LIFE STORY

BIOLOGY FOR SCHOOL & COLLEGE

F M SULLIVAN

Oliver & Boyd

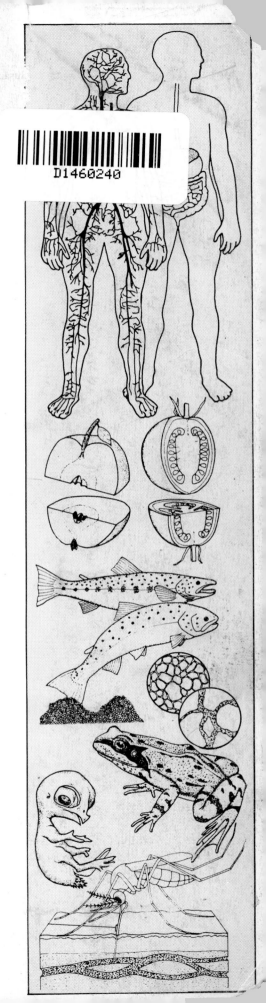

The author and publishers wish to thank Susan Griggs Agency Ltd for permission to use the
photograph on the cover of this book.

Oliver & Boyd
Robert Stevenson House
1–3 Baxter's Place
Leith Walk
Edinburgh EH1 3BB

A Division of Longman Group UK Ltd.

First published 1986

© Frank McCahill 1986

Illustrated by Frank McCahill, Stephen Gibson, Nancy Bryce,
Will Rankine and Caleb Rutherford

Set in 10/12pt Plantin (Linotron)

Produced by Longman Group (FE) Ltd
Printed in Hong Kong

ISBN 0-05-003685-8

CONTENTS

Section 17: The Endocrine System   194

Section 18: Genetics and Evolution   201

Section 19: Soil   217

Section 20: People and Micro-organisms   227

Section 21: Pollution and Conservation   223

SECTION 1

Living Things

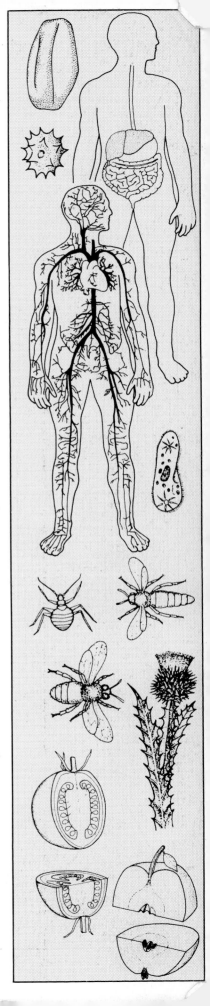

Living things

Biology is the study of living things, and living things are known as **organisms**. There are millions of different kinds of organisms. With some of them, it is obvious that they are alive. With others, it is not so easy to tell. In fact, some non-living objects, such as cars and computers, can seem to have more 'life' in them than many organisms. However, when we look closely, we find that all organisms have certain abilities in common. These are called the **characteristics** of living organisms and they are listed on this page. At some stage in their lives, all organisms show each of these characteristics. Non-living things may be able to manage some of them, but never all.

1 MOVEMENT
All organisms move. Some organisms, mainly animals, are very active and can move from place to place. The movements of others are so slow that they are hardly noticeable.

2 FEEDING
All organisms need food for energy, growth and repair. Some organisms, namely the green plants, can make their own food from very simple ingredients. These organisms are known as **autotrophs** (*auto*: self; *troph*: feed).

The others, known as **heterotrophs**, stay alive by feeding on other organisms (*hetero*: other; *troph*: feed).

3 RESPIRATION
All organisms need energy to stay alive. They get this energy from their food. Respiration is the name given to the complicated chemical process by which living cells release the energy stored in food.

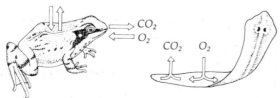

Note: respiration usually involves an organism taking oxygen from the air and returning carbon dioxide to the air. For this reason, the word 'respiration' is commonly taken to mean simply 'breathing'.

4 EXCRETION
Living cells perform a large number of different chemical reactions. These processes together make up the organism's **metabolism**. Excretion is the removal of waste substances formed during metabolism.

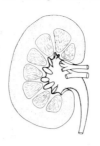 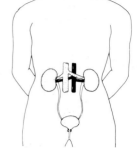

In many animals, including humans, the most important organs of excretion are the kidneys.

5 REPRODUCTION
All organisms eventually die. Successful reproduction – the production of young – makes sure that the species does not die out.

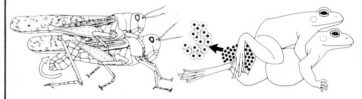

One type of reproduction, called **sexual reproduction**, leads to young which differ slightly from their parents. This produces a lot of variety within a species, giving it a better chance of survival.

6 GROWTH
At some stage in their lives, all organisms grow. Plants, in fact, tend to go on growing throughout their lives. Growth does not mean merely getting bigger. As organisms grow, they tend to change and develop as well as become larger.

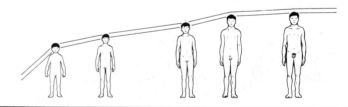

7 SENSITIVITY (also called irritability)
Sensitivity is an organism's ability to notice changes taking place around it and to react to them. Animals tend to be very sensitive. This is vital if they are to find food, escape danger, etc.

 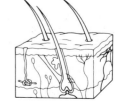

Plants are less sensitive than animals, though they can detect and react, if slowly, to changes in light, gravity, and sometimes other stimuli.

Classification: putting living things into groups

There are many, many different kinds of living things in the world. To make it easier to study them, it is useful to split them up into smaller groups of organisms which have certain things in common. This is called **classification**.

First of all, if we look at all the different kinds of living things, we find that we can split them into two very large groups. These groups are the **Animal Kingdom** and the **Plant Kingdom**.

The Animal Kingdom

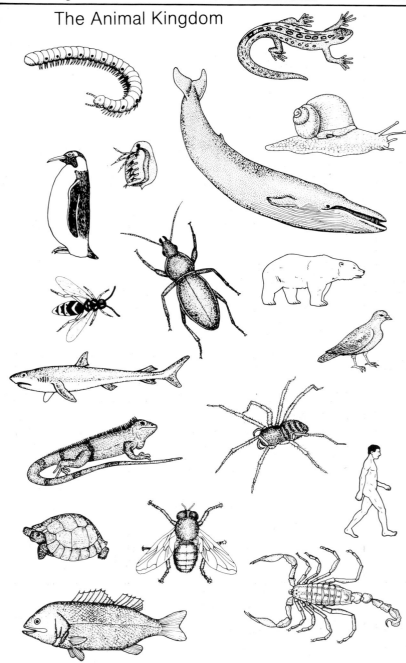

The Plant Kingdom

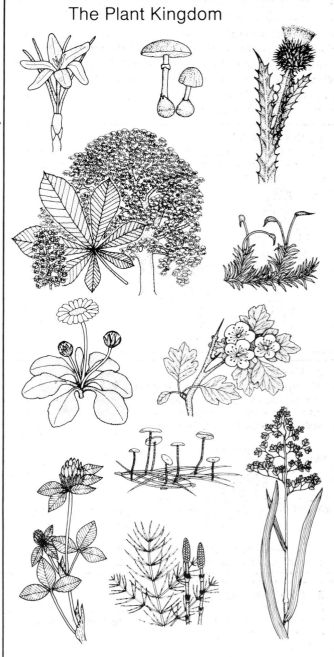

Certain features are common to the Animal Kingdom:
1 Animals usually can move around easily.
2 Animals are very sensitive to their surroundings and react quickly to changes.
3 Animals cannot make their own food from simple substances. They must have food readymade into complex things like proteins, sugars, fats, etc.
4 All parts of an animal's body grow, but they grow for only part of the animal's life.
5 Animal cells have *no* cell walls, large vacuoles, or chloroplasts (see page 14).

The features which are common to the Plant Kingdom are:
1 Plants usually stay in one place.
2 Plants are not very sensitive and react slowly to changes.
3 Plants can make their own food by **photosynthesis** (see pages 88–9).
4 Plants grow all their lives, but only at certain growing points.
5 Plant cells have **cell walls**, large **vacuoles** and often **chloroplasts**.

The animal kingdom

The two kingdoms of the living world can be split into a number of smaller groups called **phyla** (sing: *phylum*). Into each **phylum** we put all those organisms which seem to be built to a similar plan. The main phyla in the Animal Kingdom are listed below.

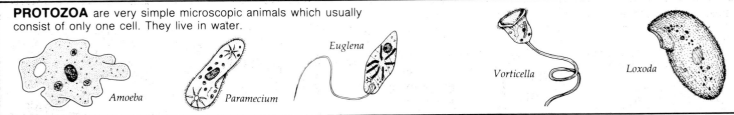

PROTOZOA are very simple microscopic animals which usually consist of only one cell. They live in water.

Euglena
Vorticella
Loxoda
Amoeba
Paramecium

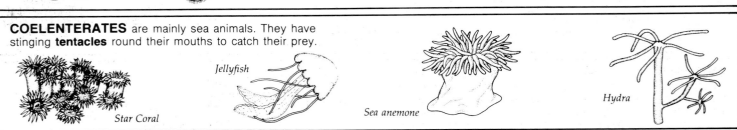

COELENTERATES are mainly sea animals. They have stinging **tentacles** round their mouths to catch their prey.

Jellyfish
Sea anemone
Hydra
Star Coral

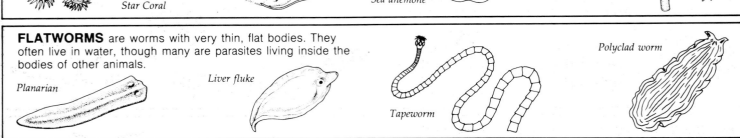

FLATWORMS are worms with very thin, flat bodies. They often live in water, though many are parasites living inside the bodies of other animals.

Polyclad worm
Planarian
Liver fluke
Tapeworm

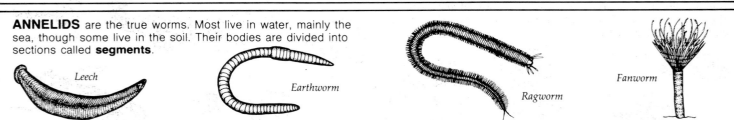

ANNELIDS are the true worms. Most live in water, mainly the sea, though some live in the soil. Their bodies are divided into sections called **segments**.

Leech
Earthworm
Ragworm
Fanworm

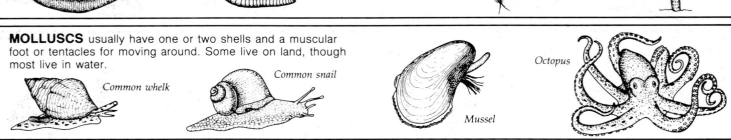

MOLLUSCS usually have one or two shells and a muscular foot or tentacles for moving around. Some live on land, though most live in water.

Octopus
Common whelk
Common snail
Mussel

ECHINODERMS all live in the sea. Their bodies are built on five rays or arms which are sometimes brought round to form a ball.

Brittle star
Sea urchin
Starfish
Feather star

ARTHROPODS are the largest group in the Animal Kingdom. Their bodies are divided into segments and their legs have moving joints. They have a hard outer covering called an **exoskeleton**. Exoskeletons cannot grow much, so, as the animal gets bigger, the old cover is shed to reveal a new, bigger one underneath (see page 6).

CHORDATES are a group composed mainly of the **vertebrates**. Vertebrates are animals with a supporting skeleton of bone or cartilage inside their bodies. All other animals are known as **invertebrates**.

The vertebrates

Vertebrates are animals which have a supporting skeleton of bone or cartilage (gristle) inside their bodies. They make up most of the **chordate** phylum. The vertebrates can be split into five smaller groups called **classes**. The five classes of vertebrates are the fish, the amphibians, the reptiles, the birds and the mammals.

FISH live in water and use their gills to absorb dissolved oxygen from it. Their skins are covered with scales. They have no limbs. Instead they have fins for swimming. They lay lots of tiny eggs which do not have shells. They lay these in the water. Fish are **cold-blooded**.

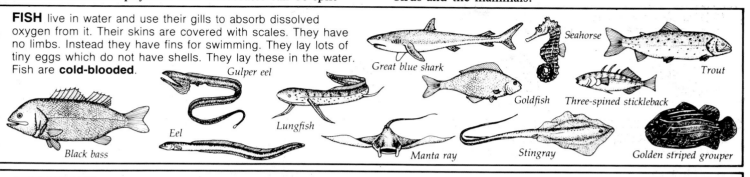

Great blue shark
Seahorse
Trout
Gulper eel
Goldfish
Three-spined stickleback
Eel
Lungfish
Black bass
Manta ray
Stingray
Golden striped grouper

AMPHIBIANS live in fresh water or in damp places. They absorb oxygen from the air either by using their lungs or their moist skins. Their skins have no covering. They have four legs. They mate in water, where they lay their small eggs. Again, these eggs do not have shells. Amphibians are cold-blooded.

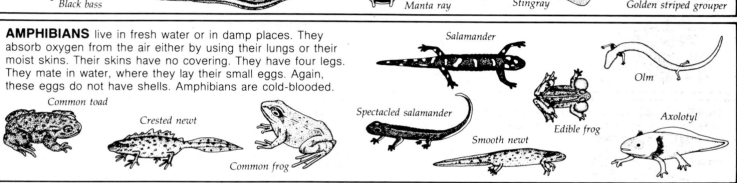

Salamander
Olm
Common toad
Crested newt
Spectacled salamander
Axolotyl
Smooth newt
Edible frog
Common frog

REPTILES live mainly on land, although some live in water. They breathe using lungs. Their skins are covered with scales. They have four legs. Their eggs, which have soft shells, are laid on land. They are cold-blooded.

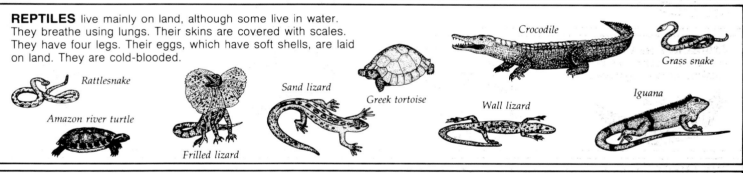

Crocodile
Grass snake
Rattlesnake
Sand lizard
Greek tortoise
Iguana
Amazon river turtle
Wall lizard
Frilled lizard

BIRDS live on land. They breathe using lungs. Their skins are covered with feathers. They have two legs, two wings and can usually fly. They lay their eggs, which have hard shells, on land. They are **warm-blooded**.

Mute swan
Emu
Sparrowhawk
Emperor penguin
Gannet
Heron
Pigeon

MAMMALS live mostly on land. They breathe using lungs. Their skins are usually covered with hair. They have legs. Their tiny, unshelled eggs are fertilised inside the female's body where they also grow. The young are born live and are fed with milk from the mother. Mammals are warm-blooded.

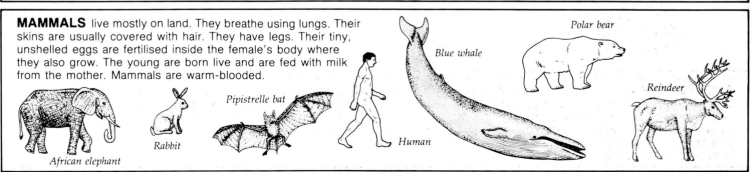

Polar bear
Blue whale
Reindeer
Pipistrelle bat
African elephant
Rabbit
Human

The arthropods

The arthropods make up the largest animal phylum. They are **invertebrates**. This means that they have no skeleton inside their bodies. They do, however, have a tough outer covering called an **exoskeleton**. This is made of a strong substance called **chitin**. Arthropods' bodies are divided into a number of sections called **segments**. They have legs with movable joints. The arthropod phylum can be divided into four classes – the **insects**, the **crustaceans**, the **arachnids** and the **myriapods**.

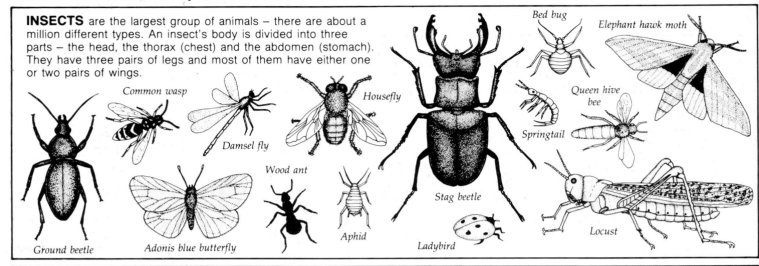

INSECTS are the largest group of animals – there are about a million different types. An insect's body is divided into three parts – the head, the thorax (chest) and the abdomen (stomach). They have three pairs of legs and most of them have either one or two pairs of wings.

Common wasp
Damsel fly
Housefly
Bed bug
Elephant hawk moth
Queen hive bee
Springtail
Wood ant
Stag beetle
Aphid
Ground beetle
Adonis blue butterfly
Ladybird
Locust

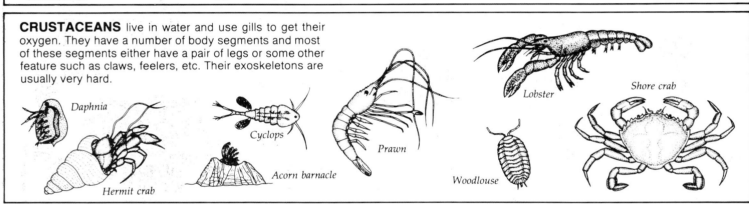

CRUSTACEANS live in water and use gills to get their oxygen. They have a number of body segments and most of these segments either have a pair of legs or some other feature such as claws, feelers, etc. Their exoskeletons are usually very hard.

Daphnia
Cyclops
Lobster
Shore crab
Prawn
Woodlouse
Acorn barnacle
Hermit crab

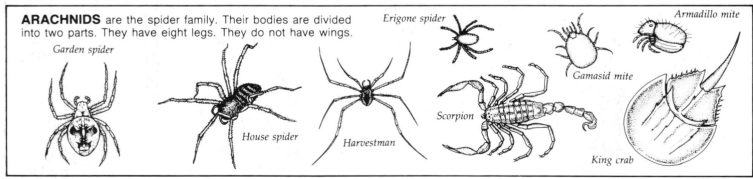

ARACHNIDS are the spider family. Their bodies are divided into two parts. They have eight legs. They do not have wings.

Erigone spider
Armadillo mite
Garden spider
Gamasid mite
House spider
Harvestman
Scorpion
King crab

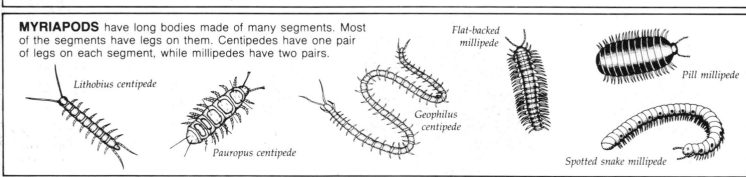

MYRIAPODS have long bodies made of many segments. Most of the segments have legs on them. Centipedes have one pair of legs on each segment, while millipedes have two pairs.

Flat-backed millipede
Pill millipede
Lithobius centipede
Geophilus centipede
Pauropus centipede
Spotted snake millipede

The flowering plants

The Plant Kingdom can be divided into plants which produce flowers and plants which do not. The flowering plants are known as **angiosperms**.

Angiosperms are those plants which reproduce sexually by means of special organs called flowers (see page 186). After **fertilisation** the flowers produce seeds. Inside each seed is an **embryo** plant. The embryo has either one or two seed leaves which are called **cotyledons**. Species of plants whose seeds have only one cotyledon on the embryo are called **monocotyledons**. Plants whose seeds have two cotyledons on the embryo are called **dicotyledons**.

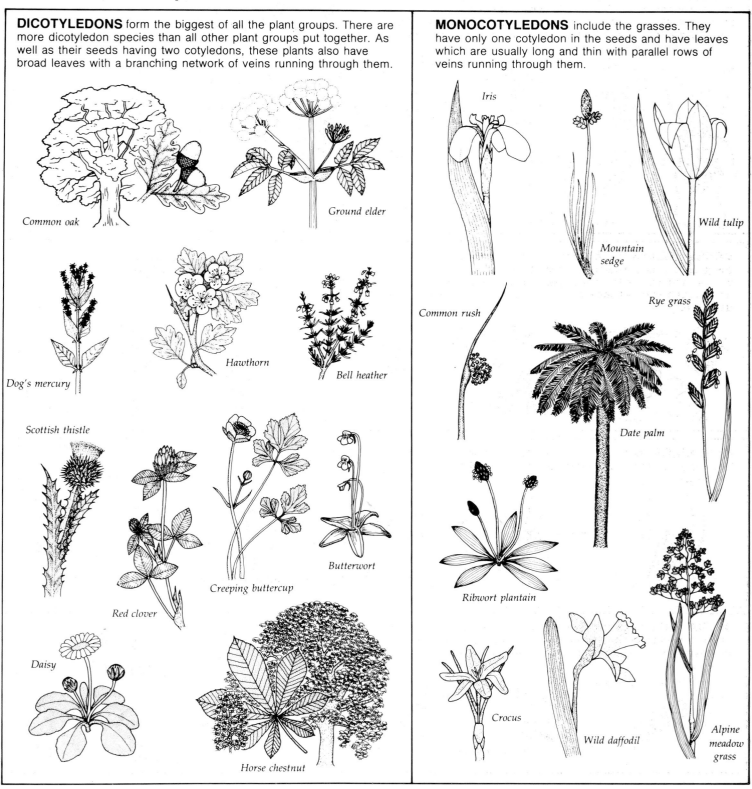

DICOTYLEDONS form the biggest of all the plant groups. There are more dicotyledon species than all other plant groups put together. As well as their seeds having two cotyledons, these plants also have broad leaves with a branching network of veins running through them.

Common oak

Ground elder

Dog's mercury

Hawthorn

Bell heather

Scottish thistle

Red clover

Creeping buttercup

Butterwort

Daisy

Horse chestnut

MONOCOTYLEDONS include the grasses. They have only one cotyledon in the seeds and have leaves which are usually long and thin with parallel rows of veins running through them.

Iris

Mountain sedge

Wild tulip

Common rush

Rye grass

Date palm

Ribwort plantain

Crocus

Wild daffodil

Alpine meadow grass

The non-flowering plants

The major groups of plants which do not produce flowers are the **thallophytes**, the **bryophytes**, the **pteridophytes** and the **gymnosperms**.

THALLOPHYTES are the simplest plant types. They have no roots, stems or leaves. They include the **bacteria** (see pages 20–1), the algae and the fungi.

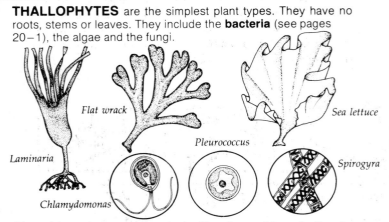

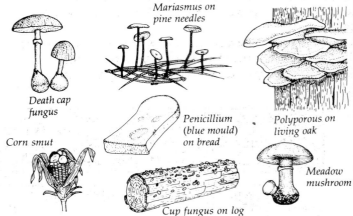

Algae (sing: *alga*) are water plants. They have **chlorophyll** and so can make their own food by **photosynthesis** (see pages 88–9). They range from large seaweeds over 60 metres long to tiny single-celled organisms.

Fungi (sing: *fungus*) have no chlorophyll and so cannot make their own food. They either feed on living organisms (**parasitic** fungi) or on dead material (**saprophytic** fungi). Fungi are made of tiny threads called **hyphae**.

BRYOPHYTES include the mosses and the liverworts. They are simple plants which live in damp places. They have no roots, but instead have tiny threads called **rhizoids**. They have chlorophyll for food making.

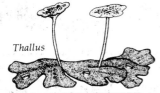

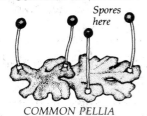

Mosses have simple leaves with no veins. They spread by **spores** from the **capsule**.

Liverworts have no leaves. They have a flat **thallus** with capsules of spores.

PTERIDOPHYTES include the ferns and horsetails. Like higher plants, they have roots, stems, leaves and a system of veins. However, they reproduce by spores. They have chlorophyll for food making.

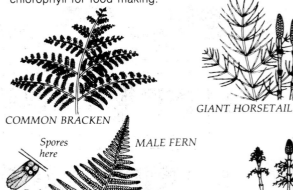

Ferns have large, flat leaves which uncurl as they grow. Spores develop under these.

Horsetails' stalks have rings of tiny leaves and a sort of cone with spores at the top.

GYMNOSPERMS are grouped together with the angiosperms (flowering plants) in a **phylum** of plants which produce seeds. These are known as the **spermatophytes**. Like angiosperms, they have roots, stems, leaves and a vascular (vein) system. However, unlike them, their seeds are not found inside fruits The gymnosperms include the **conifers**. These are mainly evergreen trees with needle or scale-like leaves. Their seeds are produced inside wooden cones.

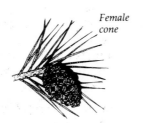

More classification

About one and a half million different kinds of living organisms have been discovered to date and new types are being found all the time. One way to begin our study of this bewildering variety of creatures is to organise them into more manageable groups. This is called **classification** (see page 3).

The first step in identifying an organism is to assign it to a **Kingdom**, either the Plant Kingdom or the Animal Kingdom. The organism is then assigned to a series of smaller groups. From largest to smallest, these groups are the **phylum, class, order, family, genus** and **species**. The species is the basic group. A species is a group of organisms which are so similar to each other that they can breed successfully together, producing offspring which can also breed successfully. We would say they were the same kind of organism. The scheme below shows how four cat-like species of animal are classified.

Animal Kingdom

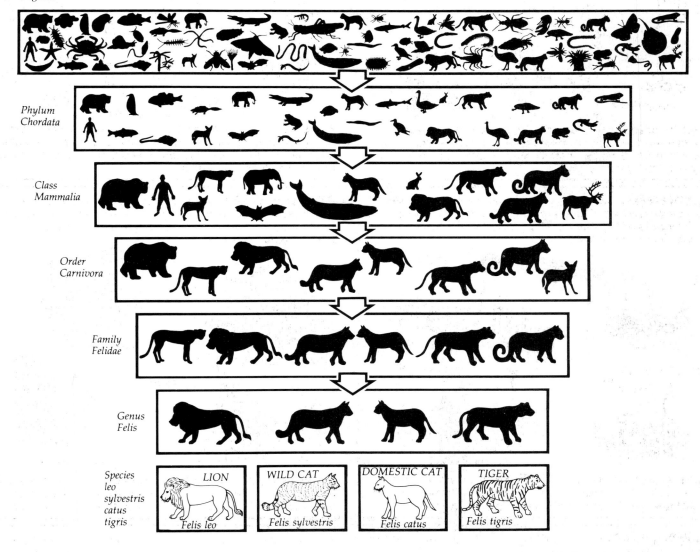

The scientific names of the 'cats' are written underneath their common or everyday names. This way of naming organisms was first used about two hundred years ago by a biologist named Linnaeus. In this system, which is called the **binomial system** (*bi*: two; *nom*: name), each organism is given two names, both in Latin. The name of the genus is put first, written with a capital letter. The species' name follows, written always with a small letter.

Of course, people often prefer to use an organism's common name, to say lion rather than *Felis leo*, for example.

However, not all the one and a half million species known to us have a common name. Also, common names are different in different languages. Even in one country, some organisms may be known by five or six common names. When the binomial system is used, every biologist knows exactly which species is being discussed and there is no chance of confusion or mistakes.

Note: names should always be printed in italics or underlined.

Identifying organisms: branching keys

There are so many different kinds of living organisms in the world that it would be impossible to learn to recognise them all. Therefore, if we find an organism which we wish to identify, we use a key. The simplest type of key to use is a **branching key**. Below is a branching key to identify any of the thirteen vertebrates illustrated.

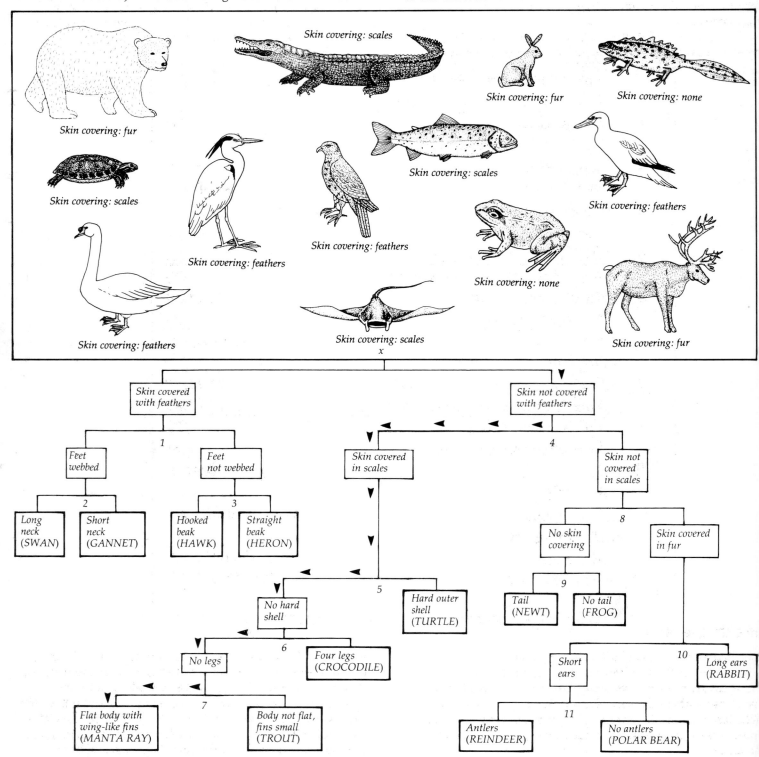

Skin covering: fur

Skin covering: scales

Skin covering: fur

Skin covering: none

Skin covering: scales

Skin covering: scales

Skin covering: feathers

Skin covering: feathers

Skin covering: feathers

Skin covering: none

Skin covering: feathers

Skin covering: scales
x

Skin covering: fur

Skin covered with feathers — Skin not covered with feathers

1

Feet webbed — Feet not webbed

2
Long neck (SWAN) — Short neck (GANNET)

3
Hooked beak (HAWK) — Straight beak (HERON)

Skin covered in scales — Skin not covered in scales

4

5
No hard shell — Hard outer shell (TURTLE)

6
No legs — Four legs (CROCODILE)

7
Flat body with wing-like fins (MANTA RAY) — Body not flat, fins small (TROUT)

8
No skin covering — Skin covered in fur

9
Tail (NEWT) — No tail (FROG)

10
Short ears — Long ears (RABBIT)

11
Antlers (REINDEER) — No antlers (POLAR BEAR)

To find the name of any of these vertebrates, first we examine it closely, then we go along the branch which describes it. For example, organism x does not have feathers, so we go along the branch marked 'Skin not covered with feathers'. This branch leads us to another two descriptions. We choose the next description which fits our organism and go along that branch, and so on. Eventually we will come to our organism's name. (On the key above, the path we would take to identify organism x is marked with arrows.)

Identifying organisms: numbered keys

The problem with **branching keys** like the one on the previous page is that they can take up too much space. To get round this, we can convert them into **numbered keys** like the one below, to identify the same thirteen vertebrates.

Down the left of this key is a row of numbers. Each number has two descriptions for you to choose between.

Opposite each description is the next number to go to. For example, if the animal's skin is covered with feathers, you go to 1. If it is not, you go to 4, and so on. When you come to a name instead of a number, then that is the name of the organism. (The path you would take to identify organism x is marked on the key by an underline.)

	Skin covered with feathers	(1)
	Skin not covered with feathers	(4)
1	Feet webbed	(2)
	Feet not webbed	(3)
2	Long neck	SWAN
	Short neck	GANNET
3	Straight beak	HERON
	Hooked beak	HAWK
4	Skin covered in scales	(5)
	Skin not covered in scales	(8)
5	Hard outer shell	TURTLE
	No hard shell	(6)
6	Four legs	CROCODILE
	No legs	(7)
7	Body not flat, fins small	TROUT
	Flat body with wing-like fins	MANTA RAY
8	No skin covering	(9)
	Skin covered in fur	(10)
9	Tail	NEWT
	No tail	FROG
10	Long ears	RABBIT
	Short ears	(11)
11	Antlers	REINDEER
	No antlers	POLAR BEAR

Making a key

The first step in making a key is to split the organisms to be included in the key into two groups. In the two examples given, they have been split into those with feathers and those without feathers. Each of these groups is then split into two smaller groups. We continue doing this until there is only one organism left in a group. We then include its name.

For the branching key, the description which fits the members of each new group is put at the end of a new branch.

To convert a branching key into a numbered key we first give each branch a number, starting on the left and working right across the key. (The numbers have been added to the key on the previous page.) These numbers are then written down the left of the page along with the descriptions to be found at each branch of that number. We then go through each branch in turn, putting on the right-hand side where that description leads to. For example, on the branching key, the description 'Skin covered with feathers' leads to branch one, so we put '1' on the right opposite that description. Similarly, 'Feet webbed' leads to branch two, so '2' goes on the right opposite that description. We continue adding numbers or names to the right-hand side until the key is complete.

SECTION 2

Cells

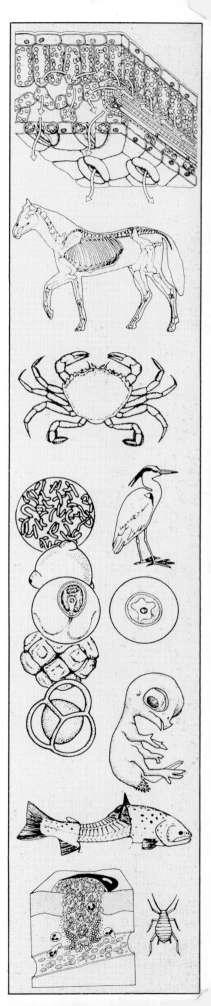

Cells: the building bricks of life

If we look at living things under a microscope, we find that they are made of tiny 'building bricks' called cells. Organisms range in size from only one cell to many millions of cells. Each cell is filled with a living material called **protoplasm**, although, as is shown in the diagram below, there are a number of differences between plant cells and animal cells.

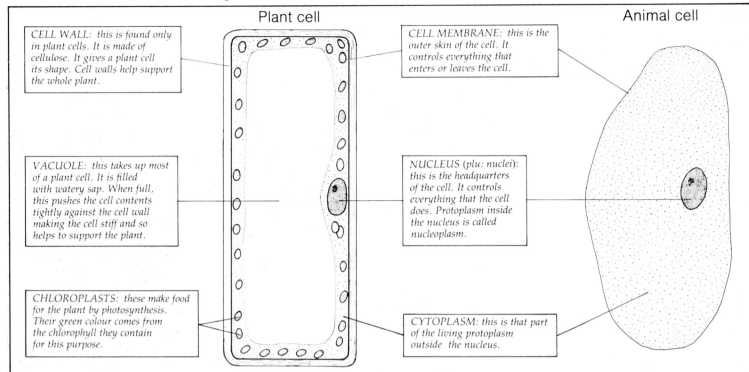

Plant cell

CELL WALL: this is found only in plant cells. It is made of cellulose. It gives a plant cell its shape. Cell walls help support the whole plant.

VACUOLE: this takes up most of a plant cell. It is filled with watery sap. When full, this pushes the cell contents tightly against the cell wall making the cell stiff and so helps to support the plant.

CHLOROPLASTS: these make food for the plant by photosynthesis. Their green colour comes from the chlorophyll they contain for this purpose.

Animal cell

CELL MEMBRANE: this is the outer skin of the cell. It controls everything that enters or leaves the cell.

NUCLEUS (plu: nuclei): this is the headquarters of the cell. It controls everything that the cell does. Protoplasm inside the nucleus is called nucleoplasm.

CYTOPLASM: this is that part of the living protoplasm outside the nucleus.

Although all cells have the same basic structure as those shown above, their actual appearance will depend on where they come from. This is because cells have different jobs to do. As they mature they take on the different shapes and sizes which will best suit them to their task. This process by which cells become different, so they can do their own particular jobs, is called **differentiation**. Cells of the same type are often found grouped together in an organism. These groups of similar cells are called **tissues**. Various cells and tissues are shown in the diagrams below.

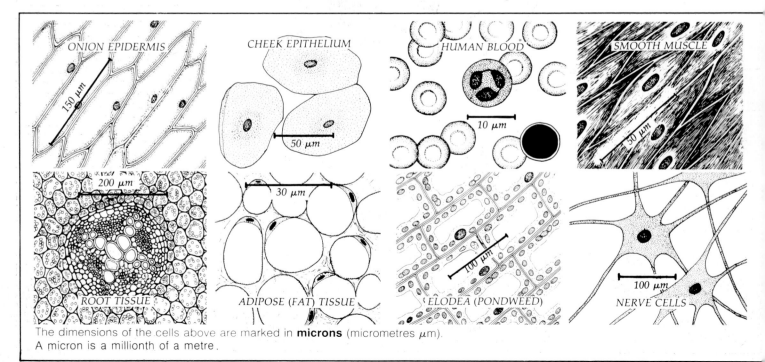

ONION EPIDERMIS
150 μm

CHEEK EPITHELIUM
50 μm

HUMAN BLOOD
10 μm

SMOOTH MUSCLE
50 μm

200 μm
ROOT TISSUE

30 μm
ADIPOSE (FAT) TISSUE

100 μm
ELODEA (PONDWEED)

100 μm
NERVE CELLS

The dimensions of the cells above are marked in **microns** (micrometres μm).
A micron is a millionth of a metre.

Cells: a closer look

The very best light microscopes can magnify up to 1500 times (×1500). For higher magnifications, an **electron microscope** must be used. In an electron microscope the picture is produced by 'shining' beams of tiny particles called electrons on to the specimen. An image is then either formed on a sort of television screen, or a photograph called an **electron micrograph** is made. Electron microscopes can achieve magnifications of up to one million times.

Using an electron microscope, cells can be seen in great detail. Many features, invisible under the light microscope, can be made out. The diagrams below illustrate the structure of cells as revealed by the electron microscope.

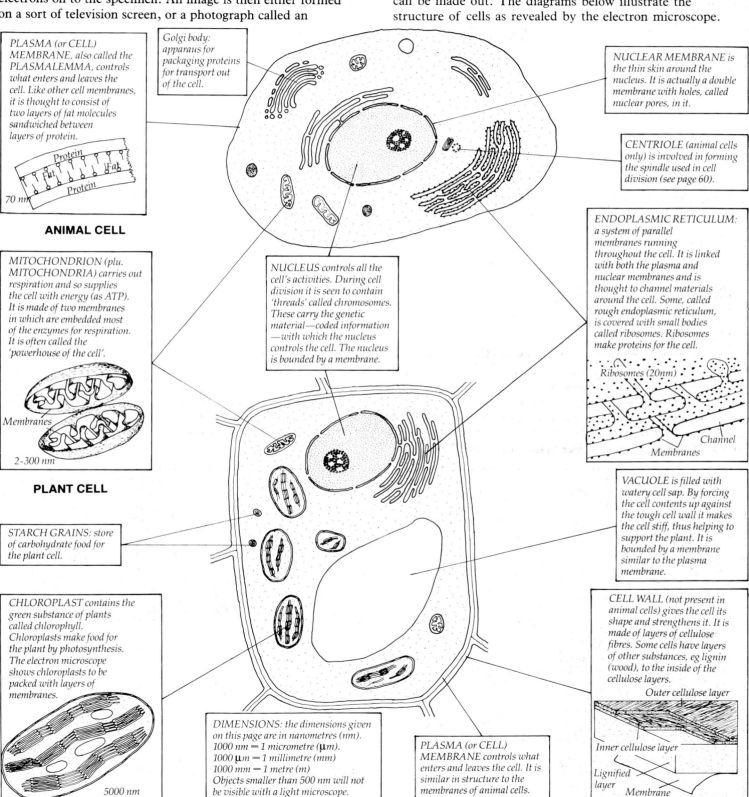

PLASMA (or CELL) MEMBRANE, also called the PLASMALEMMA, controls what enters and leaves the cell. Like other cell membranes, it is thought to consist of two layers of fat molecules sandwiched between layers of protein.

Protein
Fat
Protein
70 nm

ANIMAL CELL

Golgi body: apparaus for packaging proteins for transport out of the cell.

NUCLEAR MEMBRANE is the thin skin around the nucleus. It is actually a double membrane with holes, called nuclear pores, in it.

CENTRIOLE (animal cells only) is involved in forming the spindle used in cell division (see page 60).

MITOCHONDRION (plu. MITOCHONDRIA) carries out respiration and so supplies the cell with energy (as ATP). It is made of two membranes in which are embedded most of the enzymes for respiration. It is often called the 'powerhouse of the cell'.

Membranes
2-300 nm

PLANT CELL

NUCLEUS controls all the cell's activities. During cell division it is seen to contain 'threads' called chromosomes. These carry the genetic material—coded information—with which the nucleus controls the cell. The nucleus is bounded by a membrane.

ENDOPLASMIC RETICULUM: a system of parallel membranes running throughout the cell. It is linked with both the plasma and nuclear membranes and is thought to channel materials around the cell. Some, called rough endoplasmic reticulum, is covered with small bodies called ribosomes. Ribosomes make proteins for the cell.

Ribosomes (20nm)
Channel
Membranes

STARCH GRAINS: store of carbohydrate food for the plant cell.

VACUOLE is filled with watery cell sap. By forcing the cell contents up against the tough cell wall it makes the cell stiff, thus helping to support the plant. It is bounded by a membrane similar to the plasma membrane.

CHLOROPLAST contains the green substance of plants called chlorophyll. Chloroplasts make food for the plant by photosynthesis. The electron microscope shows chloroplasts to be packed with layers of membranes.

5000 nm

DIMENSIONS: the dimensions given on this page are in nanometres (nm).
1000 nm = 1 micrometre (μm)
1000 μm = 1 millimetre (mm)
1000 mm = 1 metre (m)
Objects smaller than 500 nm will not be visible with a light microscope.

PLASMA (or CELL) MEMBRANE controls what enters and leaves the cell. It is similar in structure to the membranes of animal cells.

CELL WALL (not present in animal cells) gives the cell its shape and strengthens it. It is made of layers of cellulose fibres. Some cells have layers of other substances, eg lignin (wood), to the inside of the cellulose layers.

Outer cellulose layer
Inner cellulose layer
Lignified layer
Membrane

Mitosis: making new cells

A **multicellular** (many-celled) organism may be made of many billions of cells. For such an organism to function properly, each cell must be able to do its own job correctly. How do cells 'know' what they must do? The answer lies inside their **nucleus**. The nucleus of every cell contains a complete 'plan' for 'making' and 'operating' the organism. This plan is in the form of thousands of chemical units called **genes**. Each gene is an 'instruction' which tells the nucleus how to carry out a particular task. Every cell in an organism contains a complete set of genes, although in its lifetime no cell needs to call on more than a fraction of them. The nucleus' store of precious genes helps to explain its behaviour when new cells are being made.

New cells come into being through the process of **cell division**. A parent cell splits and two identical daughter cells are formed. Many single-celled organisms reproduce in this way. In multicellular organisms, the process is repeated to form more and more cells.

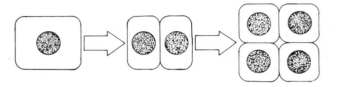

At first, the daughter cells are small since each receives only half the parent cell's **cytoplasm**. Later they grow to full size. The nucleus, though, is different. From the very start, each daughter cell has a complete nucleus. In fact, it is during cell division that we can see most clearly how the nucleus is made up. It consists of a number of small 'threads' called **chromosomes**. Each species has its own set number of chromosomes. Human cells, for example, have 46 chromosomes, onion cells have 16, etc.

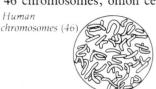
Human chromosomes (46)

Onion chromosomes (16)

We now know that the chromosomes carry the genes, packed inside them in long chains. Therefore, during cell division, it is essential that each daughter cell is given a complete set of chromosomes. To achieve this, the parent nucleus first doubles its number of chromosomes and then divides to give each daughter nucleus a complete set. This process is called **mitosis**. The diagrams below show how mitosis occurs in an animal cell containing six chromosomes.

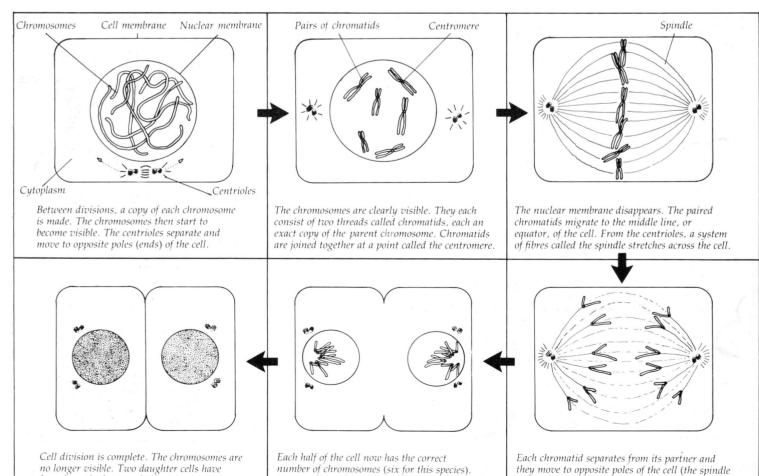

Chromosomes   Cell membrane   Nuclear membrane
Cytoplasm   Centrioles

Between divisions, a copy of each chromosome is made. The chromosomes then start to become visible. The centrioles separate and move to opposite poles (ends) of the cell.

Pairs of chromatids   Centromere

The chromosomes are clearly visible. They each consist of two threads called chromatids, each an exact copy of the parent chromosome. Chromatids are joined together at a point called the centromere.

Spindle

The nuclear membrane disappears. The paired chromatids migrate to the middle line, or equator, of the cell. From the centrioles, a system of fibres called the spindle stretches across the cell.

Cell division is complete. The chromosomes are no longer visible. Two daughter cells have been formed whose nuclei contain six chromosomes identical to the original six of the parent cell.

Each half of the cell now has the correct number of chromosomes (six for this species). New nuclear membranes form around them and the cytoplasm starts to divide.

Each chromatid separates from its partner and they move to opposite poles of the cell (the spindle is thought to be involved in this). The chromatids are now considered to be daughter chromosomes.

Therefore, the growth of an organism depends on two things: cell division and cell enlargement. New cells are added by divisions and these new cells, small at first, absorb food and grow. As they grow, they begin to change in shape and form. This is called **differentiation**. Eventually, a range of different types of cells is produced, each type perfectly suited to do its own particular job in the organism. Usually, after differentiation, a cell cannot divide any more.

Normally, large numbers of cells of the same type are found working together in an organism. A group of similar cells like this is called a **tissue**. The formation and the jobs of a few tissues from the human body are illustrated below.

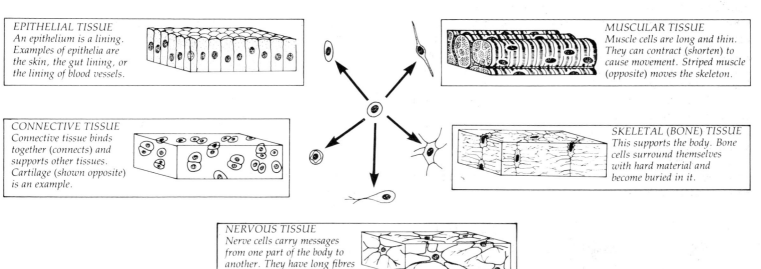

EPITHELIAL TISSUE
An epithelium is a lining. Examples of epithelia are the skin, the gut lining, or the lining of blood vessels.

CONNECTIVE TISSUE
Connective tissue binds together (connects) and supports other tissues. Cartilage (shown opposite) is an example.

NERVOUS TISSUE
Nerve cells carry messages from one part of the body to another. They have long fibres to communicate with each other.

MUSCULAR TISSUE
Muscle cells are long and thin. They can contract (shorten) to cause movement. Striped muscle (opposite) moves the skeleton.

SKELETAL (BONE) TISSUE
This supports the body. Bone cells surround themselves with hard material and become buried in it.

MITOSIS AND GROWTH IN PLANTS

There are a number of differences between plant and animal growth. In plant mitosis, **centrioles** are absent and division involves a new cell wall being formed (see below).

In a growing animal, cell divisions occur all over the body. In plants, mitosis takes place only in certain tissues called **meristems** which occur at the tip of every root.

Plants grow throughout their lives, animals stop growing when adult. Cell divisions in animals only occur in tissues, such as blood and epithelia, where cells wear out and must be replaced.

Finally, cell enlargement is more important for plant growth than animal growth. This is due mainly to the formation of **vacuoles** which take up most of the space in a plant cell.

The diagrams opposite show the position and appearance of developing and growing cells in a plant root.

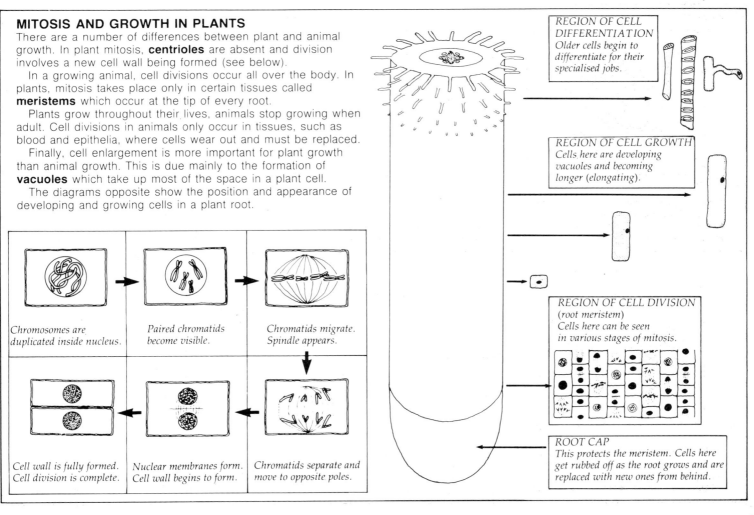

REGION OF CELL DIFFERENTIATION
Older cells begin to differentiate for their specialised jobs.

REGION OF CELL GROWTH
Cells here are developing vacuoles and becoming longer (elongating).

REGION OF CELL DIVISION
(root meristem)
Cells here can be seen in various stages of mitosis.

ROOT CAP
This protects the meristem. Cells here get rubbed off as the root grows and are replaced with new ones from behind.

Chromosomes are duplicated inside nucleus.

Paired chromatids become visible.

Chromatids migrate. Spindle appears.

Chromatids separate and move to opposite poles.

Nuclear membranes form. Cell wall begins to form.

Cell wall is fully formed. Cell division is complete.

Tissues, organs and systems

To function properly all organisms must be able to carry out a number of activities. In an **organism** consisting of only one cell, a **unicellular** organism, that one cell will carry out every activity. However, in a many-celled or **multicellular** organism, this would not be practical. A multicellular organism is divided into a number of **systems**, each one designed to do its own particular job. Each system consists of a series of **organs** made of various tissues. These systems are not completely independent of one another – the health of an organism depends on all its systems, organs and cells working closely together.

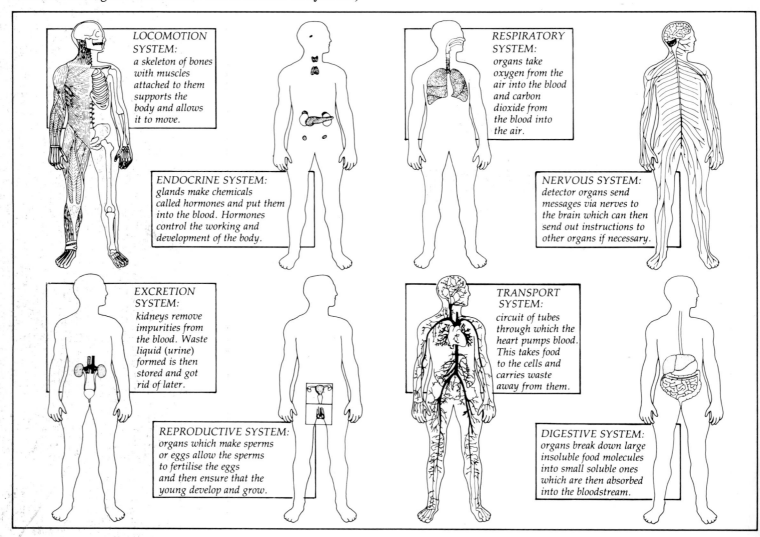

LOCOMOTION SYSTEM:
a skeleton of bones with muscles attached to them supports the body and allows it to move.

ENDOCRINE SYSTEM:
glands make chemicals called hormones and put them into the blood. Hormones control the working and development of the body.

RESPIRATORY SYSTEM:
organs take oxygen from the air into the blood and carbon dioxide from the blood into the air.

NERVOUS SYSTEM:
detector organs send messages via nerves to the brain which can then send out instructions to other organs if necessary.

EXCRETION SYSTEM:
kidneys remove impurities from the blood. Waste liquid (urine) formed is then stored and got rid of later.

REPRODUCTIVE SYSTEM:
organs which make sperms or eggs allow the sperms to fertilise the eggs and then ensure that the young develop and grow.

TRANSPORT SYSTEM:
circuit of tubes through which the heart pumps blood. This takes food to the cells and carries waste away from them.

DIGESTIVE SYSTEM:
organs break down large insoluble food molecules into small soluble ones which are then absorbed into the bloodstream.

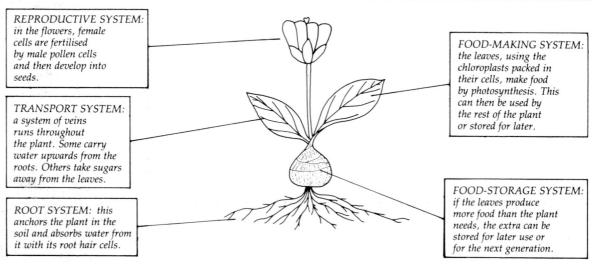

REPRODUCTIVE SYSTEM:
in the flowers, female cells are fertilised by male pollen cells and then develop into seeds.

FOOD-MAKING SYSTEM:
the leaves, using the chloroplasts packed in their cells, make food by photosynthesis. This can then be used by the rest of the plant or stored for later.

TRANSPORT SYSTEM:
a system of veins runs throughout the plant. Some carry water upwards from the roots. Others take sugars away from the leaves.

ROOT SYSTEM: this anchors the plant in the soil and absorbs water from it with its root hair cells.

FOOD-STORAGE SYSTEM:
if the leaves produce more food than the plant needs, the extra can be stored for later use or for the next generation.

SECTION 3

Ways of Living

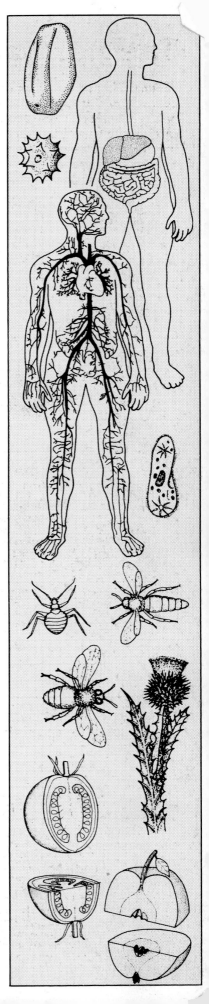

Bacteria and viruses

Bacteria (sing: *bacterium*) are very tiny, single-celled organisms, ranging in size from 0.1 up to 5 micrometres (1 mm = 1000 μm). It is possible to see them with a light microscope, but very high magnifications are required. Despite their small size, bacteria are very widespread – they are to be found almost everywhere on Earth. Many bacteria can survive in conditions which are deadly to all other forms of life.

Apart from being very much smaller than the cells of other organisms, bacterial cells differ from them in other ways. The diagram shows the structure of a bacterial cell.

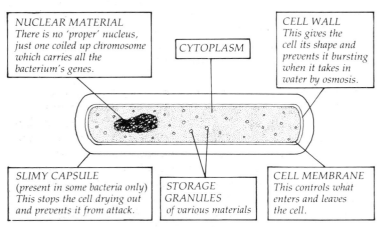

NUCLEAR MATERIAL There is no 'proper' nucleus, just one coiled up chromosome which carries all the bacterium's genes.

CYTOPLASM

CELL WALL This gives the cell its shape and prevents it bursting when it takes in water by osmosis.

SLIMY CAPSULE (*present in some bacteria only*) This stops the cell drying out and prevents it from attack.

STORAGE GRANULES of various materials

CELL MEMBRANE This controls what enters and leaves the cell.

Bacterial cells are of various shapes. The main types are the spherical **cocci** (sing: *coccus*), the rod-shaped **bacilli** (sing: *bacillus*), the comma-shaped **vibrios** and the **spiral** bacteria.

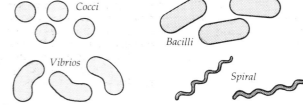

Cocci

Bacilli

Vibrios

Spiral

In some species of bacteria the cells do not occur singly. They are always found grouped together in certain ways. Among the cocci, for example, we have the following arrangements:

Streptococcus

Fours

Pairs

Packets

Clusters, e.g. staphylococcus

Most bacteria cannot move. Some types, however, possess whiplike threads called **flagella** (sing: *flagellum*). By waving their flagella they can move themselves around. Here are a few examples:

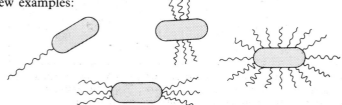

RESPIRATION
Like all organisms, bacteria must carry out some form of respiration to give them the energy they need to stay alive. Many use **aerobic respiration** (see pages 94–5), and need a supply of oxygen. The oxygen diffuses into the bacterial cell from its surroundings. Carbon dioxide is produced and this diffuses in the opposite direction out of the cell. These bacteria are called **aerobes**.

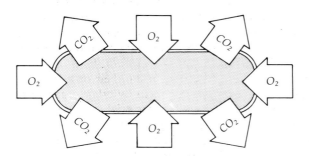

Some bacteria, however, never use oxygen. They carry out only **anaerobic respiration** (see page 96). These bacteria are called **anaerobes**. Anaerobes may be harmed, some even killed, by the presence of oxygen.

Most bacteria are a combination of those two types. They prefer to use aerobic respiration, but, if oxygen is not available, they can switch over quite happily to anaerobic respiration.

REPRODUCTION
A bacterial cell reproduces by dividing into two daughter cells. This is called **binary fission**. Before the division, the nuclear material must be copied so that each daughter cell gets a complete copy.

Under ideal conditions, bacteria can divide every 20 minutes to produce huge numbers of progeny (offspring) very quickly. Some species of bacteria also carry out a simple type of sexual reproduction.

Spores
When conditions become unsuitable for growth and reproduction, many bacteria can change themselves into smaller, toughened cells called spores.

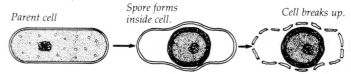

Parent cell

Spore forms inside cell.

Cell breaks up.

Thanks to its thick wall, a spore can survive being boiled, dried out, poisoned, etc. Thus in this way, the bacterial cell can remain **dormant** for many years. Then, when conditions improve, the spore **germinates** and a new cell appears.

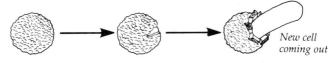

New cell coming out

Since each spore produces only one bacterial cell, this is not a method of reproduction. It is a technique for survival.

Feeding in bacteria

Bacteria obtain their food in a variety of different ways. Some bacteria are **autotrophic**, but most are **heterotrophic**.

Autotrophic bacteria can make their own food from simple ingredients such as carbon dioxide and water (*auto*: self; *troph*: feed). To do this they need a source of energy. Some, like plants, use light energy and have a type of **chlorophyll** to catch light (see page 88). In other words these bacteria are able to carry out **photosynthesis**. Other autotrophic bacteria use chemicals as their energy source. This kind of food making is called **chemosynthesis**. These bacteria include the important **nitrifying bacteria** (see pages 224–5) which increase the fertility of the soil.

Heterotrophic bacteria cannot make their own food. They must have food readymade for them by other organisms (*hetero*: other; *troph*: feed). When bacterial cells or **spores** have been carried to a suitable piece of food, they do not actually eat it. Rather, they soak it in through their cell membrane. Before this is possible, the food must be liquefied. To do this, the cell uses **digestive enzymes** as shown in the diagram below. This process is called **extracellular digestion**.

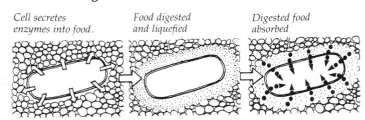

| Cell secretes enzymes into food. | Food digested and liquefied | Digested food absorbed |

Heterotrophic bacteria are often grouped together on the basis of where they obtain their food. The main groups are listed below.

Saprophytes feed on the dead bodies and wastes of other organisms, causing them to decay. This helps to keep the environment clean and, more importantly, returns to the soil the valuable minerals plants need for healthy growth.

Mutualistic bacteria form a partnership with a host organism to the benefit of them both. For example, without the mutualistic bacteria which live in their guts, herbivores could not digest the cellulose which makes up the bulk of their diet (see page 82). The root-nodule bacteria of leguminous plants (see page 86) also enjoy a mutually profitable relationship with their hosts.

Pathogenic bacteria cause diseases. They are parasites which feed on the living body of a host plant or animal. The diseases they cause are partly the result of damage they do to the host's tissues and partly to the toxins (poisons) they release into the host's system. Some bacterial toxins are among the most poisonous substances known. Some human diseases caused by pathogenic bacteria are cholera, plague, food poisoning, TB, tetanus, syphillis, typhoid, boils, diptheria and sore throats. Methods of fighting pathogenic bacteria are outlined on pages 230–1.

VIRUSES

A virus is not a living thing. It is simply a protein box which holds a tiny strand of **nucleic acid** – a substance found in the nuclei of living cells. Viruses come in various shapes, for example:

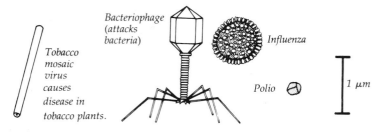

Tobacco mosaic virus causes disease in tobacco plants.

Bacteriophage (attacks bacteria)

Influenza

Polio

1 μm

These virus **particles** (they are too simple to be called cells) are extremely small and are visible only with an electron microscope. For comparison, here they are alongside a red blood cell and a medium-sized bacterial cell:

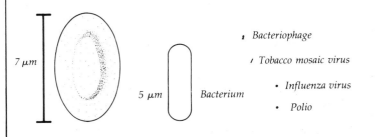

7 μm

5 μm

Bacterium

, Bacteriophage

/ Tobacco mosaic virus

• Influenza virus

• Polio

Viruses cause disease. A virus may lie dormant and lifeless for many years, yet, when it comes in contact with a suitable living cell, an amazing thing happens. The tiny virus particle 'hijacks' the host cell and 'forces' it to make hundreds of copies of itself, as shown in the diagram **below**. Eventually, the host cell dies and bursts open. The freshly-made virus particles escape and go on to infect other cells. Among the many diseases caused by viruses are smallpox, polio, influenza, chickenpox, measles, German measles and colds.

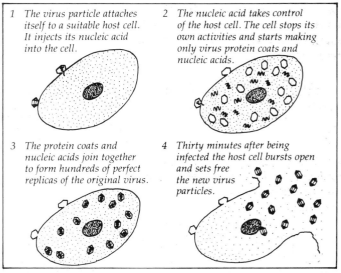

1 The virus particle attaches itself to a suitable host cell. It injects its nucleic acid into the cell.

2 The nucleic acid takes control of the host cell. The cell stops its own activities and starts making only virus protein coats and nucleic acids.

3 The protein coats and nucleic acids join together to form hundreds of perfect replicas of the original virus.

4 Thirty minutes after being infected the host cell bursts open and sets free the new virus particles.

Medically, virus infections are difficult to treat. **Antibiotics** (see pages 230–1) are no use against them. **Immunisation** is often the only defence against serious viral diseases.

Single-celled plants

There are certain activities which are typical of living things – feeding, respiration, movement, reproduction, etc. In a **multicellular** (many-celled) organism different kinds of cells get different jobs to do. However, in a **unicellular** (one-celled) organism, a single cell has to carry out all these duties. This makes single-celled organisms a bit odd. In fact, when we watch these tiny creatures under a microscope, it is sometimes difficult to decide if they are plants or animals. Because of this some people put them in a Kingdom of their own called the **Protista Kingdom**. For example, **Euglena** and **Chlamydomonas**, which are usually put in the Plant Kingdom with the **algae** (see page 8), have **chloroplasts** like plants, but they can move around just like animals.

EUGLENA lives in stagnant ponds which it often tints a bright green colour. Like plants, it has **chloroplasts** and can make its own food by **photosynthesis**. However, it is not as efficient at this as more advanced plants. Also, it can absorb dissolved food from the water and, if there is plenty about, it can live in the dark and will lose its green colour. To move around, it uses its whip-like tail called a **flagellum** (plu: *flagella*) and is helped by not having a cell wall like ordinary plant cells, but instead a flexible cover called a **pellicle** which changes shape as it moves. Euglena moves towards light which it detects with its red **eye spot**. Since it does not have a cell wall, as water entered it by **osmosis** (see pages 116–7), it would tend to fill up and burst. To prevent this, it has a **contractile vacuole** (like many animals) to get rid of excess water. Euglena reproduces by binary fission (see page 169) unless conditions are bad when it forms **cysts** to withstand them.

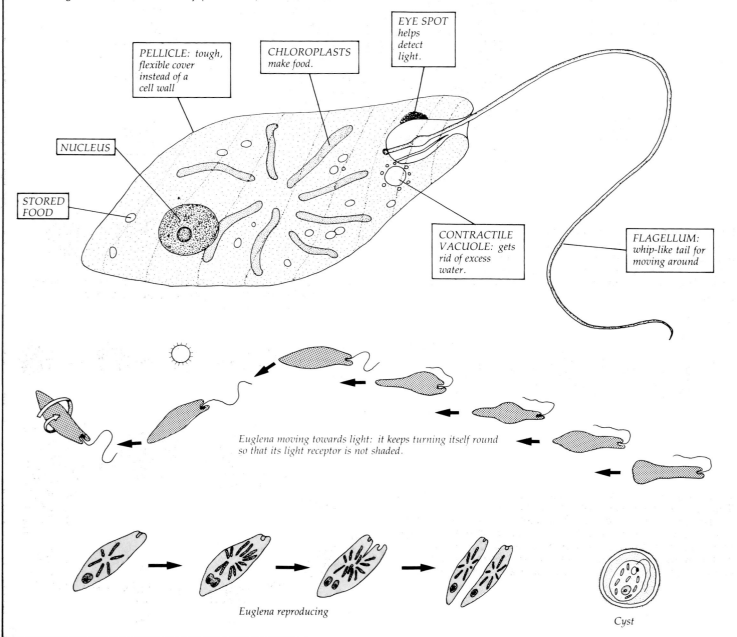

PELLICLE: tough, flexible cover instead of a cell wall

CHLOROPLASTS make food.

EYE SPOT helps detect light.

NUCLEUS

STORED FOOD

CONTRACTILE VACUOLE: gets rid of excess water.

FLAGELLUM: whip-like tail for moving around

Euglena moving towards light: it keeps turning itself round so that its light receptor is not shaded.

Euglena reproducing

Cyst

CHLAMYDOMONAS lives in water in ponds and ditches and in summer it can multiply so fast that it turns the water green. Like other plants, it has a cell wall made of **cellulose** and it has one large chloroplast with which it makes all its food. However, like animals, it can move using its two flagella. It uses its red eye spot to detect light and it will swim towards it. It also has contractile vacuoles to get rid of excess water. Chlamydomonas reproduces in different ways depending on the conditions of its environment.

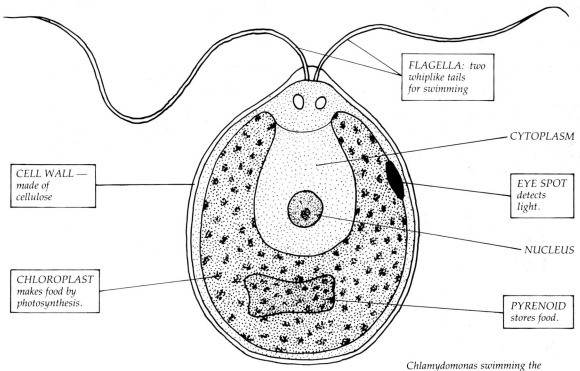

FLAGELLA: two whiplike tails for swimming

CYTOPLASM

CELL WALL — made of cellulose

EYE SPOT detects light.

NUCLEUS

CHLOROPLAST makes food by photosynthesis.

PYRENOID stores food.

If the conditions are not really suitable for growth, Chlamydomonas can enter a resting state. Divisions take place to produce eight daughter cells, but, instead of being released, these divide themselves. The walls become soft and wet and it stays in this form, called a **palmella**, until conditions get better and they are all let out.

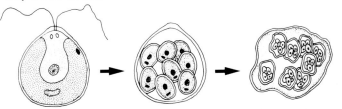

Palmella

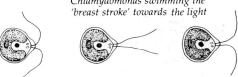

Chlamydomonas swimming the 'breast stroke' towards the light

In ideal conditions, Chlamydomonas reproduces very quickly by **binary fission**. Up to eight daughter cells may be produced before they escape.

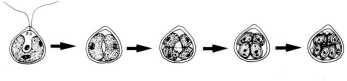

In very dry or cold conditions, sexual reproduction takes place. The cell contents divide again and again to make up to 32 tiny sex cells or **gametes**. These are released into the water where they fuse together in pairs. The cells formed, called **zygotes**, grow a thick wall which can stand severe drought. Now known as **zygospores**, they are blown away. If they land in favourable conditions, they burst open to release new Chlamydomonas.

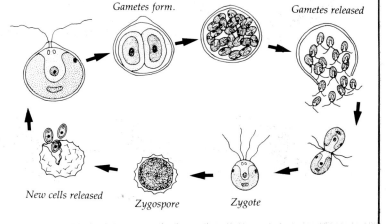

Gametes form.

Gametes released

New cells released

Zygospore

Zygote

Single-celled animals

Unicellular animals are called **protozoans**. Although protozoans are so small we have to use a microscope to see them, their single cell can do all the things for which larger animals need many different kinds of cells. Two common protozoans are **Amoeba** and **Paramecium**.

AMOEBA live in water, including water in the soil. They have no definite shape since their shape changes as they move. Being so small, they can get all their oxygen from the water around them. Dissolved oxygen simply diffuses through their thin skins. Similarly, carbon dioxide and any dissolved waste diffuses out of the cell into the water. Some of their activities are shown below.

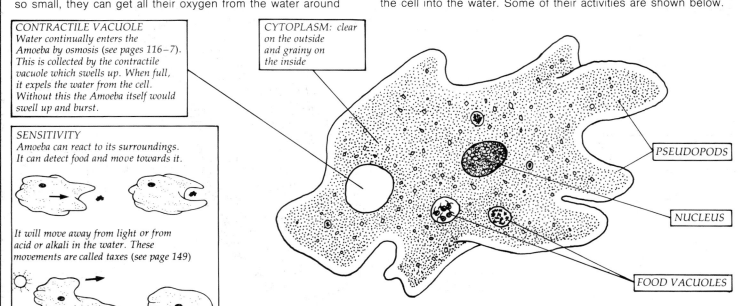

CONTRACTILE VACUOLE
Water continually enters the Amoeba by osmosis (see pages 116–7). This is collected by the contractile vacuole which swells up. When full, it expels the water from the cell. Without this the Amoeba itself would swell up and burst.

SENSITIVITY
Amoeba can react to its surroundings. It can detect food and move towards it.

It will move away from light or from acid or alkali in the water. These movements are called taxes (see page 149)

CYTOPLASM: clear on the outside and grainy on the inside

PSEUDOPODS

NUCLEUS

FOOD VACUOLES

Movement
A finger of cytoplasm, called a **pseudopod**, forms on the amoeba. The rest of the cytoplasm slowly flows into this, moving the organism along. Pseudopods can be put out in any direction.

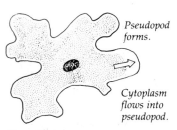

Pseudopod forms.

Cytoplasm flows into pseudopod.

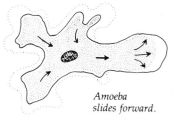

Amoeba slides forward.

Reproduction
Once an Amoeba has grown to a certain size, its nucleus divides to form two daughter nuclei. The cytoplasm then splits and the two daughter Amoeba are formed. This is called **binary fission**.

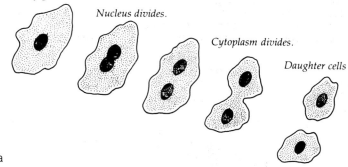

Fully-grown Amoeba

Nucleus divides.

Cytoplasm divides.

Daughter cells

Feeding
Amoeba feeds by a process called **phagocytosis**. It simply flows round a food particle and takes it into its cytoplasm where it forms a **food vacuole**. Enzymes are added to digest the food and the nutrients diffuse through the cytoplasm. Any waste is left behind as the Amoeba flows away.

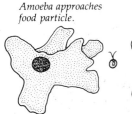

Amoeba approaches food particle.

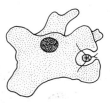

Food surrounded by cytoplasm

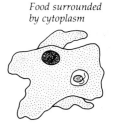

Digestive enzymes added to food vacuole

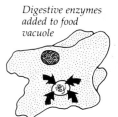

Food digested and absorbed

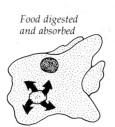

Waste left behind

PARAMECIUM lives in stagnant water containing decaying plant material. It feeds on the bacteria which cause the decay. Unlike Amoeba, it has a fixed shape. Like Amoeba, it is small enough to get all its oxygen from the water around it and to get rid of its carbon dioxide and dissolved waste into it. Some of Paramecium's other activities are shown below.

Movement

Rhythmic beating of the water by the **cilia** (rows of tiny hairs) rows the Paramecium along.

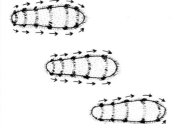

If it comes to an obstacle, it stops, backs up, turns 30°, then moves off. It goes on doing this until it gets by.

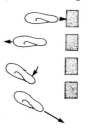

This is called the **avoiding reaction**.

CONTRACTILE VACUOLE
This gets rid of excess water which enters the cell by osmosis (see pages 116–7). The channels collect the water from the cytoplasm and lead it to the vacuole. When full, the vacuole expels the water through the membrane.

NUCLEUS

CYTOPLASM: *clear outside, grainy inside*

CHANNELS

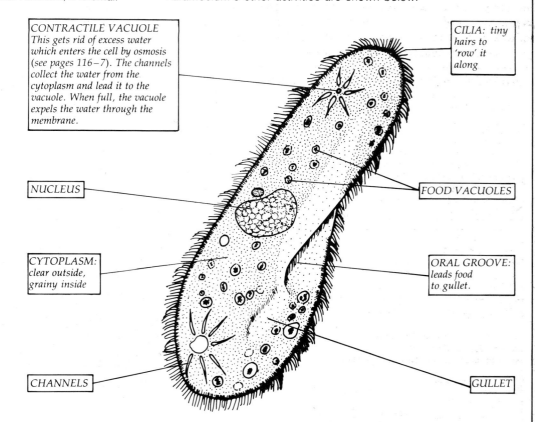

CILIA: *tiny hairs to 'row' it along*

FOOD VACUOLES

ORAL GROOVE: *leads food to gullet.*

GULLET

Feeding

The cilia round the **oral groove** brush the food down to the gullet. There it enters the cytoplasm, forming a food vacuole. Enzymes are added to digest it and the nutrients diffuse into the cytoplasm. As it is digested, it is moved in a circular path round the cell – a process known as **cyclosis**. Waste is put out through a weak spot in the membrane called the **anal pore**.

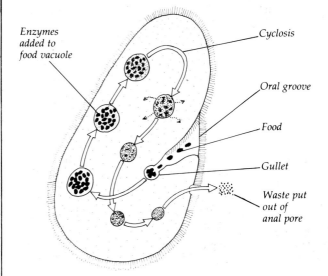

Enzymes added to food vacuole

Cyclosis

Oral groove

Food

Gullet

Waste put out of anal pore

Reproduction

Paramecium can reproduce very quickly (up to several times a day) by binary fission. First, two nuclei divide, then the cytoplasm is split to give two daughter cells.

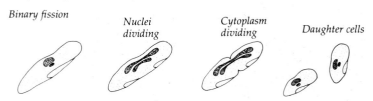

Binary fission

Nuclei dividing

Cytoplasm dividing

Daughter cells

Paramecium can also reproduce sexually. Two individuals come together and exchange parts of their nuclei. They then separate and each divides to give four new cells. This gives variety and strength to the species.

Sexual reproduction

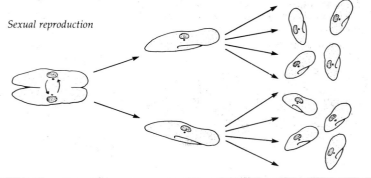

Spirogyra: a many-celled alga

Spirogyra is an **alga** (see page 8) which forms a green scum on the water of ponds and ditches. It consists of long threads or **filaments**. Each filament is a long chain of Spirogyra cells joined end to end. Spirogyra is a **multicellular** organism. However, unlike most multicellular organisms, Spirogyra cells are not given special jobs to do. Each cell can survive quite happily on its own. Indeed if cells are broken off, they often soon develop into separate filaments of their own. Being green plants, they can make their own food by **photosynthesis**. Their **gas exchange** needs (see page 112) for this and for respiration are simply met by dissolved gases diffusing in and out of the cells. Similarly, any minerals they need for growth simply diffuse in from the surrounding water.

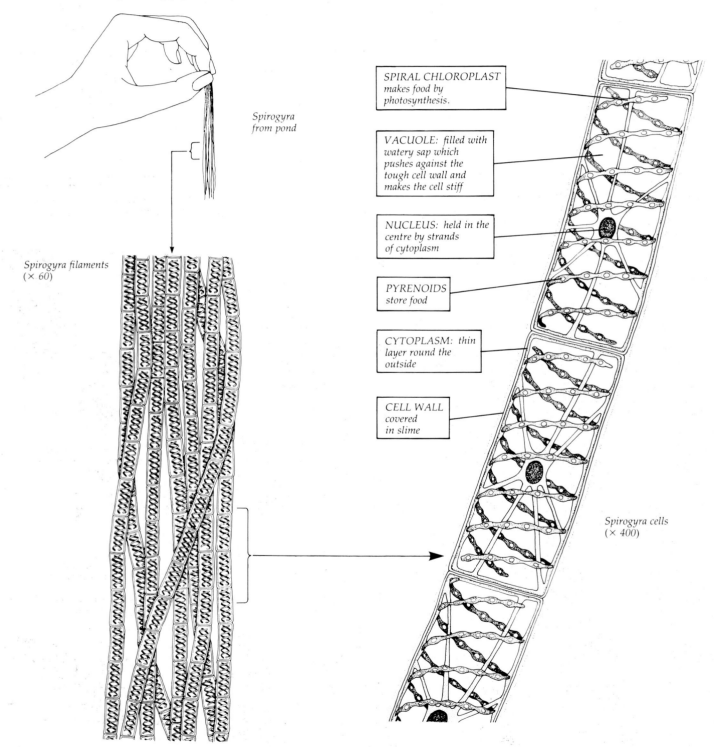

Spirogyra from pond

Spirogyra filaments (× 60)

SPIRAL CHLOROPLAST *makes food by photosynthesis.*

VACUOLE: *filled with watery sap which pushes against the tough cell wall and makes the cell stiff*

NUCLEUS: *held in the centre by strands of cytoplasm*

PYRENOIDS *store food*

CYTOPLASM: *thin layer round the outside*

CELL WALL *covered in slime*

Spirogyra cells (× 400)

New cells are added to the Spirogyra filament by **binary fission** of the older cells. Once a Spirogyra cell has grown to a certain length, it splits in the middle into the daughter cells. Unlike single-celled algae, the daughter cells do not separate, but stick together, so making the chain longer.

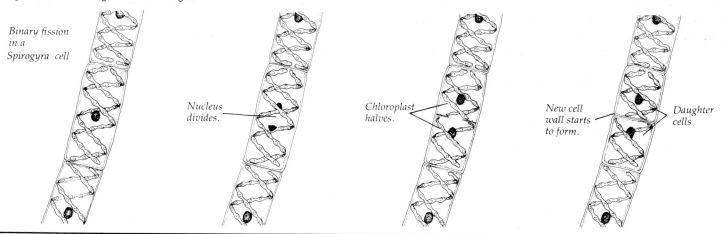

Binary fission in a Spirogyra cell

Nucleus divides.

Chloroplast halves.

New cell wall starts to form.

Daughter cells

SEXUAL REPRODUCTION IN SPIROGYRA takes place

when growing conditions become poor, for example, when there is drought or when the water becomes cooler in the autumn. Its purpose is to produce tough, resistant cells called **zygospores** which can survive in bad conditions and be ready to form new filaments when things improve. It begins with two filaments coming to lie side by side.

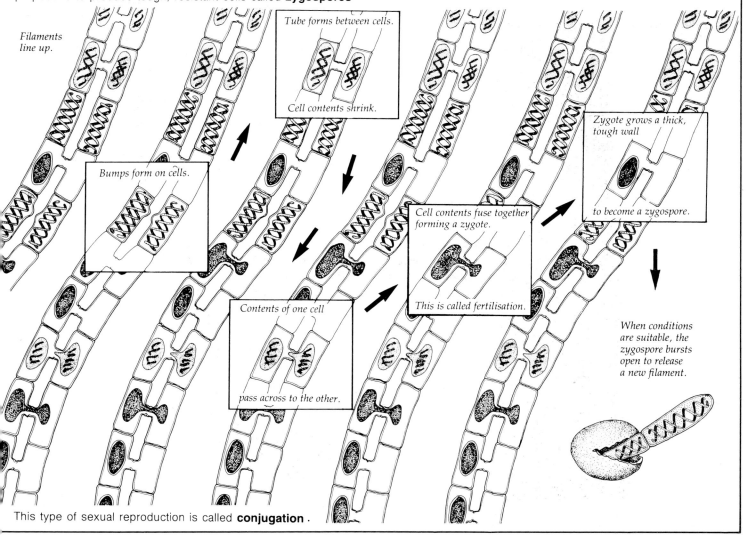

Filaments line up.

Tube forms between cells.

Cell contents shrink.

Bumps form on cells.

Contents of one cell pass across to the other.

Cell contents fuse together forming a zygote.

This is called fertilisation.

Zygote grows a thick, tough wall

to become a zygospore.

When conditions are suitable, the zygospore bursts open to release a new filament.

This type of sexual reproduction is called **conjugation**.

Mucor: a fungus

Mucor belongs to a group of plants called **fungi** (sing: *fungus*). Unlike most plants, fungi cannot make their own food by **photosynthesis**. Like animals they must get their food readymade for them. They do this in two ways. Some are **parasites** which feed on the tissues of other organisms while they are still living. Others, like Mucor, digest and absorb the remains of dead plants and animals. These fungi are called **saprophytes** (see also page 85). Saprophytes do a very important job. They cause dead organisms to decay, leaving behind simple substances which plants can use to help them to grow.

Mucor spreads by means of tiny cells called **spores** which are carried around by the air or by animals. When a spore lands on a suitable piece of moist food – bread, jam, or even dung – it germinates and tiny threads called **hyphae** (sing: *hypha*) grow from it. The hyphae are hollow tubes filled with liquid. They are not split up into separate cells. They grow down into the food and from their tips come digestive juices which dissolve the food so that it can be absorbed into the hyphae. They cannot go down too deep since they get their oxygen from the air around them. The deeper they go, the less oxygen there is.

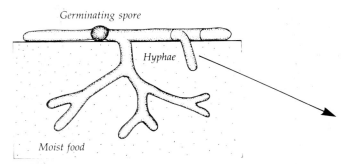

Germinating spore

Hyphae

Moist food

As the fungus develops, it appears as a fluffy white area on the surface of the food. This tangle of hyphae of which a fungus is made is called a **mycelium** (plu: *mycelia*). In Mucor little black dots appear on the mycelium. These are spore cases and give Mucor its common name of **pin mould**.

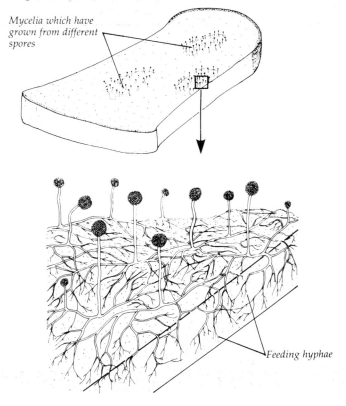

Mycelia which have grown from different spores

Feeding hyphae

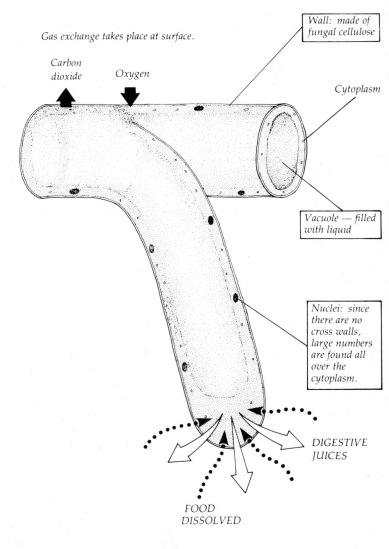

Gas exchange takes place at surface.

Wall: made of fungal cellulose

Carbon dioxide

Oxygen

Cytoplasm

Vacuole — filled with liquid

Nuclei: since there are no cross walls, large numbers are found all over the cytoplasm.

DIGESTIVE JUICES

FOOD DISSOLVED

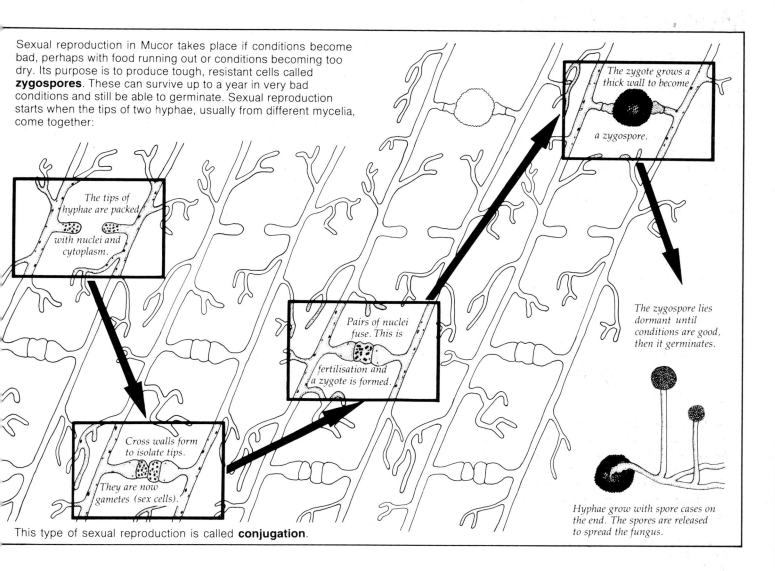

Sexual reproduction in Mucor takes place if conditions become bad, perhaps with food running out or conditions becoming too dry. Its purpose is to produce tough, resistant cells called **zygospores**. These can survive up to a year in very bad conditions and still be able to germinate. Sexual reproduction starts when the tips of two hyphae, usually from different mycelia, come together:

The tips of hyphae are packed with nuclei and cytoplasm.

Cross walls form to isolate tips.

They are now gametes (sex cells).

Pairs of nuclei fuse. This is fertilisation and a zygote is formed.

The zygote grows a thick wall to become a zygospore.

The zygospore lies dormant until conditions are good, then it germinates.

Hyphae grow with spore cases on the end. The spores are released to spread the fungus.

This type of sexual reproduction is called **conjugation**.

Once the mycelium is well established, branches start to grow upwards from the thicker hyphae at the surface. The tips of these branches are packed with **nuclei** and **cytoplasm**. The tips develop into black spore cases (also called **sporangia**), and inside them the nuclei and cytoplasm form into hundreds of tiny spores. Eventually the spore cases burst, releasing the spores. The spores are carried away by the wind or insects until they land on a piece of moist food where they begin the cycle again. The spores can survive for a long time and still germinate successfully.

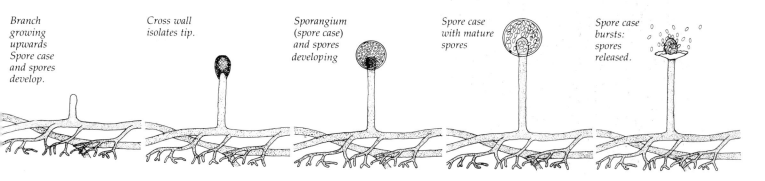

Branch growing upwards Spore case and spores develop.

Cross wall isolates tip.

Sporangium (spore case) and spores developing

Spore case with mature spores

Spore case bursts: spores released.

Liverwort: a non-flowering plant

Liverworts are small green plants that live in damp shady places, on stones, on the banks of ponds or streams, or on wet soil. The first plants that managed to move successfully from the water on to the land many millions of years ago are thought to have been quite like the liverworts alive today. Water plays a very important part in the life cycle of a liverwort. Liverworts are spread by tiny cells called **spores** carried by the wind. If a spore of the common liverwort **Pellia**, for example, lands on a suitable damp spot, it will germinate and grow into a sort of leaf called a **thallus**.

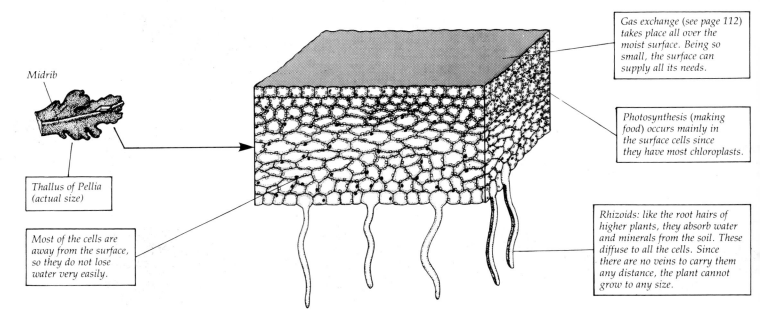

Midrib

Thallus of Pellia (actual size)

Most of the cells are away from the surface, so they do not lose water very easily.

Gas exchange (see page 112) takes place all over the moist surface. Being so small, the surface can supply all its needs.

Photosynthesis (making food) occurs mainly in the surface cells since they have most chloroplasts.

Rhizoids: like the root hairs of higher plants, they absorb water and minerals from the soil. These diffuse to all the cells. Since there are no veins to carry them any distance, the plant cannot grow to any size.

This part of Pellia's life cycle takes part in early spring. In early summer male and female sex organs appear. The male sex organs are called **antheridia** (sing: *antheridium*). The antheridia make tiny male **gametes** (sex cells) called **sperms**. Each sperm has two **flagella** so it can swim to the female organs. Each female organ, called an **archegonium** (plu: *archegonia*), contains a female egg cell waiting to be fertilised. When the plant is wet, the sperms burst from the antheridia and swim along the surface of the plant to the archegonia. One sperm fuses with each egg to form a **zygote** or fertilised egg.

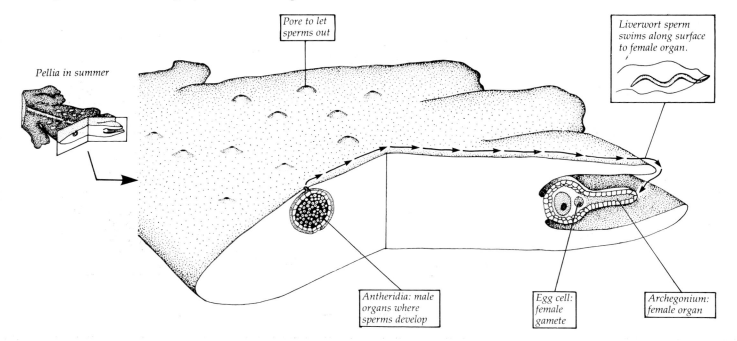

Pore to let sperms out

Liverwort sperm swims along surface to female organ.

Pellia in summer

Antheridia: male organs where sperms develop

Egg cell: female gamete

Archegonium: female organ

After fertilisation, the zygote grows into an embryo plant. It has a foot which takes nourishment from the parent plant and a stalk with a capsule full of spores at the end.

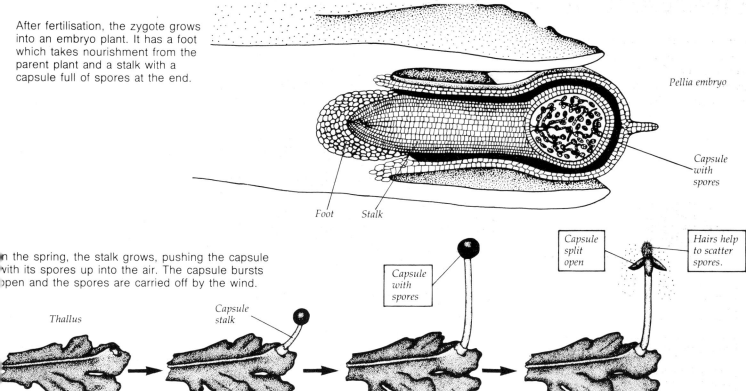

Pellia embryo

Capsule with spores

Foot *Stalk*

In the spring, the stalk grows, pushing the capsule with its spores up into the air. The capsule bursts open and the spores are carried off by the wind.

Capsule split open

Hairs help to scatter spores.

Capsule with spores

Thallus

Capsule stalk

THE ALTERNATION OF GENERATIONS

In the life of Pellia, there are two distinct stages or generations. Firstly, there is the **sexual generation**. This is the plant which produces the gametes (sex cells) sperms and eggs. This is called the **gametophyte** (*gameto:* gamete: *phyte* plant). After the sexual generation comes the **asexual generation** (see page 169). This is the plant which produces the spores. This is called the **sporophyte** (*sporo:* spore; *phyte:* plant). Although the sporophyte stays on the parent plant, it is, in fact, a separate organism. This situation, where the two generations continually follow one another, is called the alternation of generations. Mosses and ferns have a similar life cycle.

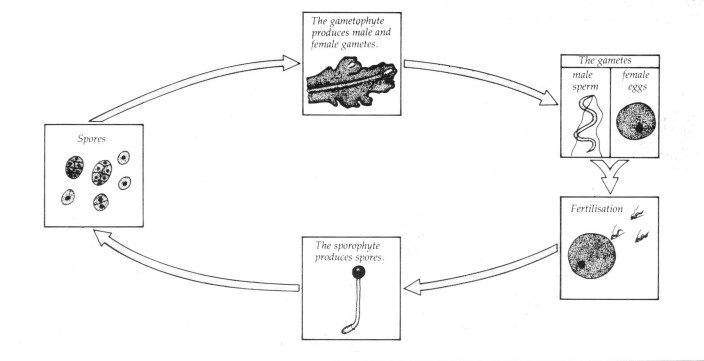

The gametophyte produces male and female gametes.

The gametes

male sperm | *female eggs*

Spores

Fertilisation

The sporophyte produces spores.

31

Hydra: a coelenterate

Hydra is a small member of the **coelenterates** – the jelly-fish family. Hydra lives attached to water plants in ponds and streams. It is really just a hollow tube with a hole at one end for a mouth. Round the mouth is a ring of 'arms' called tentacles. Hydra lives by catching small water creatures and consuming them. It is a **multicellular** (many-celled) animal but, unlike Spirogyra (see pages 26–7), as Hydra grows, its cells **differentiate** (become different) from each other so that they become suited to do one particular job. The diagram below shows the structure of a Hydra and the kinds of cell it is made of.

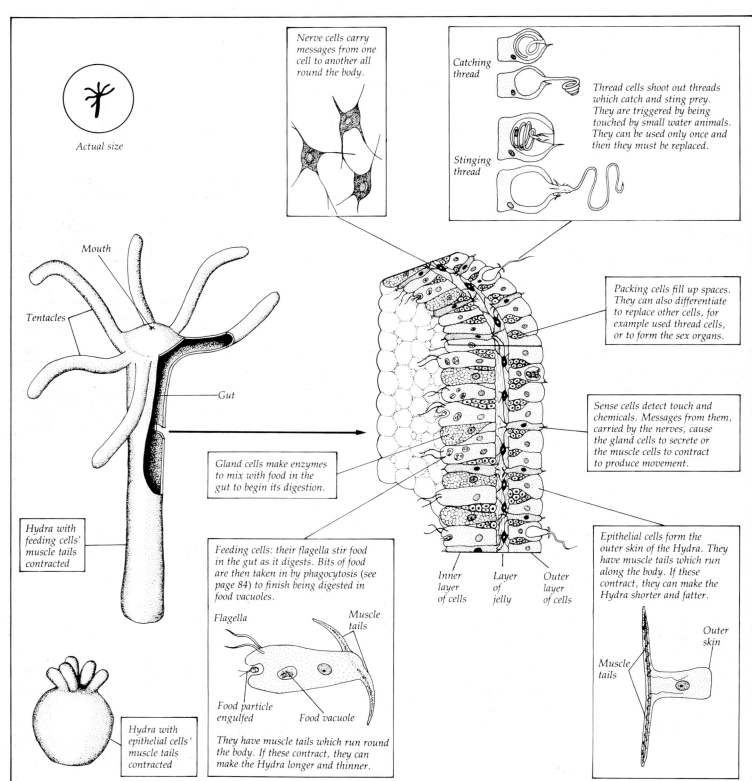

Actual size

Nerve cells carry messages from one cell to another all round the body.

Catching thread

Stinging thread

Thread cells shoot out threads which catch and sting prey. They are triggered by being touched by small water animals. They can be used only once and then they must be replaced.

Mouth

Tentacles

Gut

Packing cells fill up spaces. They can also differentiate to replace other cells, for example used thread cells, or to form the sex organs.

Sense cells detect touch and chemicals. Messages from them, carried by the nerves, cause the gland cells to secrete or the muscle cells to contract to produce movement.

Gland cells make enzymes to mix with food in the gut to begin its digestion.

Hydra with feeding cells' muscle tails contracted

Feeding cells: their flagella stir food in the gut as it digests. Bits of food are then taken in by phagocytosis (see page 84) to finish being digested in food vacuoles.

Inner layer of cells

Layer of jelly

Outer layer of cells

Epithelial cells form the outer skin of the Hydra. They have muscle tails which run along the body. If these contract, they can make the Hydra shorter and fatter.

Flagella

Muscle tails

Food particle engulfed

Food vacuole

They have muscle tails which run round the body. If these contract, they can make the Hydra longer and thinner.

Muscle tails

Outer skin

Hydra with epithelial cells' muscle tails contracted

HYDRA IN ACTION

The different types of cells which make up the Hydra do not act on their own. They work as a team so that the animal can do everything needed to survive and to reproduce itself.

Feeding

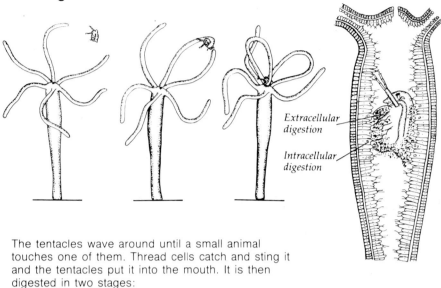

Extracellular digestion

Intracellular digestion

The tentacles wave around until a small animal touches one of them. Thread cells catch and sting it and the tentacles put it into the mouth. It is then digested in two stages:
1 **Extracellular** (outside the cell) digestion – enzymes from the gland cells break it into smaller pieces in the gut.
2 **Intracellular** (inside the cell) digestion – small bits are taken in by the feeding cells which finish digestion. The amino acids, etc., which this produces, can then diffuse to the surrounding cells.

Movement

Apart from feeding movements, Hydra can move itself from place to place like this:

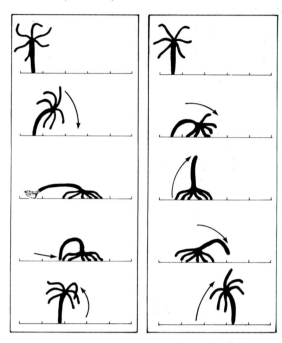

Movement and other cell activities require oxygen. Dissolved oxygen diffuses from the water into all the Hydra's cells. Carbon dioxide, or other waste which is produced, diffuses from the cells into the water.

Asexual reproduction

When growing conditions are good, small bumps called buds appear on Hydra. These develop into 'baby' Hydra and, when they are big enough, they break away to live on their own. Asexual, or vegetative, reproduction like this is very common in plants, but can only happen in very simple animals.

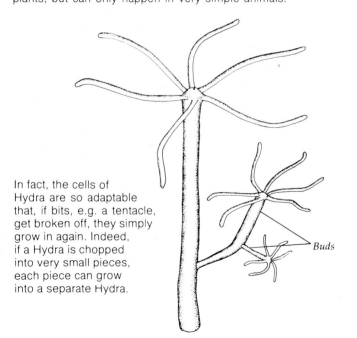

In fact, the cells of Hydra are so adaptable that, if bits, e.g. a tentacle, get broken off, they simply grow in again. Indeed, if a Hydra is chopped into very small pieces, each piece can grow into a separate Hydra.

Buds

Sexual reproduction

In the autumn, when conditions become poor, Hydra grows sex organs – several male organs called **testes** and one female **ovary**. These ripen at different times. So, when the male sex cells, called sperms, are ready, they burst from the testes and swim to the ovary of another Hydra:

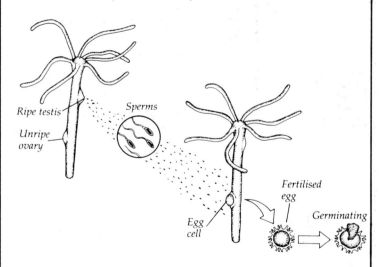

Ripe testis

Unripe ovary

Sperms

Fertilised egg

Germinating

Egg cell

There one sperm fuses with (fertilises) the single egg made by the ovary. The fertilised egg, or **zygote**, grows a tough coat and falls to the bottom of the pond. It can survive the winter like this and, when better weather comes, it can germinate and form a new Hydra.

Tapeworm: a flatworm

Tapeworms are a group of flatworms which live as **parasites** inside the intestines of vertebrates, including humans. A parasite is an organism which lives off another organism, called the **host**, while the host is still alive. A parasite usually causes some kind of harm to its host. A tapeworm leads a very comfortable protected life inside its host and so its body is very simple. It does not need a mouth or a digestive system since its flat body has enough surface to absorb all the food it needs, ready digested, from the host's gut. It has very simple nerves and muscles since there are no enemies to run away from. Since there is no oxygen in the host's gut, it uses **anaerobic respiration** (see page 96) and any waste produced is put out into the gut. This leaves the tapeworm two main problems: first, it must stop itself being pushed out of the host's gut; second, since each host can only support one tapeworm, it needs a method of reproduction which will spread the infection to other hosts. The pork tapeworm shows how these problems are solved. Pork tapeworms grow inside humans who have eaten infected pork.

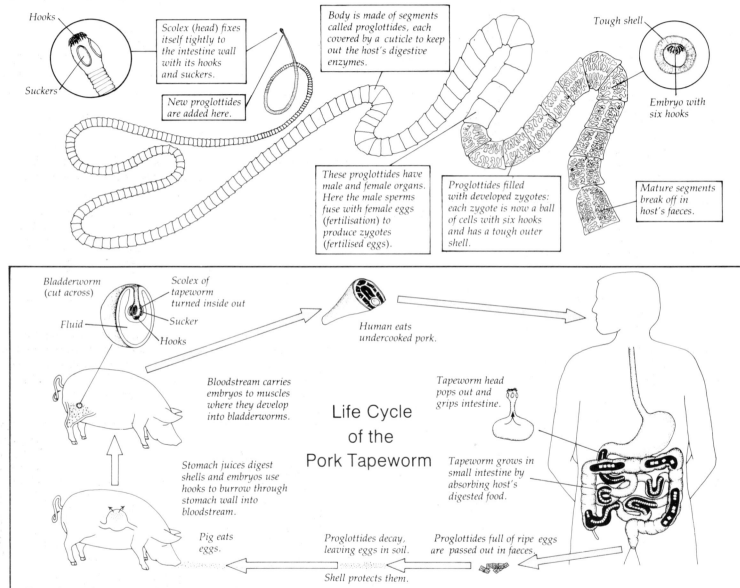

Hooks

Suckers

Scolex (head) fixes itself tightly to the intestine wall with its hooks and suckers.

New proglottides are added here.

Body is made of segments called proglottides, each covered by a cuticle to keep out the host's digestive enzymes.

These proglottides have male and female organs. Here the male sperms fuse with female eggs (fertilisation) to produce zygotes (fertilised eggs).

Proglottides filled with developed zygotes: each zygote is now a ball of cells with six hooks and has a tough outer shell.

Tough shell

Embryo with six hooks

Mature segments break off in host's faeces.

Bladderworm (cut across)

Scolex of tapeworm turned inside out

Fluid

Sucker

Hooks

Human eats undercooked pork.

Bloodstream carries embryos to muscles where they develop into bladderworms.

Tapeworm head pops out and grips intestine.

Life Cycle of the Pork Tapeworm

Tapeworm grows in small intestine by absorbing host's digested food.

Stomach juices digest shells and embryos use hooks to burrow through stomach wall into bloodstream.

Pig eats eggs.

Proglottides decay, leaving eggs in soil.

Shell protects them.

Proglottides full of ripe eggs are passed out in faeces.

Thus the pork tapeworm has two hosts. The human, where it grows to maturity and may live for up to 20 years, is called the **primary host**. The pig, which spreads the tapeworm to humans, is called the **secondary host**. By using the pig, a source of human food, in this way, the tapeworm makes sure that it will be eaten by humans. Even so, the chances that a pig will eat tapeworm eggs are still very small. So, the tapeworm must produce vast numbers of eggs.

Tapeworms are not necessarily very dangerous. Apart from having to eat a lot or losing weight, a healthy human may not notice them. However, in children or adults weakened perhaps by starvation, tapeworms may cause pain or even vomiting. Also, tapeworm eggs may get into the bloodstream and lodge in vital organs, including the brain, and cause serious illness or even death. In most countries, such problems are prevented by keeping human sewage away from pigs and by carefully inspecting pork. Thorough cooking of meat will kill tapeworms.

There are other kinds of tapeworm, but, in every case, the secondary host forms part of the diet of the primary host.

Earthworm: an annelid

Earthworms belong to the **phylum** of **annelids** – the true worms. Their bodies are made of a number of rings called **segments**.

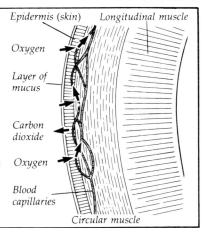

Segments

Mouth

Saddle: used in reproduction

A partition separates each segment, though the gut, nerves and blood vessels pass through it.

Longitudinal muscle makes the body shorter and fatter.

Circular muscle makes the body longer and thinner.

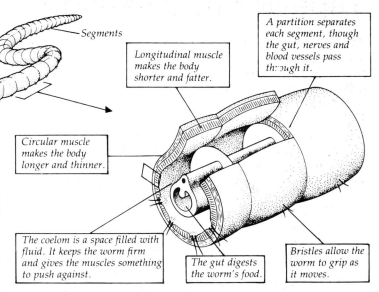

The coelom is a space filled with fluid. It keeps the worm firm and gives the muscles something to push against.

The gut digests the worm's food.

Bristles allow the worm to grip as it moves.

The worm can absorb all the oxygen it needs through its surface. The oxygen dissolves in a layer of slimy **mucus** on the skin and diffuses into the body. However, the worm is just too big for the oxygen to reach everywhere by diffusion, so, it gets picked up by the **haemoglobin** in the blood flowing through the skin capillaries and this takes it all over the body. Carbon dioxide leaves the body in the opposite direction.

Epidermis (skin)   Longitudinal muscle

Oxygen

Layer of mucus

Carbon dioxide

Oxygen

Blood capillaries

Circular muscle

All earthworms have both male and female sex organs, therefore each worm can produce both male sperm and female egg cells. However, they do not let their eggs become fertilised by their own sperm. The first stage in sexual reproduction occurs when two worms come to the surface on a warm damp night to exchange sperm.

Sperms leave male openings and swim along sperm grooves into the opening of the other worm.

Worms are held together by mucus from the saddles and also by some of the bristles.

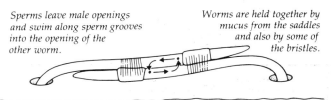

All worms eat some soil and digest any plant remains in it. This is finely ground up inside them and when they deposit it back in the earth, it is good for the soil's texture. Some worms leave it on the surface as **worm casts** and this helps to mix the different layers of soil.

Once each worm has some of the other's sperm, they go back into their burrows. Over the next few months they use the sperm to fertilise their eggs. The fertilised eggs are laid inside **cocoons** made by the saddle. About twelve weeks after the cocoons are laid, one worm hatches from each cocoon.

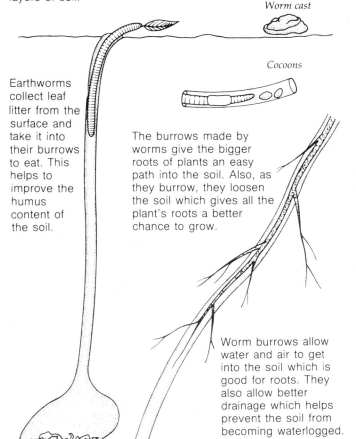

Worm cast

Cocoons

Earthworms collect leaf litter from the surface and take it into their burrows to eat. This helps to improve the humus content of the soil.

The burrows made by worms give the bigger roots of plants an easy path into the soil. Also, as they burrow, they loosen the soil which gives all the plant's roots a better chance to grow.

Worm burrows allow water and air to get into the soil which is good for roots. They also allow better drainage which helps prevent the soil from becoming waterlogged.

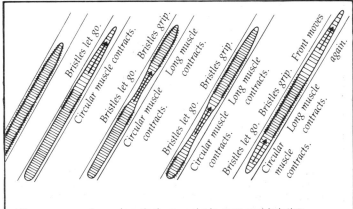

Bristles let go. Circular muscle contracts. Bristles let go. Bristles grip. Long muscle contracts. Bristles grip. Bristles let go. Circular muscle contracts. Bristles let go. Long muscle contracts. Circular muscle contracts. Bristles grip. Bristles let go. Bristles grip. Front moves again. Circular muscle contracts. Long muscle contracts.

Worms move by using their muscle layers and bristles together. The circular muscles contract and stretch part of the body forward. This part then grips on with its bristles and contracts its longitudinal muscles to get thicker again. This process of stretching, gripping and thickening starts at the head and works backwards towards the tail.

The bee: a social insect

Honey bees belong to the **arthropod phylum**. The arthropods are a large group of **invertebrates** whose bodies are divided into sections called **segments** and whose legs are jointed. Honey bees belong to the largest **class** in the arthropod phylum – the insects. An insect's body is divided into three parts: the **head**, the **thorax** and the **abdomen**. Insects have six legs and they usually have wings, often two pairs. The parts of the honey bee's body are shown in the diagram below.

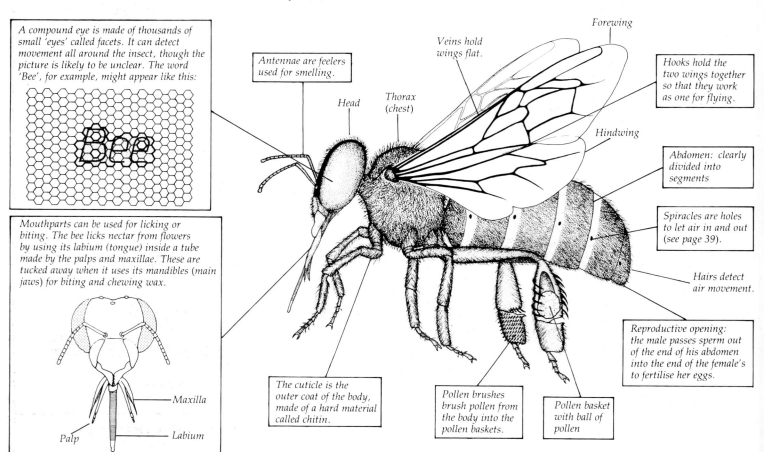

A compound eye is made of thousands of small 'eyes' called facets. It can detect movement all around the insect, though the picture is likely to be unclear. The word 'Bee', for example, might appear like this:

Mouthparts can be used for licking or biting. The bee licks nectar from flowers by using its labium (tongue) inside a tube made by the palps and maxillae. These are tucked away when it uses its mandibles (main jaws) for biting and chewing wax.

Maxilla
Palp
Labium

Antennae are feelers used for smelling.

Head

Thorax (chest)

Veins hold wings flat.

Forewing

Hooks hold the two wings together so that they work as one for flying.

Hindwing

Abdomen: clearly divided into segments

Spiracles are holes to let air in and out (see page 39).

Hairs detect air movement.

Reproductive opening: the male passes sperm out of the end of his abdomen into the end of the female's to fertilise her eggs.

The cuticle is the outer coat of the body, made of a hard material called chitin.

Pollen brushes brush pollen from the body into the pollen baskets.

Pollen basket with ball of pollen

LIFE OF THE HONEY BEE

Honey bees are **social insects**. This means that they live together in large numbers. A hive or nest can have up to 80 000 bees living in it. A hive is a very organised community and each bee has its own part to play in it. There are three types of bees in a hive – the **queen**, the **workers** and the **drones**.

The workers do all the work.

Worker
(sterile female)

The drones provide sperm.

Drone
(fertile male)

The queen lays eggs.

Queen
(fertile female)

Most bees in a hive are workers. Workers are female but their reproductive organs do not develop so they are **sterile**. However, their food-gathering organs are much bigger than the queen's or the drones'. In summer they live for three to four weeks before they die from overwork. Some of the jobs they do are shown on page 37.

The drones are male bees. They develop from eggs which have not been fertilised. There may be a few hundred in a hive, but, on the 'wedding flight', only one or two can catch and mate with the queen. They live for about five weeks, but all of them are killed or driven off by the workers before the winter.

When a new queen hatches, she flies off with the drones (males) and mates in mid-air with one or two. Since she can store sperm, she need mate only once in her life (she can live up to five years). Back at the hive, she lays eggs, often thousands each day. A hive has only one queen since the first queen to emerge stings to death any rivals before they hatch out.

Workers gather food

Scout bees fly off to find food. When they do, they go back to the hive and do a kind of dance on the comb. Watching this, the others can tell how far away and in what direction to go to get the food.

ROUND DANCE

Round dance (food near)

Food less than 100 m away – the faster the dance, the nearer the food

TAIL WAGGING DANCE

Figure of eight dance (food far)

Direction of waggle run indicates direction of food. Speed of waggle run indicates distance.

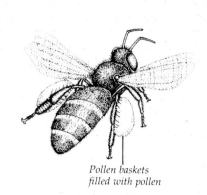

Worker uses long tongue to lick up nectar.

Tongue

Nectary

Pollen baskets filled with pollen

Workers take nectar and pollen from flowers. These are later used as food, with extra nectar being stored as honey. Bees are important for they **pollinate** lots of flowers and any extra honey they make can be harvested by humans as a source of food.

Workers make the combs

Workers have a special gland to make **wax**. With their special mandibles, they mould this into six-sided boxes called **cells**. The queen lays eggs in these cells. Large cells, called **queen cells**, are used for rearing new queens. Old cells are used to store honey or a mixture of nectar and pollen called **bee bread**. The cells are hung in a double layer called a **comb**.

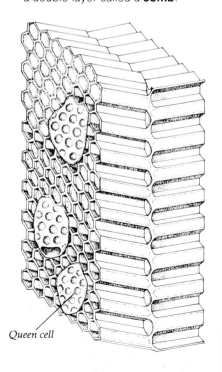

Queen cell

Workers feed the young

The queen lays one egg in each cell. This hatches into a grub or **larva**. The workers feed it until it is ready to turn into a **pupa**, then they cap its cell with wax. The new bee later chews its way out. It takes about three weeks for an egg to develop into a new worker.

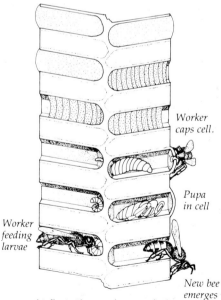

Worker caps cell.

Pupa in cell

Worker feeding larvae

New bee emerges

At first, the grubs are fed a rich food called **royal jelly**. They are then switched to bee bread. Young queens, however, are fed only on royal jelly and this makes them turn into queens instead of workers.

Workers guard the hive

Insects with the wrong smell are stung if they try to enter the hive.

Workers regulate temperature

If the hive is too hot, they fan the air with their wings to cool it.

If it is too cool, they swarm over the combs to keep the eggs and larvae warm.

Swarming

The queen and workers survive the winter by feeding on their stores of food from the summer. In spring, before the new queen hatches, the old queen and most of the workers leave to set up a new nest elsewhere. This is called swarming.

Swarm of bees in a tree

The butterfly

Butterflies belong to the class of insects, the largest class in the **arthropod phylum**. Arthropods are animals which have jointed legs and whose bodies are divided into a number of sections called **segments**. The arthropods are **invertebrates**. Their bodies are supported, not by bones, but by a tough outer covering called an **exoskeleton**. The body is in three parts – the **head**, **thorax** and **abdomen**. Attached to the thorax are six legs and usually, as is the case with the butterfly, two pairs of wings.

Most insects are land animals and some of the adaptations which allow them to survive on land are described below. The butterfly we are looking at on these two pages is a common one known as the Large White or Cabbage White Butterfly (Latin name: *Pieris brassicae*).

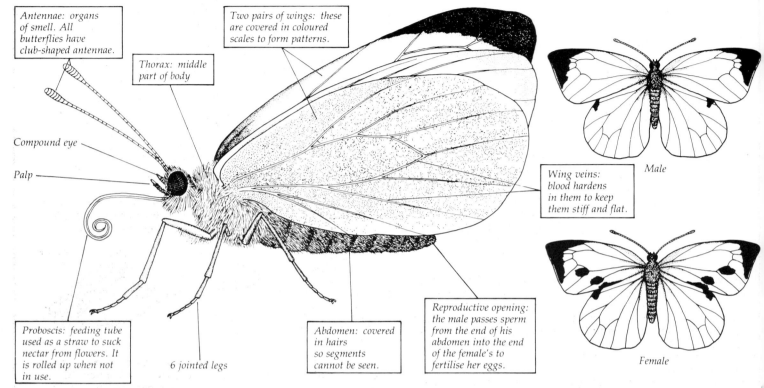

Antennae: organs of smell. All butterflies have club-shaped antennae.

Two pairs of wings: these are covered in coloured scales to form patterns.

Thorax: middle part of body

Compound eye

Palp

Wing veins: blood hardens in them to keep them stiff and flat.

Male

Proboscis: feeding tube used as a straw to suck nectar from flowers. It is rolled up when not in use.

6 jointed legs

Abdomen: covered in hairs so segments cannot be seen.

Reproductive opening: the male passes sperm from the end of his abdomen into the end of the female's to fertilise her eggs.

Female

MOVEMENT AND FLIGHT

The exoskeleton of an insect is called the **cuticle**. The cuticle is waterproof, a major advantage for a land animal since it reduces water loss. It is made mainly of a very hard substance called **chitin**. This supports the body and protects it from damage. It does not stop movement, however. Pairs of muscles inside the exoskeleton can move the joints in this fashion:

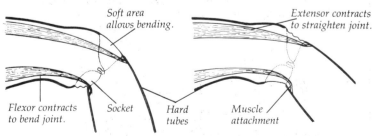

Soft area allows bending.

Extensor contracts to straighten joint.

Flexor contracts to bend joint.

Socket

Hard tubes

Muscle attachment

This is possible because, wherever movement is needed, between leg joints, say, or body segments, there is no chitin. This makes the cuticle thin and flexible at that point, so allowing movement to take place.

Butterflies, in fact, do not walk much. Instead, they use their legs for perching on flowers. Caterpillars, on the other hand, since they have no wings, must walk. To help them get about, they have six true legs like the adult butterfly, but they also have **prolegs**. These are pads covered with hooks which they use to grip with as they move their bodies.

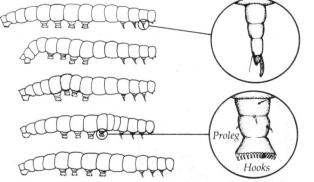

Proleg

Hooks

One major reason for the success of the insects on land has been their ability to fly. Like the leg muscles, the muscles which move the wings, are inside the exoskeleton. In the butterfly, unlike in some other insects, the flight muscles are attached directly to the wings, which they move as shown in the diagram below.

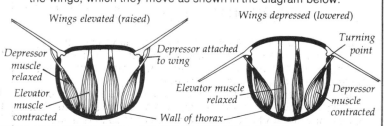

Wings elevated (raised)

Wings depressed (lowered)

Depressor muscle relaxed

Elevator muscle contracted

Depressor attached to wing

Turning point

Elevator muscle relaxed

Wall of thorax

Depressor muscle contracted

FEEDING

Adult butterflies feed on **nectar**, a sugary liquid produced by flowers. They uncoil their long **proboscis**, place it inside a flower and, using it like a straw, they suck up the nectar. The proboscis is in two parts which are hooked together. They can be taken apart for cleaning.

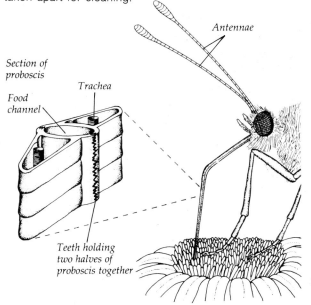

Antennae

Section of proboscis

Trachea

Food channel

Teeth holding two halves of proboscis together

Butterflies are useful because, as they feed from flowers, they also pollinate them (see page 188). The completely different feeding methods of the caterpillars, however, make them a serious pest. In place of a proboscis, a caterpillar has hard jaws called **mandibles**. It uses these to cut up and chew cabbage leaves for its food. This can cause considerable damage.

Sense organs

Butterflies have two large **compound** eyes. They cannot see clearly with these, but they can judge distances and they can detect the slightest movement around them. Each eye is made of thousands of separate 'seeing units' called **ommatidia**. Each ommatidium detects a small part of the view around the insect.

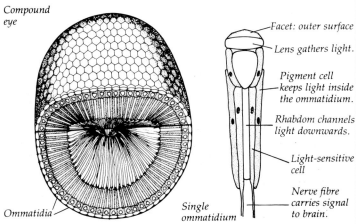

Compound eye

Facet: outer surface

Lens gathers light.

Pigment cell keeps light inside the ommatidium.

Rhabdom channels light downwards.

Light-sensitive cell

Nerve fibre carries signal to brain.

Ommatidia

Single ommatidium

The main organs of smell are the two long **antennae**, although the palps are also used. The palps, however, are really for tasting with. Strangely, the feet also contain taste organs, so the butterfly can actually taste with its feet.

Despite their hard cuticle, insects are very sensitive to touch. The hairs all over their bodies are, in fact, touch detectors. The tiniest movement of one of these hairs is noticed instantly.

GAS EXCHANGE

Being a land animal, the butterfly needs air to breathe. The air enters its body through holes called **spiracles** along its sides. It then passes into a network of air tubes called **tracheae** (sing: *trachea*) which has branches going to every part of the body. This is called the **tracheal system**. A fraction of it is drawn below.

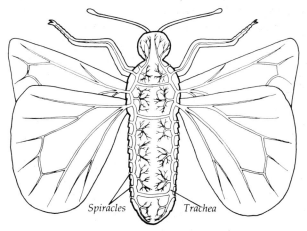

Spiracles   *Trachea*

The finest end branches in the system are tiny fluid-filled tubes called **tracheoles**. Oxygen diffuses out of the tracheoles and into the surrounding cells. Carbon dioxide diffuses the other way.

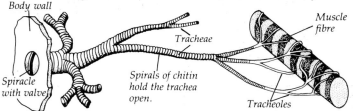

Body wall

Tracheae

Muscle fibre

Spiracle with valve

Spirals of chitin hold the trachea open.

Tracheoles

To cut down on the amount of water lost from the spiracles, they are equipped with valves. These are opened only when the insect needs air. When it is very active, it can increase its air supply by making pumping movements with its abdomen. This is called **ventilation**.

REPRODUCTION

Cabbage White butterflies live as adults for only about three weeks. During that time they mate. The males are attracted to the females by their scent. The eggs are fertilised inside the female's body (internal fertilisation). She then lays them, up to 100 at a time, by sticking them to the underside of a cabbage leaf.

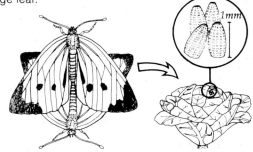

1mm

Protected from drying out by the tough, waterproof egg shells, the **larvae** (caterpillars) hatch out in about a week. Their first meal is their egg shell. They then start eating the leaf on which they were laid. The butterfly develops from the caterpillar by a process called **complete metamorphosis** (see pages 182–3). Cabbage Whites produce two broods (generations) each year, one in May/June and one in August/September.

Mosquito: insect danger

Many insects are beneficial to people. These are the ones which pollinate flowers, produce honey, eat harmful organisms and provide food for useful ones. Other insects cause damage and disease. Throughout the centuries one insect has caused more suffering and death than any other. That insect is the tiny mosquito or gnat. The male mosquito which feeds on nectar is harmless enough. The female, however, sucks blood. Without a meal of blood, she cannot produce eggs.

The mouthparts of the female mosquito, shown in the diagram below, are perfectly adapted for this unpleasant habit.

MOSQUITO SUCKING BLOOD

The mouthparts of the female mosquito contain four sharp daggers or **stylets**. The skin is pierced with these. Saliva is then injected into the wound. (Mosquito saliva contains an agent which prevents blood clotting.) Blood can then be sucked up easily through the tube-like **proboscis**. An organism, like the mosquito, which feeds on another, still living, organism is called a **parasite**. Its victim is called the **host**.

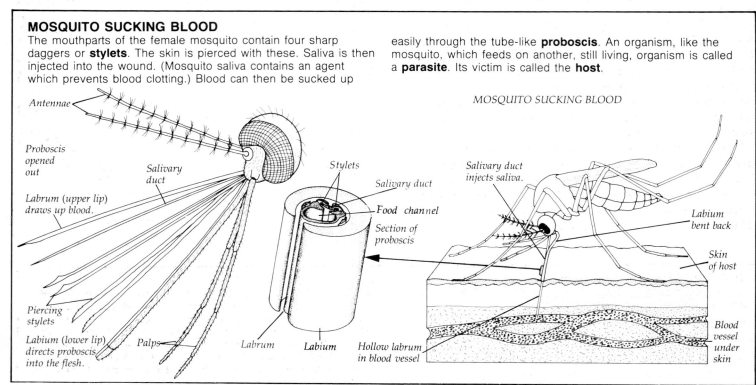

MOSQUITO SUCKING BLOOD

Malaria and the anopheline mosquito

All mosquitos can be annoying, but there are certain species, known as **anopheline mosquitos**, which are also very dangerous. These mosquitos, which mainly live in hot countries, may carry **malaria**. Malaria has long been the world's number one killer disease. In 1955, for example, it was estimated that 250 million people, one tenth of the world's population, were suffering from malaria. Two and a half million of these died of the disease. Anopheline mosquitos do not actually *cause* malaria. Malaria is caused by another parasite. This is a microscopic single-celled animal: a **protozoan** called **Plasmodium**. When an infected mosquito pierces the skin to obtain blood, plasmodium parasites are injected into the bloodstream along with the saliva. Within half an hour all the Plasmodium have lodged within liver cells where they multiply in number over the next week or two.

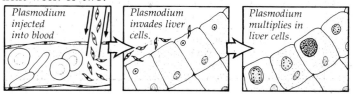

The parasites then leave the liver and invade red blood cells. More multiplication takes place and, finally, the blood cells burst open, releasing the Plasmodium and various **toxins** (poisons) into the blood.

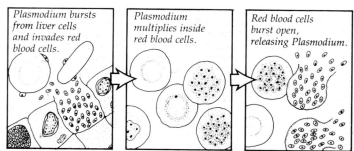

The parasites find fresh red blood cells to attack and two days later these too explode, and so on.

The actual course of the disease is in four stages.

The incubation period
As the parasites multiply in the liver, there are no symptoms. Towards the end of this period (6–16 days) the person starts to feel unwell.

The shivering fit
Although the body temperature is really above normal, the patient begins to shiver, feels cold and is unable to get warm. This lasts about an hour.

The fever
The patient becomes burning hot with temperatures up to 41.1°C. During this stage the infected blood cells are bursting open. The fever lasts several hours.

The sweating stage
For the next two to three hours sweat pours from the patient. Usually, the victim, although weak, recovers. Sometimes, however, the symptoms become so severe that death results. Without medical treatment, these attacks will be repeated, usually every two days for a few weeks. Even then, though the person seems fully recovered, the disease returns in a few months or a few years. There are a number of **anti-malarial drugs** available which can prevent attacks and eventually cure the disease.

Where do anopheline mosquitos pick up malarial parasites in the first place? The answer is from humans. When the mosquito sucks the blood of an infected human into its stomach, it also sucks in Plasmodium. The parasite breeds in the insect's stomach and then moves on to the salivary glands, ready to be injected with the saliva into the next host. An animal such as the mosquito, which transmits a parasite or disease from one individual to another is called a **vector** or carrier. While anopheline mosquitos are the vectors of malaria, other species of mosquito are vectors of other diseases such as yellow fever.

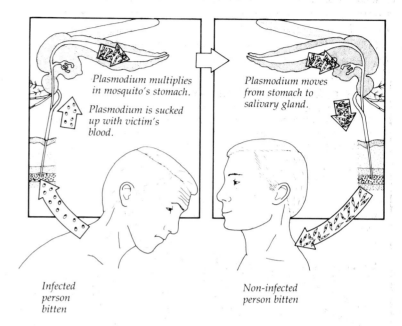

Plasmodium multiplies in mosquito's stomach.

Plasmodium is sucked up with victim's blood.

Plasmodium moves from stomach to salivary gland.

Infected person bitten

Non-infected person bitten

THE CONTROL OF MALARIA
Once the cause of malaria was known, it became possible to control it. This can be done in a number of ways:

By attacking Plasmodium
Mosquitos are not born carriers of malaria. They pick up the malarial parasite (*Plasmodium*) when they suck the blood of an infected human. The chances of this are reduced if:
(a) infected persons take antimalarial drugs to clear *Plasmodium* from their blood;
(b) non-infected persons in malarial areas take anti-malarial drugs to prevent *Plasmodium* from getting a hold.
The oldest drug known to be successful against malaria is **quinine**, first used in the seventeenth century.

By preventing mosquito bites
Malaria can only be caught from the bite of an infected female Anopheline mosquito. In malarial areas, this is prevented by:
(a) wearing clothing which covers arms and legs;
(b) covering open windows and doors with fine wire mesh to keep mosquitos out and screening beds and tents with muslin mosquito netting. (It is especially important that infected persons are screened from mosquitos to stop the disease from spreading.)
(c) spraying houses with a contact insecticide such as DDT. When the adult mosquito lands on this, it dies. One spraying gives protection for several months. However, if insecticides are used in large quantities, they can cause problems, for example, the insects become immune to them and they no longer work. Also, the insecticides remain active for a very long time and may harm other animals, especially when concentrated by food chains (see pages 234–5).

By attacking mosquito larvae and pupae
For hundreds of years, malaria has been associated with marshes and swamps. It was thought to be caused by the foul gases which rise from such places. The disease, in fact, took its name from the Italian words for 'bad air' (*mala*: bad; *aria*: air). We now know what the connection really is. Mosquitos need water to breed. The female mosquito lays her eggs on the surface of water. When these become larvae and pupae (see below), they stay underwater. They need air to breath, however, and they get this through a breathing tube to the surface. Mosquitos will breed in any patch of still water – puddles, lakes, marshes, even wells will do.

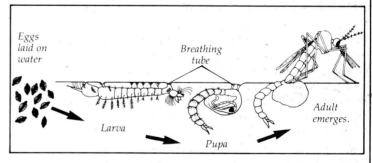

Eggs laid on water

Breathing tube

Adult emerges.

Larva

Pupa

The larva stage is a most vulnerable period in a mosquito's life and it can be attacked by:
(a) spraying the water with oil. This causes the insects to sink and they drown. If the spray contains an insecticide, it is even more effective.
(b) stocking lakes or wells with small minnows which like to feed on the larvae and pupae.
(c) draining the swamps. This is the best long-term solution.
By waging war on the disease using the methods outlined above, whole countries, such as the USA, the USSR, Italy, and Holland, have been completely freed of malaria. It is hoped that sometime in the not too distant future malaria will be completely wiped out.

Fish: the brown trout

Fish belong to the **phylum chordata**. They are vertebrates, which means they have a backbone and skeleton inside their bodies to support them. In some fish, called **cartilaginous** fish, the skeleton is made of a flexible material called **cartilage**. The cartilaginous fish include the sharks and the rays. Most fish, however, have much harder, bony skeletons.

Fish are **cold-blooded** animals. This means that the temperature of their bodies rises and falls with the water temperature around them. They are, of course, completely **aquatic** animals and they are well adapted for their life underwater. There are about 27 000 different species of fish of all shapes and sizes (see page 5). However, to get a general idea of what fish are like, we will look at just one species here: the brown trout (Latin name: *Salmo trutta*).

THE TROUT

The trout lives in clear, fast-running fresh water in rivers, lakes and streams where it feeds on insects, small crustaceans and small fish. Its body is between 15 and 35 cm long and is protected by a layer of fine scales. Slimy mucus spread over the surface of the scales keeps out water and prevents infection.

Water is a very dense substance in which to move about, so 60% of the trout's body is made of muscle. The body is also slender and streamlined to offer the minimum of resistance to the passing water. Fins, stiffened by bony struts, are used to adjust and correct the swimming movements.

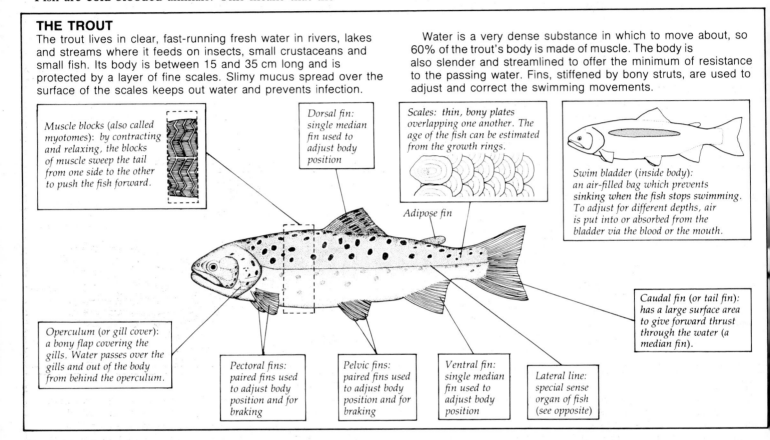

Muscle blocks (also called myotomes): by contracting and relaxing, the blocks of muscle sweep the tail from one side to the other to push the fish forward.

Dorsal fin: single median fin used to adjust body position

Scales: thin, bony plates overlapping one another. The age of the fish can be estimated from the growth rings.

Adipose fin

Swim bladder (inside body): an air-filled bag which prevents sinking when the fish stops swimming. To adjust for different depths, air is put into or absorbed from the bladder via the blood or the mouth.

Caudal fin (or tail fin): has a large surface area to give forward thrust through the water (a median fin).

Operculum (or gill cover): a bony flap covering the gills. Water passes over the gills and out of the body from behind the operculum.

Pectoral fins: paired fins used to adjust body position and for braking

Pelvic fins: paired fins used to adjust body position and for braking

Ventral fin: single median fin used to adjust body position

Lateral line: special sense organ of fish (see opposite)

Swimming

A fully-grown trout can swim comfortably at speeds of up to about 32 km/h. To achieve this it sweeps its tail from side to side. The large tail fin pushes against the water and the trout is propelled forward.

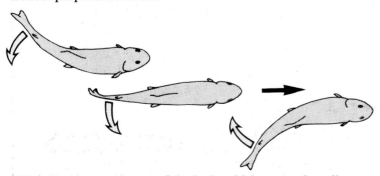

The curving movements of the body which sweep the tail back and forth are caused by contracting and relaxing muscle blocks (**myotomes**) along the sides of the fish. As the myotomes on one side contract, those on the opposite side are relaxed. Waves of contraction and relaxation pass along the body from head to tail, constantly changing the body's S-shaped curve.

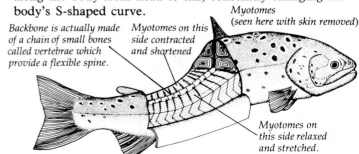

Backbone is actually made of a chain of small bones called vertebrae which provide a flexible spine.

Myotomes on this side contracted and shortened

Myotomes (seen here with skin removed)

Myotomes on this side relaxed and stretched.

By finely adjusting the amount of air in its **swim bladder**, the trout can stay without effort at whichever depth it prefers. It is in fact 'weightless' in the water. Many fish, including the cartilaginous fish, have no swim bladder. If they stop swimming, they slowly sink to the bottom. To prevent this happening they have to move their fins, especially their **pectoral fins**.

As it moves forward, the body of a fish is likely to undergo three other kinds of movement. These are **rolling,** **pitching** and **yawing** (see diagram below). The fish can control the degree of these movements by using its fins.

Rolling causes the fish to twist through the water. The dorsal and ventral fins form a keel to prevent this.

These and the tail fin are called median fins since they run along the mid-line of the fish.

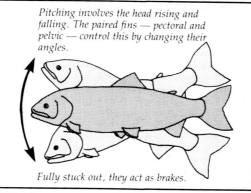

Pitching involves the head rising and falling. The paired fins — pectoral and pelvic — control this by changing their angles.

Fully stuck out, they act as brakes.

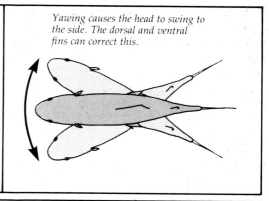

Yawing causes the head to swing to the side. The dorsal and ventral fins can correct this.

GAS EXCHANGE

Using special organs called gills, fish can absorb oxygen which is dissolved in the water around them. They draw water into their mouths and pass it over the gills. Oxygen diffuses over the gill surfaces into the blood. Carbon dioxide diffuses out of the blood in the opposite direction. The water is then pushed out the side of the head. Active fish, like the trout, need shallow or fast-flowing water which contains a lot of dissolved oxygen. The large area of very thin gas exchange surface and the rich blood supply to the gills make them very efficient at gas exchange.

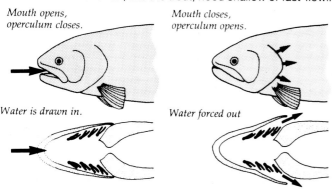

Mouth opens, operculum closes.

Water is drawn in.

Mouth closes, operculum opens.

Water forced out

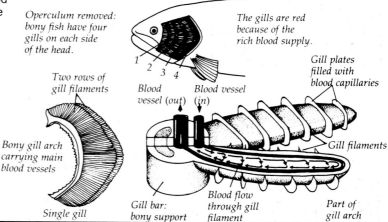

Operculum removed: bony fish have four gills on each side of the head.

The gills are red because of the rich blood supply.

Two rows of gill filaments

Bony gill arch carrying main blood vessels

Single gill

Blood vessel (out)

Blood vessel (in)

Gill plates filled with blood capillaries

Gill filaments

Gill bar: bony support

Blood flow through gill filament

Part of gill arch

SENSE ORGANS

The trout can see, hear, taste and smell. Its well-developed vision is especially important to it, as it uses it when hunting food. In addition to these senses, all fish have an extra sense organ called the **lateral line**. Visible as a line along the side of the fish, it has the following structure:

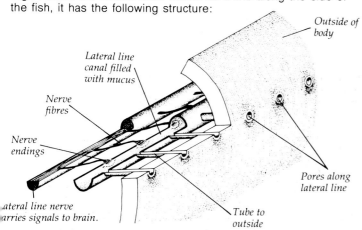

Lateral line canal filled with mucus

Nerve fibres

Nerve endings

Lateral line nerve carries signals to brain.

Outside of body

Pores along lateral line

Tube to outside

Vibrations in the water are transmitted through the mucus to trigger the nerve endings, which then send signals to the brain. Using its lateral line, the fish is instantly aware of disturbance in the water around it. This is useful when swimming in poor light, when hunting, or when being pursued by predators.

REPRODUCTION

Trout breed in the autumn. The female selects a gravelly spot on the riverbed and with her tail digs a shallow trench called a **redd**. Into this she lays her eggs, thousands at a time. The male then covers them with sperm. Thus, fertilisation is external (see page 173). The fertilised eggs are then covered with gravel and abandoned.

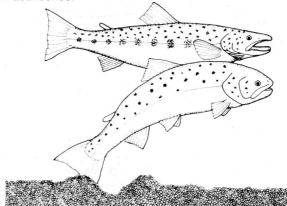

The eggs take between two and three months to hatch and, during that time, they are protected by the gravel. The gravel also allows river water to flow constantly through the eggs so they are well supplied with oxygen. Details of how trout eggs develop after hatching are given on page 184.

The frog: an amphibian

Frogs belong to the **phylum chordata**. They are vertebrates. This means they have a supporting backbone and skeleton inside their bodies. They are also **amphibians**, members of the class *amphibia*, along with toads, newts and salamanders.

The word amphibian means 'a double life'. Amphibians are called this because they are well adapted to live both on land and in water. What is more, most adult amphibians, even if they spend all their lives on land, must return to water to breed. When the young hatch, they are completely aquatic, similar in many ways to fish. As they develop, they have to undergo a complete **metamorphosis** (change of form) to equip them for life on land. On land they prefer moist habitats.

There are about 3000 species of amphibians. The species described and illustrated below is the common frog (Latin name: *Rana temporaria*).

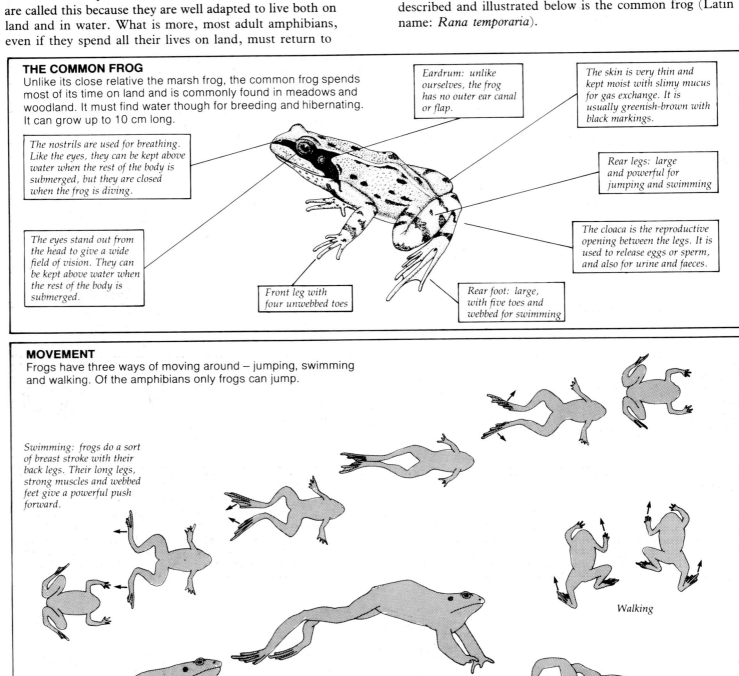

THE COMMON FROG
Unlike its close relative the marsh frog, the common frog spends most of its time on land and is commonly found in meadows and woodland. It must find water though for breeding and hibernating. It can grow up to 10 cm long.

The nostrils are used for breathing. Like the eyes, they can be kept above water when the rest of the body is submerged, but they are closed when the frog is diving.

The eyes stand out from the head to give a wide field of vision. They can be kept above water when the rest of the body is submerged.

Eardrum: unlike ourselves, the frog has no outer ear canal or flap.

The skin is very thin and kept moist with slimy mucus for gas exchange. It is usually greenish-brown with black markings.

Rear legs: large and powerful for jumping and swimming

The cloaca is the reproductive opening between the legs. It is used to release eggs or sperm, and also for urine and faeces.

Front leg with four unwebbed toes

Rear foot: large, with five toes and webbed for swimming

MOVEMENT
Frogs have three ways of moving around – jumping, swimming and walking. Of the amphibians only frogs can jump.

Swimming: frogs do a sort of breast stroke with their back legs. Their long legs, strong muscles and webbed feet give a powerful push forward.

Walking

Jumping: the long back legs with their powerful muscles provide the energy for take off. The tough, springy front legs absorb the shock of landing.

GAS EXCHANGE

For the frog, as for other animals, efficient gas exchange needs a thin, moist surface to dissolve oxygen and let it pass into the body (and also to let carbon dioxide out). There must also be enough of this gas exchange surface to supply all of the organism's needs. The more active an animal is, the greater is the volume of oxygen it uses and the larger is the amount of gas exchange surface it requires.

The frog has three gas exchange surfaces available to it. These are the skin, the lining of the mouth, and the lungs. The use it makes of these depends on how much energy it is using up.

Through the skin If the frog is not too active, its skin has enough surface area to absorb all the oxygen it needs. The skin is kept moist by a layer of slimy mucus. Oxygen dissolves in the mucus, then diffuses easily through the thin skin into the thick network of blood vessels just beneath it. Carbon dioxide diffuses out of the blood in the opposite direction. This is called **cutaneous gas exchange** (cutis: skin). Unfortunately, having to keep the skin moist causes a lot of water to be lost. This is why frogs live in moist habitats.

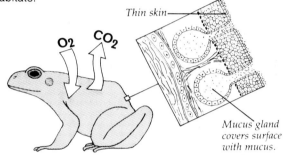

O2 CO2

Thin skin
Mucus gland covers surface with mucus.

Through the mouth Gentle movements of the floor of the mouth as shown here take air in and out of the mouth, through the nostrils. Oxygen dissolves and passes into the bloodstream. This acts as a back-up system for the skin.

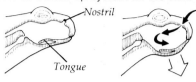 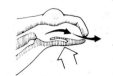

Nostril
Tongue

By the lungs When a frog becomes more energetic, its skin and mouth just do not have enough surface area to absorb all the oxygen it needs. The frog must then use its lungs. These are two small, spongy sacs, the moist walls of which have lots of blood vessels to carry away oxygen. The frog does not breathe rhythmically as we do. It takes violent gulps of air only when it needs it. In this way, water loss from the lungs is kept to a minimum.

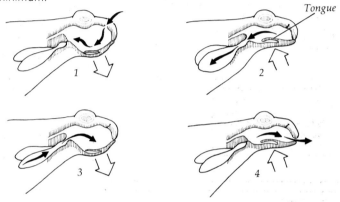

Tongue
1   2
3   4

FEEDING

Frogs feed on small animals such as worms, slugs, beetles, flies, and other insects. Large victims are simply gobbled up and quickly swallowed. Smaller prey, even insects in flight, can be taken with the long, sticky tongue as shown here.

 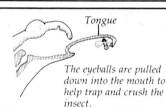 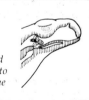

Tongue
The eyeballs are pulled down into the mouth to help trap and crush the insect.

HIBERNATION

Like all amphibians, frogs are cold–blooded. This means that their body temperature rises and falls with the temperature of their surroundings. This, together with lack of food in winter, causes amphibians in cold climates to go into a kind of hibernation for the cold months. Frogs bury themselves in the mud in and around ponds. They do not actually sleep, but they lie still, eat nothing and breathe only through their skins. They surface again in the spring.

REPRODUCTION

After hibernation frogs journey to their breeding ponds. The small males cling tightly to the backs of the females. They may swim around like this for several days. Then, underwater, with their cloaca close together, the eggs are laid by the female and quickly covered with sperm by the male. Thus, fertilisation is external. The frogs then leave the eggs to hatch on their own. Details of the tadpoles' development are given on page 184.

 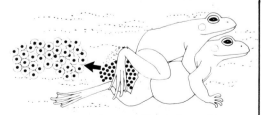

A pad of tough, horny material grows on the male's hand for holding on.

The mating position, called being in amplexus, may be maintained for a day.

45

Birds

The class *aves* to which birds belong is part of the **phylum chordata**. Birds are vertebrates, having a backbone and skeleton inside their bodies. They are **warm-blooded**. This means that a bird can hold its body temperature steady at about 40°C, no matter how hot or cold its environment might be. This has allowed birds to thrive in all parts of the world.

The vast majority of birds can fly, although they cannot all do so. This ability is another reason for the success of the class. To make flight possible, a bird's body has become adapted in many ways. Some of these adaptations for flight are detailed in the diagrams below.

All birds, and only birds, have feathers. The feather is the bird's own special 'invention'. There are about 8700 species of birds. Here are some characteristics typical of them:

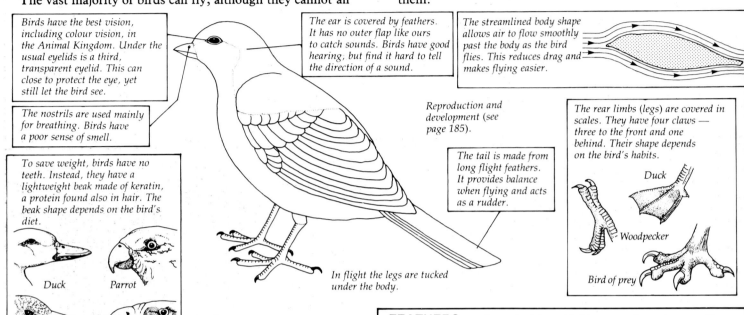

Birds have the best vision, including colour vision, in the Animal Kingdom. Under the usual eyelids is a third, transparent eyelid. This can close to protect the eye, yet still let the bird see.

The nostrils are used mainly for breathing. Birds have a poor sense of smell.

To save weight, birds have no teeth. Instead, they have a lightweight beak made of keratin, a protein found also in hair. The beak shape depends on the bird's diet.

Duck

Parrot

Kingfisher

Eagle

The ear is covered by feathers. It has no outer flap like ours to catch sounds. Birds have good hearing, but find it hard to tell the direction of a sound.

Reproduction and development (see page 185).

The tail is made from long flight feathers. It provides balance when flying and acts as a rudder.

The streamlined body shape allows air to flow smoothly past the body as the bird flies. This reduces drag and makes flying easier.

The rear limbs (legs) are covered in scales. They have four claws — three to the front and one behind. Their shape depends on the bird's habits.

Duck

Woodpecker

Bird of prey

In flight the legs are tucked under the body.

THE CLOACA is the bird's single opening for both waste and sex. The sex organs, both male and female, the gut and the kidneys all empty into it.

To save water, the kidneys do not produce a liquid urine. Instead, they remove the **nitrogenous waste** (see pages 120–1) as a white paste of **uric acid**. This mixes with the dark faeces before dropping out of the cloaca

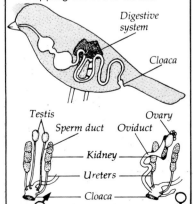

Digestive system

Cloaca

Testis

Ovary

Sperm duct

Oviduct

Kidney

Ureters

Cloaca

GAS EXCHANGE in birds has to be unusually rapid and efficient. Being both warm-blooded and able to fly, birds use a lot of energy and so they need large amounts of oxygen. To supply this, they have large **air sacs** leading from their two small lungs. On breathing in, the air sacs fill. On breathing out, this air flows right through the lungs and gas exchange takes place. There is never any stale air left in the lungs and heavy lung tissue is replaced with lightweight air sacs. Also, to breathe, the **sternum** is moved up and down. Flapping the wings moves it faster, so that flying increases the bird's rate of breathing.

Trachea

Air sacs

Lungs

FEATHERS are important to a bird in a number of ways. They give it its streamlined body shape. They insulate it against extreme heat or cold, especially when fluffed out with a layer of air trapped underneath. They give it its colour. Finally, they provide a large area of wing for very little weight. There are several

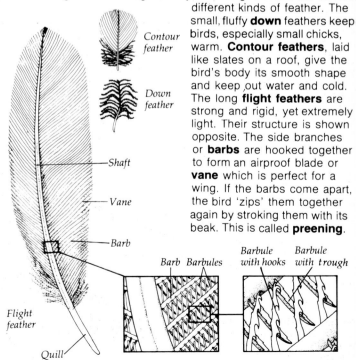

Contour feather

Down feather

Shaft

Vane

Barb

Flight feather

Quill

different kinds of feather. The small, fluffy **down** feathers keep birds, especially small chicks, warm. **Contour feathers**, laid like slates on a roof, give the bird's body its smooth shape and keep out water and cold. The long **flight feathers** are strong and rigid, yet extremely light. Their structure is shown opposite. The side branches or **barbs** are hooked together to form an airproof blade or **vane** which is perfect for a wing. If the barbs come apart, the bird 'zips' them together again by stroking them with its beak. This is called **preening**.

Barb Barbules

Barbule with hooks

Barbule with trough

THE SKELETON

THE SKELETON of a bird is built to the same basic plan as those of other vertebrates, including ourselves. However, it is adapted for flight in a number of ways.

(a) The bones are hollow and very light. Some contain air sacs from the lungs.

(b) The number of bones is reduced to save weight.

(c) Some bones are fused together to form a rigid frame to withstand the flying movements.

(d) The sternum (breast bone) has a large keel to take the flight muscles.

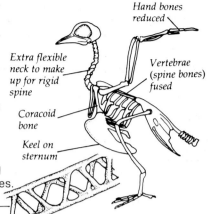

Hand bones reduced

Extra flexible neck to make up for rigid spine

Vertebrae (spine bones) fused

Coracoid bone

Keel on sternum

Struts for strength

THE FLIGHT MUSCLES

THE FLIGHT MUSCLES which raise and lower the wings can make up to 20% of a bird's total weight. The wing is brought down by the strong **pectoralis major** muscle and pulled up by the smaller **pectoralis minor**. Both are attached to the large keel on the sternum.

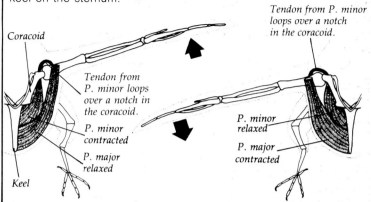

Coracoid

Tendon from P. minor loops over a notch in the coracoid.

P. minor contracted

P. major relaxed

Keel

Tendon from P. minor loops over a notch in the coracoid.

P. minor relaxed

P. major contracted

THE WINGS

THE WINGS are the forelimbs of the bird. Their bones are those of the bird's 'arms' and 'hands'. Although the actual limb is thin, the long flight feathers growing from it transform it into a broad, flat blade. When this is brought downwards, its large surface area pushes against the air and lifts the bird upwards. Further lift comes from the shape of the wing. In cross section, this has an **aerofoil** shape, similar to an aeroplane wing. When flowing past an aerofoil, air moves faster above it than below it. The slow-moving air has a higher pressure than the fast-moving air above it. This pushes the aerofoil upwards.

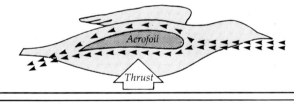

Aerofoil

Thrust

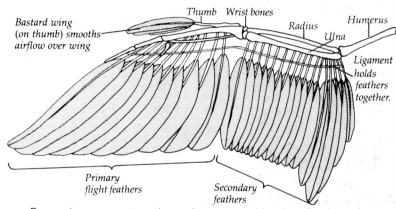

Bastard wing (on thumb) smooths airflow over wing

Thumb *Wrist bones* *Radius* *Humerus* *Ulna*

Ligament holds feathers together.

Primary flight feathers

Secondary feathers

Forward movement, or thrust, is generated by the wings being held at an angle as they beat. This pushes air backwards and thrusts the bird forwards.

FLYING

With their lightweight, streamlined bodies, strong flight muscles and large, aerodynamic wings, birds are perfectly adapted to flying. Flapping the wings provides enough lift and thrust to get the bird airborne and keep it there. Here is how a pigeon uses its wings:

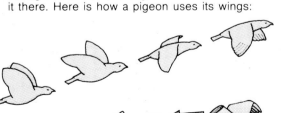

Lift

Downstroke

Upstroke

Thrust

By changing the angle of the wing as it beats up and down, the bird can achieve forward thrust, on both the upstroke and the downstroke.

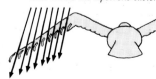

On the upstroke, the primary flight feathers are turned so that air can pass between them. This reduces air resistance and makes the upstroke easier.

On the downstroke, the flight feathers are tight against each other, making an airproof blade. In this way, as much air as possible is pushed down by the wing.

Gliding and soaring

Because of the aerofoil nature of its wings, a bird can glide in the air for some time without flapping its wings. By making use of upcurrents of air caused by heat, cliffs, etc., a bird can actually rise and soar. Large sea birds such as the albatross can fly over the sea for weeks on end like this.

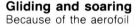

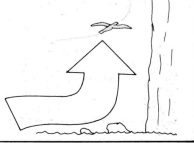

The structure of flowering plants

Herbaceous plants

Plants with stems which stay mostly soft and green throughout their lives are said to be **herbaceous**. This limits their size, usually to less than a metre or so. The diagram opposite shows a typical herbaceous plant. Like other flowering plants, it has two main parts – a **root system** below ground and a **shoot system** above.

The root system

Many plants have a single main root or **tap root** with **lateral roots** (side roots) branching from it. This is called a **tap root system**. Other species have a bunch of similar-sized roots growing from the base of the stem. This is called a **fibrous root system**. Sometimes, when we plant a cutting for example, roots can sprout from stems or even leaves. These are called **adventitious roots**. Fibrous roots may also be called this.

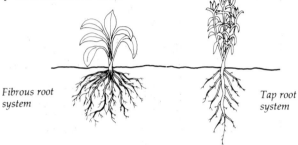

Fibrous root system

Tap root system

The root system anchors the plant in the soil and collects water and minerals from it. The job of absorbing water is done mainly by the delicate **root hairs** which grow near the root tips. Details of root structure and root growth are given on pages 118 and 170. Some plants, for example carrots, may use their roots to store food.

The shoot system

The shoot system consists of stems carrying leaves, flowers and buds. At the tip of each stem is the **terminal bud**, also called the **apical bud**. This is the stem's main growing point (see page 193), and also the place where new leaves and flowers start. The angle between stem and leaf is called an **axil**. In it there is usually a small bud known as an **axillary bud**. Axillary buds are normally **dormant**. This means that they will not grow unless the terminal bud is removed. In some species, however, they *do* develop to form side or lateral stems.

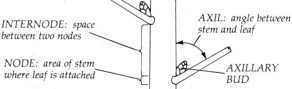

INTERNODE: space between two nodes

NODE: area of stem where leaf is attached

AXIL: angle between stem and leaf

AXILLARY BUD

A stem's job is to support the leaves, flowers and fruits of the plant and to transport materials around the plant. Details of these features are given on **pages 134 and 148**. Stems may also do other jobs. They may spread along the ground as **runners** or they may remain underground to serve as food storage organs such as bulbs, corms and rhizomes (see page 170).

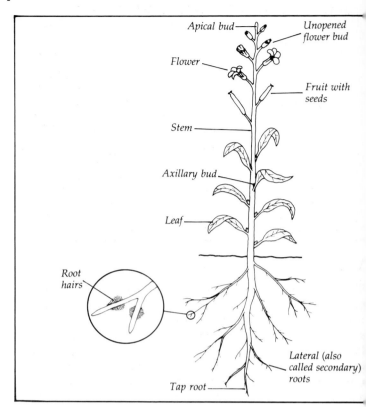

Apical bud

Unopened flower bud

Flower

Fruit with seeds

Stem

Axillary bud

Leaf

Root hairs

Lateral (also called secondary) roots

Tap root

The leaf

A leaf's most important job is to make food for a plant by **photosynthesis** (see pages 88–9). Since it needs light for this, the main part of a leaf is a flat blade or **lamina**, whose job is to catch as much light as possible. **Dicotyledon** leaves usually have a stalk called the **petiole** which merges into the **midrib** of the leaf. From the midrib a network of veins spreads throughout the lamina.

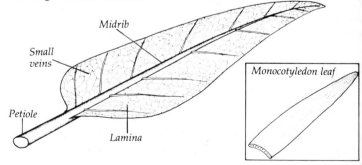

Midrib

Small veins

Monocotyledon leaf

Petiole

Lamina

The typical **monocotyledon** leaf is different. It is long and narrow with parallel veins running through it. The leaf's veins help to hold it flat. Their main purpose, however, is to supply the leaf with minerals and water and to take out surplus food.

There are many different shapes of leaf and these are useful in identifying plants. Leaves are also arranged along stems in a variety of ways so that they do not block each other's light. The internal structure of leaves is detailed on **page 92**. The structure of flowers, which are really special sort of leaves, is described on pages 186–7. A collection of flowers on a stem is called an **inflorescence**.

THE LIFETIMES OF HERBACEOUS PLANTS

Herbaceous plants are either annuals, biennials or perennials.

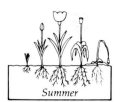
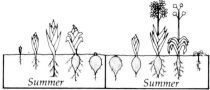

Annuals grow from seed, mature and die in one growing season, e.g. lettuce, wheat, marigolds.

Biennials take two years to develop. In the first year they grow from seed and produce leaves. They store food in their roots and the following year they produce flowers and seeds. They then die. Examples are carrots, cabbages and foxgloves.

Perennials can go on flowering year after year. Each season they store food underground as bulbs, corms, tubers, rhizomes, etc. They die back in winter, then, next growing season, they use the food stores to produce new flowering shoots and seeds, e.g. iris, daffodil.

Woody perennials

The growing stems of many plants do not stay soft and green for long. They quickly develop a hard core of wood which strengthens and thickens them. This is called **secondary thickening** (see page 136). Each year another layer of wood is formed round the layer from the previous one. The **epidermis** of these woody plants, too, is rapidly replaced by a much tougher coat of bark. Air is only allowed to penetrate the stem through breaks in the bark called **lenticels** (see page 112).

The strength of their wood allows these plants to go on growing, year after year, without the shoots dying off in winter. They are known, therefore, as **woody perennials**. Some, such as privet and hawthorn, which are used for hedges, stay fairly small. These are called **shrubs**. Others, the **trees**, develop a thick main stem, or trunk, and can often grow to great heights.

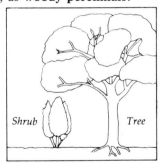

Leaf fall

Abscission or leaf fall happens to most plants. **Evergreens**, such as holly, lose a few of their leaves all the year round. Others, the **deciduous** plants, shed all of their leaves each autumn. Their leaf fall is necessary because in winter it is difficult for them to absorb water from the cold soil. With water losses through **transpiration** from their leaves, they would soon be in difficulties. Evergreen leaves have extra thick **cuticles** or other features to help them reduce their water loss.

In many species leaf fall begins with the growth of a band of cells right across the base of the **petiole**. This is called the **absciss layer**. Beneath this a layer of corky cells develops. The absciss cells then gradually become loose until eventually the leaf is held on only by the veins. Wind or frost breaks these and the leaf falls off.

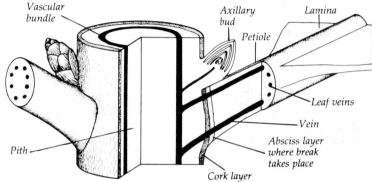

When the leaf breaks off, it leaves behind a mark on the stem called the **leaf scar**. This has been sealed off by the layer of cork so that it does not become infected.

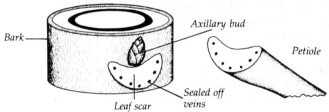

Winter buds

During the summer, large terminal buds develop at the ends of the branches. Each bud contains the next season's leaves or flowers, tightly packed and ready for fast growth as soon as the winter is over. These delicate organs are surrounded by hard **bud scales** which prevent them drying out and protect them from insects, birds and cold. The growth of terminal buds is dealt with on the next page.

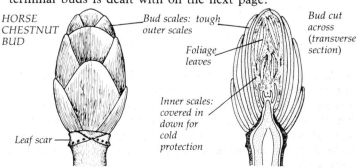

49

Twigs

With its young leaves and flowers already partly developed inside its terminal buds, the woody perennial has a head start for growth when winter is over. Once conditions have improved, the leaves inside the buds start to swell. This forces apart the bud scales and lets the leaves and flowers out. The bud scales eventually fall off, leaving a ring of marks around the twig. This ring is called a **girdle** or **bud scale** scar. The twig's increase in length each year is due entirely to the growth of the shoot which emerges from the terminal bud. Since each girdle scar on the twig marks the position of one year's terminal bud, the distance between the scars shows how much the twig grew that year. The older parts of the twig grow no longer, but they do develop an extra layer of wood each year and so get thicker (see page 136).

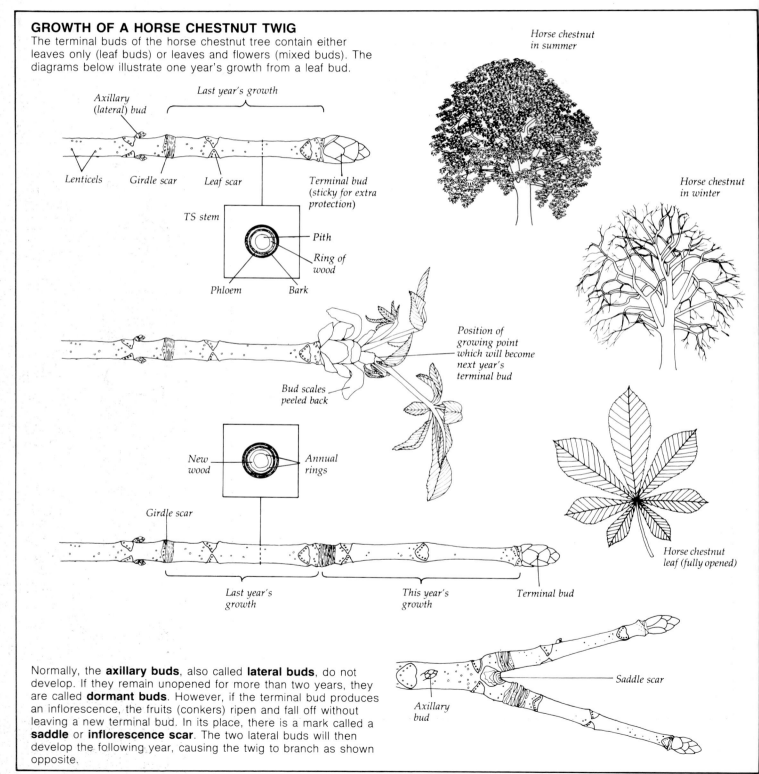

GROWTH OF A HORSE CHESTNUT TWIG

The terminal buds of the horse chestnut tree contain either leaves only (leaf buds) or leaves and flowers (mixed buds). The diagrams below illustrate one year's growth from a leaf bud.

Axillary (lateral) bud

Last year's growth

Lenticels

Girdle scar

Leaf scar

Terminal bud (sticky for extra protection)

TS stem

Pith

Ring of wood

Phloem

Bark

Bud scales peeled back

Position of growing point which will become next year's terminal bud

New wood

Annual rings

Girdle scar

Last year's growth

This year's growth

Terminal bud

Horse chestnut in summer

Horse chestnut in winter

Horse chestnut leaf (fully opened)

Saddle scar

Axillary bud

Normally, the **axillary buds**, also called **lateral buds**, do not develop. If they remain unopened for more than two years, they are called **dormant buds**. However, if the terminal bud produces an inflorescence, the fruits (conkers) ripen and fall off without leaving a new terminal bud. In its place, there is a mark called a **saddle** or **inflorescence scar**. The two lateral buds will then develop the following year, causing the twig to branch as shown opposite.

SECTION 4

Chemistry of the Cell

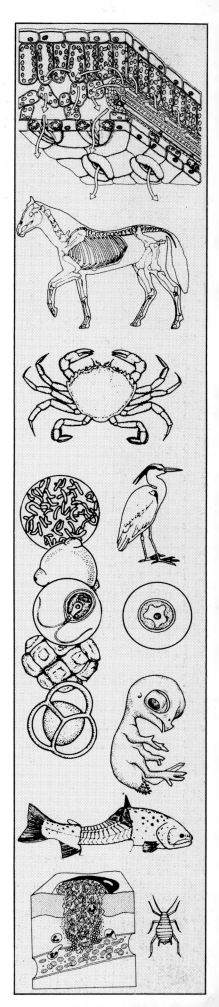

Atoms and molecules

The world around us, including all living things, consists of a vast number of different chemical substances. All of these different materials are made of tiny particles called atoms. Atoms are so small that they can hardly be seen even with the most powerful of microscopes. Ninety-two different types of atoms are found in Nature, and from these ninety-two building bricks everything else can be made. For convenience, each atom is given a symbol.

C = Carbon
H = Hydrogen
O = Oxygen
K = Potassium
Fe = Iron
P = Phosphorus

N = Nitrogen
S = Sulphur
Na = Sodium
Cl = Chlorine
Mg = Magnesium
I = Iodine

When a substance is made of just one kind of atom, it is called an **element**.

COMPOUNDS

From the 92 elements, joined together in various ways, all other substances can be made. However, to make a new substance, it is not enough to just mix different kinds of atoms together. Energy must be involved. For example, if two elements – iron (filings) and sulphur (powder) – are thoroughly mixed together, nothing happens and they can be easily separated again using a magnet or a solvent:

Iron filings and sulphur powder mixed together

Magnet attracts iron filings but leaves sulphur behind.

Sulphur dissolves in solvent but iron does not.

Filter

Sulphur solution

However, if the mixture is heated strongly to start it off, it begins to burn. Once it has stopped, the iron atoms and the sulphur atoms can no longer be separated.
This is called a **chemical reaction**. When the reaction is over, we have a new substance called iron sulphide. Although iron sulphide is made of iron atoms and sulphur atoms tightly joined

together, it no longer behaves like iron or like sulphur. A substance like this, which is made of more than one type of atom joined together, is called a **compound**.

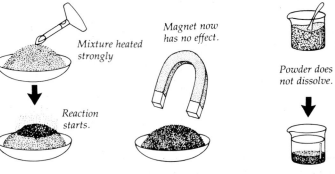

Mixture heated strongly

Magnet now has no effect.

Reaction starts.

Powder does not dissolve.

Some chemical reactions, like the one shown above, need some energy to start them and then they will give off energy of their own. Other reactions will start on their own as soon as the two substances are mixed and others need a constant supply of energy, usually heat, to make them go at all. However, in all cases, energy plays a part.

CHEMICAL EQUATIONS

To show what has happened in a chemical reaction we can write a chemical equation. For example, when glucose burns in oxygen, carbon dioxide and water are formed. This reaction can be shown as a simple word equation like this:

GLUCOSE + OXYGEN → CARBON DIOXIDE + WATER

It is better, though, to write it as a proper chemical equation

which shows the chemical formulae of the **reactants** (starting materials) and of the **products** (finishing materials):

$$C_6H_{12}O_6 + 6O_2 \rightarrow 6CO_2 + 6H_2O$$

(1 molecule of glucose) + (6 molecules of oxygen) → (6 molecules of carbon dioxide) + (6 molecules of water)

This equation shows the same number of atoms on the left-hand side as on the right. This is called a **balanced equation**.

ORGANIC COMPOUNDS

Most of the materials which make up living things are compounds of the element **carbon**. Such substances are called **organic compounds**. The smallest particle which you can get of a compound is called a **molecule**. To show the atoms of which a compound is made, we write a chemical formula, for example:

CO_2 H_2O O_2 $C_6H_{12}O_6$
carbon dioxide   water   oxygen   glucose

Carbon dioxide and glucose both contain carbon and so are organic compounds. Water and oxygen contain no carbon and are called **inorganic** molecules. Many organic molecules are very large and a simple chemical formula saying which atoms they contain is not good enough. $C_6H_{12}O_6$, for example, is the chemical formula for glucose. It is also the formula for fructose, another kind of sugar. To get round this, we write the formula in a different way which shows how the various atoms in the

molecule are joined together. Lines between the atoms represent the chemical bonds which hold the atoms together.

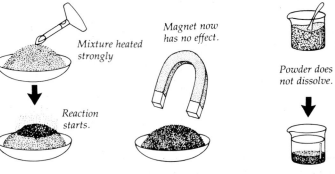

GLUCOSE

FRUCTOSE

Below are some more organic compounds commonly found in living things.

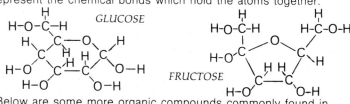

A FATTY ACID

AN AMINO ACID

Ions and pH

Many of the chemical substances which are important to living things are electrically charged. Electric charges may be either **positive** (+) or **negative** (−). Particles carrying positive charges are attracted to negatively charged particles.

Usually in living organisms the positive charges are balanced by an equal number of negative charges. This makes the system as a whole electrically **neutral**. There are occasions, however, when they are allowed to become unbalanced, for example in nerve cells.

IONS AND IONISATION

Ions are atoms or groups of atoms which carry an electric charge. Positively-charged ions are called **cations** and negatively-charged ions are called **anions**. Sodium chloride (common salt), for example, contains two kinds of ion. Half are sodium ions (Na+), each with a single positive charge, and half are chloride ions (Cl−), each carrying a single negative charge. Because of their opposite charges, the sodium and chloride ions 'stick' together to form salt. This is called an **ionic compound**. In fact, the ions arrange themselves in neat rows, as shown below, to make the salt crystals.

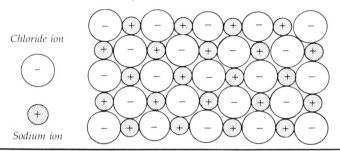

Chloride ion

Sodium ion

The following are other ions of biological interest:

NO_3^-	SO_4^{2-}	$K^{\oplus}$
Nitrate ion	*Sulphate ion*	*Potassium ion*
$OH^{\ominus}$	$NH_4^{\oplus}$	$H^{\oplus}$
Hydroxyl ion	*Ammonium ion*	*Hydrogen ion*

When an ionic compound like salt is dissolved in water, the ions, normally held together by their opposite charges, separate and begin to move freely around in the solution. This is called **ionisation**. Many compounds which are not ionic in nature can also ionise when dissolved in water. Acetic acid, for example, has the formula CH_3CO_2H. In water it ionises like this:

$$CH_3CO_2H \rightarrow CH_3CO_2^{\ominus} + H^{\oplus}$$

Water itself ionises to a very small extent:

$$H_2O \rightarrow H^{\oplus} + OH^{\ominus}$$

ACIDS, ALKALIS AND SALTS

Acids are compounds which dissolve in water to release hydrogen ions. Strong acids ionise completely, providing a lot of hydrogen ions, for example hydrochloric acid:

$$HCl \rightarrow H^{\oplus} + Cl^{\ominus}$$

Nitric acid (HNO_3) and sulphuric acid (H_2SO_4) are other examples. Acetic acid, on the other hand, ionises to a very limited extent and so makes only a weak acid.

Carbon dioxide, an important gas for living things, dissolves fairly well, giving a weak acid called carbonic acid:

$$CO_2 + H_2O \rightleftarrows H_2CO_3 \rightleftarrows H^{\oplus} + HCO_3^{\ominus} \text{ (bicarbonate ion)}$$

The bicarbonate ion is a handy form for organisms to transport their carbon dioxide. It is easily converted back to the gas.

Alkalis or bases are compounds which dissolve in water to release hydroxyl ions. Very strong alkalis include sodium hydroxide (NaOH₄) and potassium hydroxide (KOH). They ionise completely to provide a lot of hydroxyl ions like this:

$$NaOH \rightarrow Na^{\oplus} + OH^{\ominus} \qquad KOH \rightarrow K^{\oplus} + OH^{\ominus}$$

Ammonia (NH_3) is a gas produced by certain cell processes. It dissolves rapidly in water, forming a strong alkali:

$$NH_3 + H_2O \rightarrow NH_4^{\oplus} + OH^{\oplus}$$

Ammonia is harmful in high concentrations. Only organisms with a plentiful water supply can cope with it in this form.

When acids and alkalis are mixed, the free hydrogen and hydroxyl ions quickly pair off to form water molecules. The remaining ions form a salt solution of some kind. For example, if strong hydrochloric acid and sodium hydroxide solutions are carefully mixed in exactly the right amounts, salt water is produced:

$$\underbrace{Na^{\oplus} + OH^{\ominus}}_{\substack{\text{Sodium hydroxide} \\ \text{solution}}} + \underbrace{H^{\oplus} + Cl^{\ominus}}_{\substack{\text{Hydrochloric} \\ \text{acid}}} \rightarrow \underbrace{H_2O + Na^{\oplus} + Cl^{\ominus}}_{\text{Common salt solution}}$$

This is called **neutralisation**.

THE pH SCALE

This scale is used to measure how acid or alkaline a solution is. It ranges from pH 1 (very acidic) up to pH 14 (very alkaline). pH 7 is neutral (pure water). Everything below pH 7 is acid and everything above pH 7 is alkaline. Here are some examples:

Indicators

Indicators are dyes which change colour if their pH is changed. They are useful for testing the pH of solutions. Different indicators are available and each works best over its own range of pH. A few common ones are shown below.

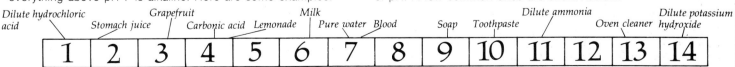

Enzymes: catalysts of the cell

A cell is a tiny chemical factory. To survive, it must be able to carry out thousands of **chemical reactions** very quickly. Unfortunately, many of its most important reactions are very slow. The cell needs some way to speed them up. In a real chemical factory there are two main ways to do this. The first is to use heat. Chemical reactions go faster when the reactants are heated. Cells, though, operate at very mild temperatures. The second method is to use a **catalyst**. A catalyst is a substance which speeds up a chemical reaction without being used up itself. A small amount of catalyst can

make a large amount of product. Cells make special **biological catalysts** to speed up their many reactions. These biological catalysts are called **enzymes**. Unlike industrial catalysts, enzymes are very **specific**. This means that an enzyme can only speed up its own particular reaction. The starting material of an enzyme is called its **substrate** and its finishing material is called its **product**. All living cells contain enzymes and all cell activities are controlled by them.

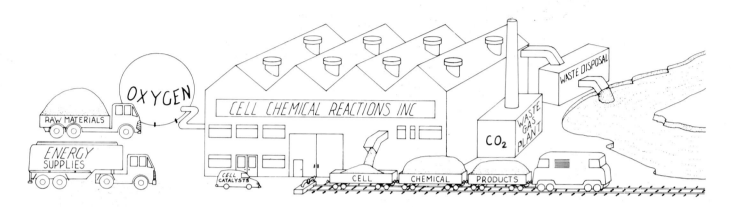

ENZYMES IN ACTION

A cell can carry out thousands of different chemical reactions. This means it needs thousands of enzymes, since each enzyme is only able to speed up one reaction. Many enzymes, like **amylase**, are able to split large molecules into smaller bits, while many others, like **phosphorylase**, take small molecules and build them into larger ones.

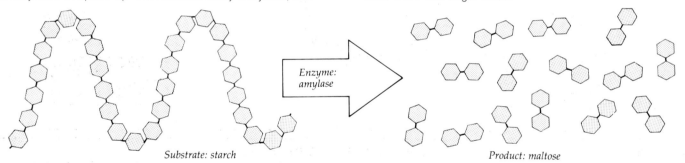

Substrate: starch

Enzyme: amylase

Product: maltose

◯ = glucose (Maltose is a 'double sugar' made of two glucoses joined together.)

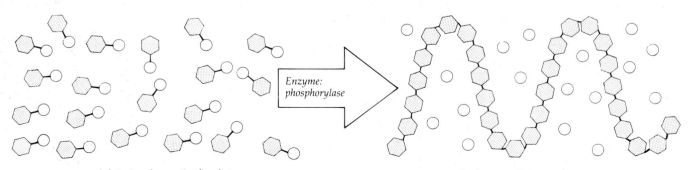

Substrate: glucose -1- phosphate

Enzyme: phosphorylase

Product: starch (+ phosphate)

⬡ = glucose-1-phosphate, a kind of sugar.

HOW ENZYMES WORK

Enzymes are made of protein. Proteins are very large molecules, made of long chains of smaller molecules called **amino acids** joined together (see page 62). In enzymes, this chain is folded so as to leave a 'pocket' on the surface of the molecule. This pocket exactly matches the shape of the enzyme's substrate which can fit into it like a key into a lock. The substrates fit into the pocket, the reaction takes place, the product is set free and the enzyme can then go on to pick up fresh substrate. Since the enzyme is re-used, only a small amount is needed. Enzymes can make cell reactions go 100 000 000 times faster than they could go by themselves.

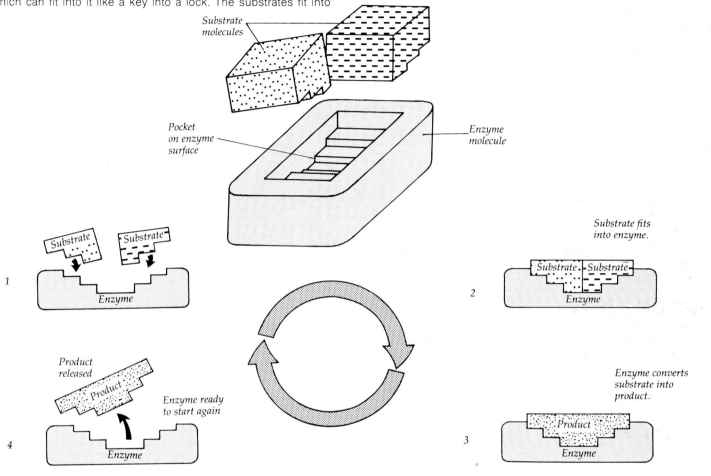

Substrate molecules

Pocket on enzyme surface

Enzyme molecule

1. Substrate / Substrate — Enzyme

2. Substrate fits into enzyme. Substrate · Substrate — Enzyme

3. Enzyme converts substrate into product. Product — Enzyme

4. Product released / Product — Enzyme ready to start again — Enzyme

---

ENZYMES AND pH

All enzymes work best at a certain pH. This is called their **optimum pH**. Most enzymes have an optimum pH of about 7 (neutral), though some prefer acid (low pH) and others prefer alkaline (high pH) conditions. If we measure how fast an enzyme can work in different pHs, we can find its optimum pH.

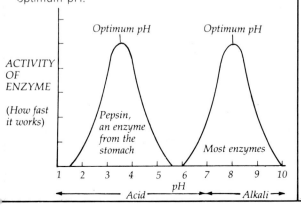

ACTIVITY OF ENZYME

(How fast it works)

Optimum pH

Optimum pH

Pepsin, an enzyme from the stomach

Most enzymes

pH: 1 2 3 4 5 6 7 8 9 10

◄— Acid ——— Alkali —►

ENZYMES AND TEMPERATURE

As the temperature rises, enzymes work faster until they reach the temperature at which they work best. This is called the **optimum temperature**. Human enzymes work best at 37 °C (body temperature). A few degrees above this the enzyme is destroyed and can no longer work. Heat destroys the special shape of the protein chain and the substrate no longer fits. We say that the enzyme has been **denatured**.

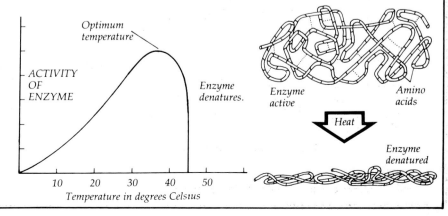

ACTIVITY OF ENZYME

Optimum temperature

Enzyme denatures.

Temperature in degrees Celsius: 10 20 30 40 50

Enzyme active

Amino acids

Heat

Enzyme denatured

SECTION 5

Energy

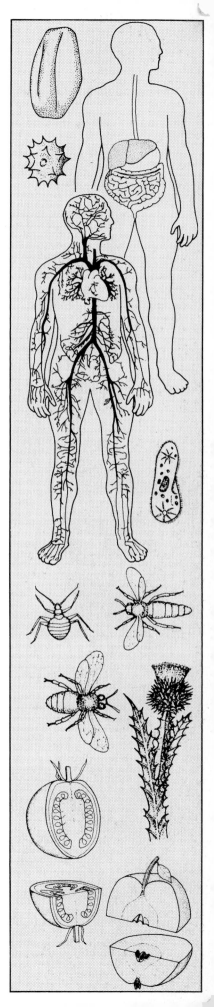

Energy

Nothing can happen without energy. It is energy which makes things work. It comes in a number of forms – light energy, heat energy, sound energy, kinetic (movement) energy, chemical energy and electrical energy. We are all familiar with light, heat, sound and kinetic energy since we can detect these easily. It is not so easy, however, to tell if an object or substance contains chemical or electrical energy.

Chemical energy is a convenient way to store energy until it is needed, while electrical energy can be sent rapidly from one place to another. However, one useful thing about energy is the fact that it can be changed from one form into another. For example, when we light a candle, the chemical energy in the wax is converted into light energy. When we switch on an electric lamp, electrical energy is changed to light energy.

Such changes of energy from one form to another are called **energy conversions**. In both of the previous examples heat energy is also produced. This always happens during energy conversions.

Life, too, depends on energy conversions. The first and most important energy conversion for living things occurs in **photosynthesis**. In photosynthesis, plants absorb energy from the sun and convert it to chemical energy which is then stored in their tissues. From these tissues, one way or another, comes the food and thus the vital energy supplies for all living things.

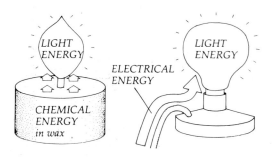

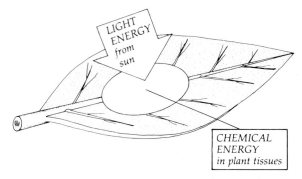

A second energy conversion process releases the stored-up chemical energy of food in forms which organisms can use to stay alive. This process is called **respiration**. Below are a few of the energy conversions carried out by living things.

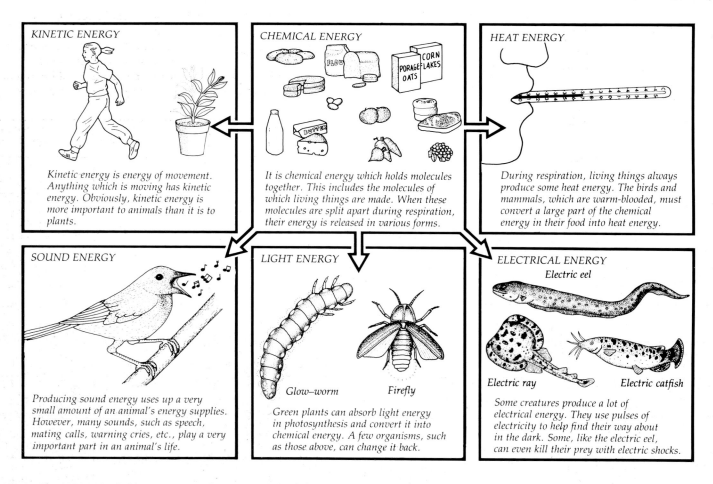

KINETIC ENERGY

Kinetic energy is energy of movement. Anything which is moving has kinetic energy. Obviously, kinetic energy is more important to animals than it is to plants.

CHEMICAL ENERGY

It is chemical energy which holds molecules together. This includes the molecules of which living things are made. When these molecules are split apart during respiration, their energy is released in various forms.

HEAT ENERGY

During respiration, living things always produce some heat energy. The birds and mammals, which are warm-blooded, must convert a large part of the chemical energy in their food into heat energy.

SOUND ENERGY

Producing sound energy uses up a very small amount of an animal's energy supplies. However, many sounds, such as speech, mating calls, warning cries, etc., play a very important part in an animal's life.

LIGHT ENERGY

Glow-worm   Firefly

Green plants can absorb light energy in photosynthesis and convert it into chemical energy. A few organisms, such as those above, can change it back.

ELECTRICAL ENERGY

Electric eel

Electric ray   Electric catfish

Some creatures produce a lot of electrical energy. They use pulses of electricity to help find their way about in the dark. Some, like the electric eel, can even kill their prey with electric shocks.

Energy in food

Scientists measure all energy in units called **kilojoules** (kJ). This includes the energy which is stored in foods. One gram of butter, for example, supplies about 33.5 kilojoules of energy. We would say that the **calorific value** of butter is about 33.5 kJ/g. (The calorific value is the energy content of the food.) Not everyone, however, uses kilojoules as their food energy unit. Many people, such as cooks and slimmers, use an older unit called the **kilocalorie** (usually shortened to **Calorie**). Measuring with this unit, butter has a calorific value of about eight calories per gram (8 Cal/g). One Calorie, therefore, equals 4.2 kilojoules.

Calories are actually units of heat energy. Food, of course, contains chemical energy. The trouble is that the chemical energy in a food is difficult to measure directly. The easiest thing to do is to burn the food so that its chemical energy is converted into heat energy. This heat is then used to warm up a quantity of water. From the rise in temperature of the water, we get a measure of the energy content/calorific value of the food. Here is a simple example:

Definitions: (a) 1 Calorie is the amount of heat energy which can warm up 1 kilogram of water by 1 degree Celsius.
(b) 1 Calorie = 4.2 kilojoules

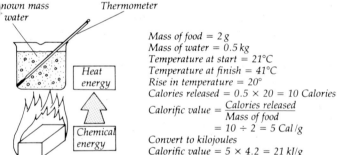

Mass of food = 2 g
Mass of water = 0.5 kg
Temperature at start = 21°C
Temperature at finish = 41°C
Rise in temperature = 20°
Calories released = 0.5 × 20 = 10 Calories
Calorific value = $\dfrac{\text{Calories released}}{\text{Mass of food}}$
  = 10 ÷ 2 = 5 Cal/g
Convert to kilojoules
Calorific value = 5 × 4.2 = 21 kJ/g

The simple set-up shown in the previous column would certainly give us a rough idea of how much energy a food contained. For more accurate measurements a device called a **food calorimeter** is used. In a food calorimeter, a small amount of food is burned very rapidly in pure oxygen. Precautions are taken to prevent heat being lost into the air before the final temperature is noted. Here is one type of food calorimeter:

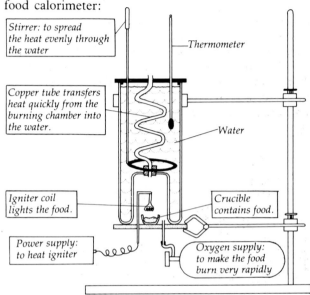

Stirrer: to spread the heat evenly through the water

Thermometer

Copper tube transfers heat quickly from the burning chamber into the water.

Water

Igniter coil lights the food.

Crucible contains food.

Power supply: to heat igniter

Oxygen supply: to make the food burn very rapidly

(*Note*: the calorimeter itself absorbs some heat and a correction has to be made for this.)

Using this and even more complicated food calorimeters, the calorific values of many different foods have been measured. The table below lists some of these. With tables like this we can work out how much energy we consume each day in our food.

FOOD	CAL VALUE	TYPICAL PORTION	FOOD	CAL VALUE	TYPICAL PORTION	FOOD	CAL VALUE	TYPICAL PORTION	FOOD	CAL VALUE	TYPICAL PORTION
APPLE	1.96 KJ/g equal to 0.47 Cal/g	294 KJ 150g 70 Cal	COFFEE (sugar, white)	3.86 KJ/g equal to 0.92 Cal/g	521 KJ 135g 124 Cal	JAM	12.15 KJ/g equal to 2.89 Cal/g	364 KJ 30g 87 Cal	PEAS (canned)	4.07 KJ/g equal to 0.97 Cal/g	407 KJ 100g 97 Cal
BANANA	1.93 KJ/g equal to 0.46 Cal/g	290 KJ 150g 69 Cal	CORNED BEEF	9.66 KJ/g equal to 2.30 Cal/g	966 KJ 100g 230 Cal	KIPPER (poached)	14.07 KJ/g equal to 3.35 Cal/g	844 KJ 60g 201 Cal	PORRIDGE	1.98 KJ/g equal to 0.47 Cal/g	198 KJ 100g 47 Cal
BEANS (baked)	4.77 KJ/g equal to 1.13 Cal/g	477 KJ 100g 113 Cal	CORN FLAKES	15.26 KJ/g equal to 3.63 Cal/g	457 KJ 30g 109 Cal	LETTUCE	0.44 KJ/g equal to 0.11 Cal/g	13 KJ 30g 3 Cal	POTATOES (boiled)	3.33 KJ/g equal to 0.79 Cal/g	333 KJ 100g 79 Cal
BUTTER	31.26 KJ/g equal to 7.44 Cal/g	938 KJ 30g 223 Cal	CUSTARD	4.32 KJ/g equal to 1.03 Cal/g	1210 KJ 280g 288 Cal	MARGARINE	32.30 KJ/g equal to 7.69 Cal/g	969 KJ 30g 231 Cal	SARDINES (canned)	11.84 KJ/g equal to 2.82 Cal/g	1184 KJ 100g 282 Cal
CAKE	9.21 KJ/g equal to 2.19 Cal/g	553 KJ 60g 131 Cal	EGG (boiled)	6.81 KJ/g equal to 1.62 Cal/g	408 KJ 60g 97 Cal	MELON	0.59 KJ/g equal to 0.14 Cal/g	89 KJ 150g 21 Cal	STEAK	7.43 KJ/g equal to 1.77 Cal/g	743 KJ 100g 177 Cal
CHEESE (cheddar)	17.78 KJ/g equal to 4.23 Cal/g	533 KJ 30g 127 Cal	EGG (fried)	11.59 KJ/g equal to 2.76 Cal/g	695 KJ 60g 166 Cal	MILK (fresh)	2.82 KJ/g equal to 0.67 Cal/g	703 KJ 250g 168 Cal	SPROUTS	1.48 KJ/g equal to 0.35 Cal/g	89 KJ 60g 21 Cal
CHICKEN (roast)	3.72 KJ/g equal to 0.89 Cal/g	372 KJ 100g 89 Cal	FISH FINGERS	9.07 KJ/g equal to 2.16 Cal/g	680 KJ 75g 162 Cal	MUSHROOMS (fried)	9.2 KJ/g equal to 2.19 Cal/g	553 KJ 60g 131 Cal	SWEETCORN (canned)	4.07 KJ/g equal to 0.97 Cal/g	407 KJ 100g 97 Cal
CHIPS	10.04 KJ/g equal to 2.39 Cal/g	1004 KJ 100g 239 Cal	GRAPES	2.53 KJ/g equal to 0.60 Cal/g	253 KJ 100g 60 Cal	ORANGE	1.23 KJ/g equal to 0.29 Cal/g	209 KJ 170g 49 Cals	TEA (milk, sugar)	1.87 KJ/g equal to 0.44 Cal/g	252 KJ 135g 60 Cal
COD (fillet)	3.57 KJ/g equal to 0.85 Cal/g	357 KJ 100g 85 Cal	HAM (lean)	8.89 KJ/g equal to 2.12 Cal/g	267 KJ 30g 64 Cal	PEANUTS (roasted)	8.89 KJ/g equal to 2.12 Cal/g	267 KJ 30g 64 Cal	TOMATO (raw)	0.59 KJ/g equal to 0.14 Cal/g	36 KJ 60g 8 Cal

Energy needs

The rate at which the body uses energy is called the **metabolic rate**. This rate differs from person to person depending on their size, age, sex and how active they are. Let's take one example: if an average-sized man lies in bed all day, completely at rest, he needs to produce about 7140 kilojoules (1700 calories) of energy just to stay alive. This amount is the **basal metabolic rate** for that person. This energy is used in the following ways:

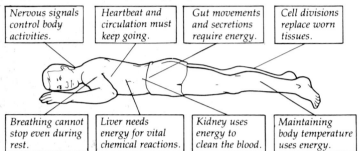

Nervous signals control body activities.

Heartbeat and circulation must keep going.

Gut movements and secretions require energy.

Cell divisions replace worn tissues.

Breathing cannot stop even during rest.

Liver needs energy for vital chemical reactions.

Kidney uses energy to clean the blood.

Maintaining body temperature uses energy.

In general, small people use less energy than larger people, children use less than adults, and females use less than males. Some people, of course, are more physically active than others, especially in the jobs they do. As the diagram in the box opposite shows, this is reflected in the amount of energy they require. Pregnant and nursing mothers must supply energy to their growing babies and so they consume more than usual themselves.

ENERGY BALANCE

If the food we eat contains more energy than we need, the body stores the surplus as fat. Fat is an ideal way to store energy because, weight for weight, fat can hold about twice as much energy as either protein or carbohydrate, for example:

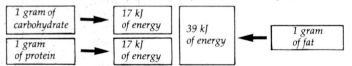

1 gram of carbohydrate → 17 kJ of energy

1 gram of protein → 17 kJ of energy

39 kJ of energy ← 1 gram of fat

Foods rich in carbohydrate and fat, especially, are easily converted into stored body fats. Too much of these can lead to obesity (fatness). Obese people tend to be fattest at certain parts of the body such as the belly or buttocks. These areas contain a lot of **adipose tissue** (fat-storing), the cells of which swell up as they fill with stored fat:

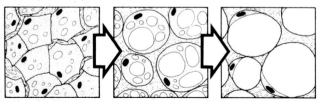

Obesity is unhealthy. It contributes to heart disease, diabetes and other illnesses. To reduce weight, many overweight people go on diets where their energy intake is reduced to less than their energy needs. The body begins to use its fat stores to make up the difference and the person loses weight. In starvation, this process goes further. The fat reserves are all used up. The body must now use other tissues such as muscle to supply its energy. The person begins to waste away and may eventually die. In a proper healthy diet, the body's energy intake should be roughly in balance with its energy needs.

Girl (15 years old)
9600 kJ per 24 hours (2285 Cal)

Boy (15 years old)
12 600 kJ per 24 hours (3000 Cal)

Woman (light work)
9450 kJ per 24 hours (2250 Cal)

Man (light work)
11 550 kJ per 24 hours (2750 Cal)

Woman (pregnant)
10 000 kJ per 24 hours (2380 Cal)

Woman (breast feeding)
11 300 kJ per 24 hours (2690 Cal)

Man (moderate work)
12 100 kJ per 24 hours (2900 Cal)

Woman (moderate work)
10 500 kJ per 24 hours (2500 Cal)

Man (fairly heavy work)
18 500 kJ per 24 hours (4400 Cal)

Man (very heavy work)
20 000 kJ per 24 hours (4800 Cal)

SECTION 6

Food

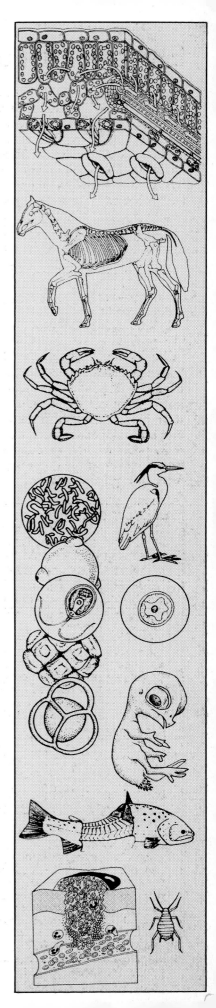

Proteins, carbohydrates and fats

All living things need food. Stored in food is the energy they need to stay alive, and from food they get the 'building' materials – the atoms and molecules – of which they are made.

Autotrophs (see page 68), like the green plants, can make their own food from very simple substances. **Heterotrophs** like ourselves must get their food in the form of complex molecules already made by other creatures.

Foods consist mainly of water. Apart from water, foods are made up of **proteins**, **carbohydrates** and **fats**.

PROTEINS are used for bodybuilding, making new body tissues and to repair worn or damaged tissues. Many substances which the body needs to work properly are made of protein. These include **enzymes, hormones** and **blood proteins**. Proteins can be used to supply energy (4 kcal/g) but they are usually too important for this. Proteins are made from atoms of carbon, hydrogen, oxygen, nitrogen and sometimes sulphur.

Proteins are built from long chains of smaller molecules called **amino acids**. There are about 20 different amino acids

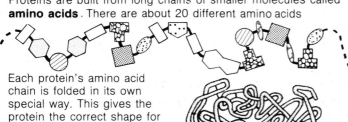

Each protein's amino acid chain is folded in its own special way. This gives the protein the correct shape for whatever job it has to do.

These foods are good sources of protein:

Animal tissues – All animal tissues and foods made by animals for their young are high in protein. Animal proteins are best as they contain all the amino acids which humans need.

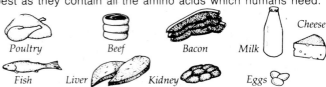

Poultry   Beef   Bacon   Milk   Cheese
Fish   Liver   Kidney   Eggs

Plant tissues – Plant tissues contain some protein. Plant foods do not have all the amino acids which humans need.

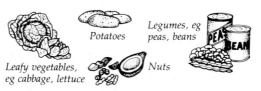

Leafy vegetables, eg cabbage, lettuce   Potatoes   Legumes, eg peas, beans   Nuts   Flour products

---

CARBOHYDRATES are the cell's main source of energy. One gram of carbohydrate supplies about four kilocalories. Carbohydrates are made from atoms of carbon, hydrogen and oxygen. Carbohydrates may be either sugars or starches.

SUGARS are the basic units of carbohydrate. The sugar most in demand by cells is glucose:

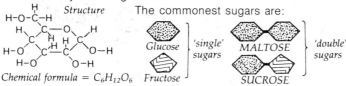

Structure

The commonest sugars are:

Glucose } 'single' sugars   MALTOSE } 'double' sugars
Fructose }   SUCROSE }

Chemical formula = $C_6H_{12}O_6$

These foods are good sources of sugar:

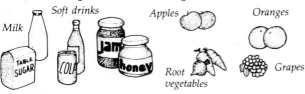

Milk   Soft drinks   Apples   Oranges   Root vegetables   Grapes

STARCHES are used to store excess energy. They are made of hundreds of glucoses joined together. When energy is needed, they are broken down to glucose which the cell can use.

Plant starch   **Glycogen** (animal starch) – stored in the liver and muscles.

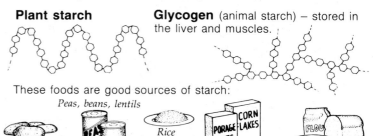

These foods are good sources of starch:

Peas, beans, lentils   Potatoes   Rice   Corn   Cereal products   Flour products

Roughage is the name given to **fibre** in the diet. It consists mainly of **cellulose** from plant tissues. Cellulose, like starch, is made of joined glucoses. Although we cannot digest it, roughage gives the diet bulk and this helps the digestive system to work properly and prevents constipation.

FATS are used to store energy. Each gram of fat contains about eight kilocalories of energy – twice as much as carbohydrate or protein. If we eat too much carbohydrate, it is changed into fat and stored. This energy can be used when needed. Fat stores also give good insulation against the cold. Fats are needed to make certain cell parts, such as membranes. Fats are made from atoms of carbon, hydrogen and oxygen.

These foods are good sources of fat:

Fat molecules are made of three **fatty acids** joined to a smaller molecule called **glycerol**:

FATTY ACID A
GLYCEROL
FATTY ACID B
FATTY ACID C

Eggs   Dairy products   Meats   Fried food, eg chips   Sardines

Using different fatty acids, various sorts of fat can be made. Some fats are solid, while others are in the form of oil.

Vitamins and minerals

The body is an incredibly complicated chemical machine. For it to work at all, it needs a supply of **proteins, fats and carbohydrates** for fuel and building materials. However, even with a good supply of these, it will not work properly without certain other special substances. These are called **vitamins** and **minerals**. Only very tiny amounts of vitamins and minerals are needed, but without them certain illnesses called **deficiency diseases** will result. Each vitamin and mineral has its own special part to play in the proper working of the body. Some of the most important of these vitamins and minerals are described below.

VITAMIN A is needed for normal growth and eyesight and for good skin. Lack of this vitamin can cause reduced growth, diseases of the eyes and can allow easy infection of the skin and of the linings of the throat and air passages. Good sources of vitamin A are:

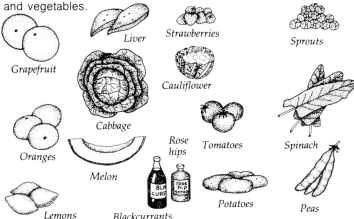

Cod liver oil, Sardines, Liver, Eggs, Carrots, Milk, Kidney, Spinach, Butter, Margarine, Cheese

Cooking has little effect on vitamin A.

VITAMIN C prevents a disease called **scurvy**. Scurvy causes weakness, sore bleeding gums, slow healing of wounds and poor growth in children. Vitamin C is found mainly in fresh fruit and vegetables.

Grapefruit, Liver, Strawberries, Sprouts, Cauliflower, Cabbage, Oranges, Melon, Rose hips, Tomatoes, Spinach, Lemons, Blackcurrants, Potatoes, Peas

The preparation of food reduces its vitamin C content. Some is destroyed during chopping or grating, some may be destroyed by heating and, if the food is boiled, some of this water-soluble vitamin is lost into the water.

VITAMIN D helps to build the minerals **calcium** and **phosphorus** into strong bones and teeth. Lack of vitamin D in children causes **rickets**, a disease where the ends of growing bones become soft and deformed. The skin can make vitamin D if it gets enough sunshine. Otherwise, these foods are good sources of the vitamin:

Eggs, Liver, White fish, Sardines, Salmon, Cod liver oil, Milk, Butter, Margarine, Cheese

Vitamin D is little affected by cooking.

VITAMIN K is needed for blood to clot properly when we are injured. It is found in spinach, cabbage, peas, cereals and potatoes. However, it is also made by bacteria (germs) in the intestine and then absorbed by the body, so, deficiency does not often occur.

VITAMIN B COMPLEX is a group of at least 11 different essential substances. They are usually found together and so were once thought to be just one vitamin. They each play a part in the processes by which our cells get their energy. The vitamin B complex includes:

Vitamin B1 (also called **thiamine**) is needed for normal growth. Without it, growth in children is stunted. Severe lack causes a disease of the nervous and digestive systems called **beri-beri**. Beri-beri is common in the East.

Vitamin B2 (also called **riboflavin**) is essential for normal growth.

Niacin (also called **nicotinic acid**) is needed for normal growth in children. Lack of the vitamin causes skin, digestive and mental disorders (a disease called **pellagra**).
The B vitamins are found in these foods:

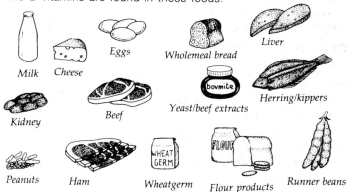

Milk, Cheese, Eggs, Wholemeal bread, Liver, Kidney, Beef, Yeast/beef extracts, Herring/kippers, Peanuts, Ham, Wheatgerm, Flour products, Runner beans

B vitamins are destroyed by heat. During cooking or baking, some of them, especially thiamine, are lost from the food.

MINERALS, unlike vitamins, are **inorganic**, that is, they contain no carbon, and they are chemically simpler substances. Important minerals include:

Calcium is needed for strong bones and teeth (without it children get rickets), for normal blood clotting and working of the muscles. It can be got from milk, cheese, bread, flour products and green vegetables.

Iron is needed to make the red blood protein called **haemoglobin**. Carried by red blood cells, this delivers oxygen to all parts of the body. Shortage of iron can cause **anaemia**. Bread, flour products, meat, green vegetables and potatoes contain iron.

Phosphorus is needed, along with calcium, for strong bones and teeth. Also, as part of **ATP** (see page 98), it helps get energy for the cells to use. Most common foods contain some.

A balanced diet

The food we eat each day is called our diet. To keep us healthy our diet must contain the correct amounts of the correct **nutrients**. The amount of food we need varies from person to person. It depends on our age, our sex and our occupation. However the daily diet of an average adult should contain:

PROTEIN 70–100 g – half of this should come from animals.	WATER 1 litre of liquid, more if sweating a lot	CARBOHYDRATE & FAT Enough to make up the energy supply – average is 2800 kilocalories.
MINERALS 12 mg of iron, 0.8 g of calcium (children need more) and small amounts of other minerals	VITAMINS Very small amounts of vitamin A, vitamin B, vitamin B, niacin, vitamin C and vitamin D	

If our diet does not supply us with the correct nutrients, we may suffer from one of the forms of **malnutrition**. Usually, in cases of malnutrition, the diet is lacking more than one nutrient, although some symptoms occur before others. However, it is possible for a person to get plenty to eat, to never feel hungry, and yet still suffer from one of the diseases of malnutrition. This is because that person's diet is not well balanced.

MALNUTRITION

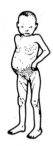

Disease: **kwashiorkor**
Cause: lack of animal protein
Symptoms: swellings, enlarged liver, anaemia

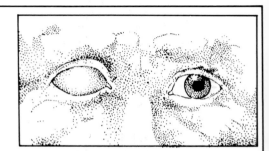

Disease: **eye disorders**
Cause: lack of vitamin A
Symptoms: night blindness (mild form), cloudy cornea, blindness (severe form)

Disease: **starvation**
Cause: lack of food
Symptoms: illness, wasting away of the muscles

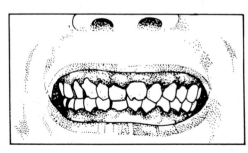

Disease: **scurvy**
Cause: lack of vitamin C
Symptoms: swollen, bleeding gums, weakness, pain

Disease: **pellagra**
Cause: lack of niacin
Symptoms: skin rashes, diarrhoea, mental illness

Disease: **beri-beri**
Cause: lack of vitamin B
Symptoms: muscular weakness, paralysis, pain, heart failure

Disease: **rickets** (children only)
Cause: lack of vitamin D
Symptoms: bones become soft and deformed leading to crippling

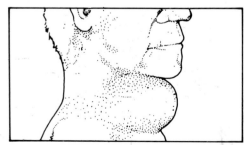

Disease: **goitre**
Cause: lack of iodine
Symptoms: swollen thyroid gland

Most foods contain a mixture of different nutrients, for example:

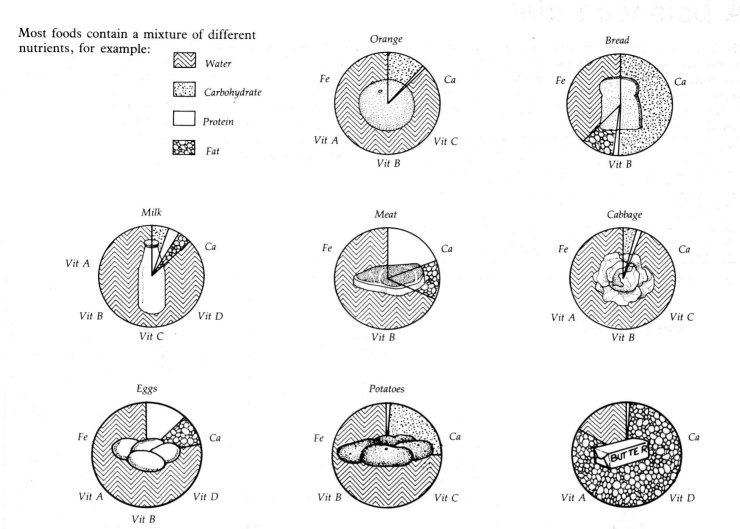

There is no perfect food. A food which is a good source of one nutrient may be completely lacking in others. The best way to make sure that our diet has all the nutrients we need to stay healthy is to eat meals which have something from all the main groups of foods. This is known as a **balanced diet**.

World food problems

Every year many thousands of people die from starvation. About 70% of the world's population – nearly 3000 million people – do not get enough to eat. The problem is greatest in the poorer developing countries, as the map below shows.

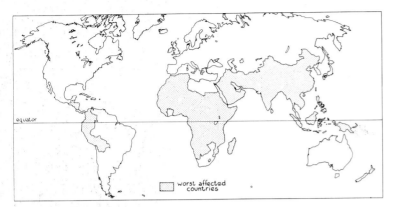

worst affected countries

equator

Along with poor diets go the diseases of malnutrition, for example, large numbers of people go blind each year due to lack of vitamin A. Many diets do not contain enough protein, especially first-class animal protein. In some countries nearly 20% of the children are suffering from protein deficiency which could affect them for life. On the other hand, people in richer countries consume far more protein than they need.

Some causes of food shortage
Overpopulation
When the number of people who die (the **death rate**) balances the number of babies born (the **birth rate**), the population does not change. For thousands of years this was more or less what happened, then because of a number of things, such as better public health measures and improvements in hygiene and medical care, the death rate, especially among young children, began to fall. Populations began to increase, first in Europe and North America, and now mainly in developing countries. The graph below shows changes in birth and death rates in one developing country – Sri Lanka.

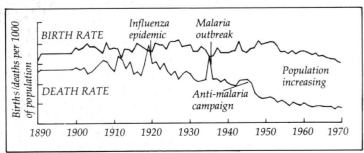

As the graph on page 236 shows, a **population explosion** is now taking place. The world population is expected to double in just 30 years. Widespread use of birth control methods (see page 181) might eventually stabilise the population, but this will take a long time. There will still be thousands of millions more mouths to feed.

Climate
Food production in any part of the world can be disrupted by bad weather. Severe winters, floods, winds and drought can all destroy or reduce crops. These effects may be only temporary, but sometimes they can be disastrous. From 1971 onwards, for example, huge areas of Africa have been hit by severe drought and thousands of people have died of starvation. Millions more are at risk. The livestock on which many depend for their livelihood have died in their millions. Life in this region may never be the same again.

Waste
Huge amounts of food are lost each year because of pests. In America, for example, these losses are put as high as 40% per year.

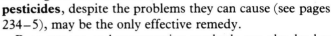

Food saved / Rats, etc. / Disea... / Inse... / Weeds...

In developing countries, where swarms of locusts can still devastate crops, the wastage is even higher. **Herbicides** and **pesticides**, despite the problems they can cause (see pages 234–5), may be the only effective remedy.

Poor storage and preservation methods can also lead to food being plentiful at one time of year and scarce at others. In some Third World countries, for instance, losses (grain through unsuitable storage can be as high as 50%.

Another type of waste occurs in meat production. More than 30% of all grain goes to feed animals. Yet, when we eat their meat, we only get 4–20% of this back. The rest is lost (see page 101). In future this loss may be reduced by usi 'artificial meat' or meat substitutes made from high protein plants such as **soya**.

Unequal distribution
In 1977 the World Food Survey estimated that there was enough food to feed everybody in the world with 7% left over, yet the developing countries went short. In fact, in rich industrialised countries the main type of malnutrition was **obesity** (fatness) caused by eating too much. So, why not simply transfer food from rich to poor countries? The answer is that even if they could afford it, the amounts needed, perhaps more than a 100 million tonnes each year, are so huge that they could neither transport it, nor distribute it to the needy. Also, large amounts of imported food, either cheap or free, depresses the local agriculture and makes the problem even worse in the long run. Food aid is best used in emergencies, where a community is face with starvation due to bad harvests caused by drought, etc

More useful in the long term is help with materials and knowledge. Small farmers can be shown how to produce more food locally, where it is needed. The development of new types of cereals such as 'miracle rice' can be a help here Properly cultivated, these can give double the yield. The hig cost of seed and fertiliser, however, is a major drawback. Many countries may also be able to obtain much needed ext animal protein by the careful use of fish and game (see page 236).

SECTION 7

Feeding

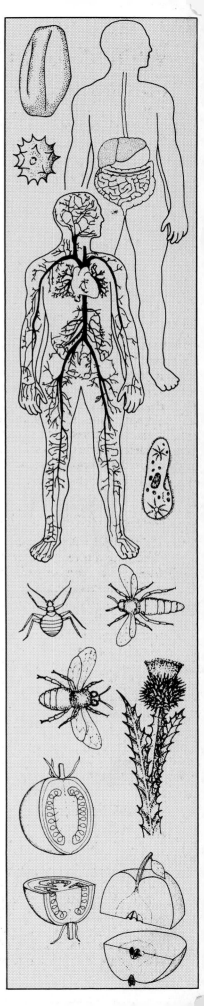

Autotrophs and heterotrophs

AUTOTROPHS (*auto*: self; *troph*: feed) are organisms which can make their own food from simple inorganic substances. The process by which they do this is called **photosynthesis** (see page 88). Green plants and algae are autotrophs. Using the energy of sunlight they turn carbon dioxide and water into sugar.

Oxygen is given off as waste. Any extra food they make is stored for later use. Other minerals, for example nitrates, are used to convert the sugar into any materials they need. Since they make the food which other organisms will feed on, they are also known as **producers**.

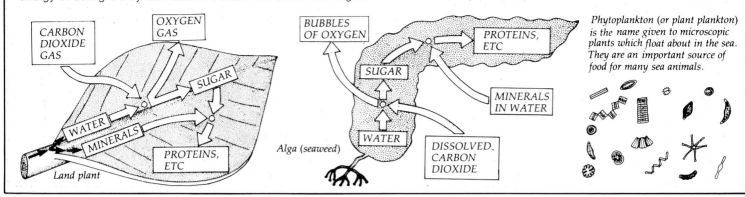

Phytoplankton (or plant plankton) is the name given to microscopic plants which float about in the sea. They are an important source of food for many sea animals.

HETEROTROPHS (*hetero*: others; *troph*: feed) are all those organisms which cannot make their own food by photosynthesis. Heterotrophs survive by eating other organisms or their remains.

Only in this way can they get the larger 'readymade' organic molecules they need to live and grow. Heterotrophs obtain their food in a variety of ways.

Carnivores are animals which catch other animals, kill them and eat them. The animals they catch form their prey and they are said to be **predators**.

Carnivorous mammal

Carnivorous insect

Herbivores are animals which eat plants.

Herbivorous mammal

Herbivorous insect

Omnivores are animals which eat both animals and plants.

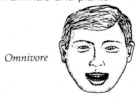

Omnivore

Parasites feed on other organisms while they are still alive.

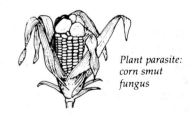

Plant parasite: corn smut fungus

Scavengers do not kill their prey. They wait for sick or injured animals to die and then eat them. They may also eat the leftovers of larger predators.

Scavenger

Filter feeders suck in water and remove the tiny food particles, both living and dead, from it.

Filter feeder

Animal parasite: flea

Detritus feeders include worms which eat mud to get out the food, and filter feeders. Detritus is the rotting remains of dead organisms which fall to the mud at the bottom of water.

Detritus feeder: lugworm

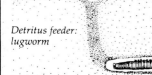

Saprophytes are the fungi and bacteria which cause dead organisms to decay. They do this by putting out digestive juices as they spread through the dead material. These digest the dead material. They then absorb the nutrients. Saprophytes do a very important job, since, when they are finished, all that is left are inorganic materials. These are then used by plants to help them grow.

Feeding in humans

Humans are **omnivores**. This means that human teeth must be able to deal with both plant and animal foods. They are therefore less specialised in shape than the teeth of other mammals. There are four basic types of teeth – **incisors, canines, premolars** and **molars**.

INCISORS: chisel-shaped teeth at the front of the mouth.

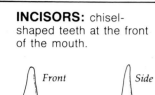

Front *Side*

Top

Incisors are used to cut pieces from food.

CANINES: pointed teeth on both sides of the incisors.

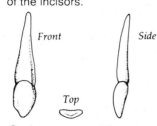

Front *Side*

Top

Canines are used for gripping and tearing.

PREMOLARS AND MOLARS: flat-topped teeth in the cheeks. They have points or **cusps**. Upper and lower cusps fit together.

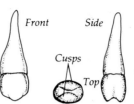
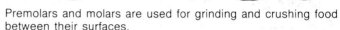

Front *Side* *Cusps* *Top* *Front* *Side* *Cusps* *Top*

Premolars and molars are used for grinding and crushing food between their surfaces.

The four types of teeth are arranged in the mouth as shown:

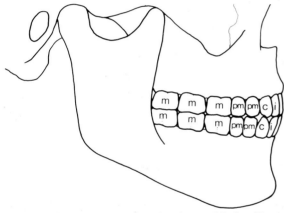

i: incisors
c: canines
pm: premolars
m: molars

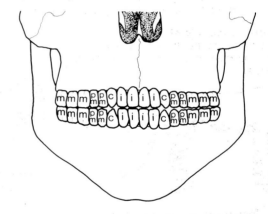

The incisors form an upper and a lower blade. Pieces of food are cut off when the jaw closes and brings these together. The canines are less useful, but a tough food, held in the hand, can be torn if held tightly between two canines. Once the front teeth have obtained a chunk of food, it is passed to the cheek teeth, i.e. the premolars and molars. These then crush it into smaller bits between their flatter surfaces, with the lower jaw making circular movements.

The main jaw muscles which control the actions of the teeth are the **temporalis** or **temple muscle** and the **masseter** or **chewing muscle**. The temporalis is concerned mainly with the front teeth, while the masseter is concerned mainly with the cheek teeth.

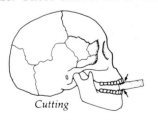
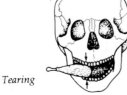

Cutting *Tearing*

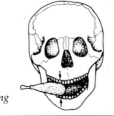

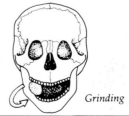
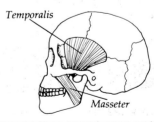

Temporalis

Grinding *Masseter*

The tooth arrangement of an animal is called its **dentition**. An animal's dentition can be written down as a **dental formula**. Since both sides of the mouth are the same, a dental formula need describe one side of the mouth only. The dental formula of an adult human is:

$$i\frac{2}{2} \qquad c\frac{1}{1} \qquad pm\frac{2}{2} \qquad m\frac{3}{3}$$

2 incisors in each side, both top and bottom

1 canine in each side, both top and bottom

2 premolars in each side, both top and bottom

3 molars in each side, both top and bottom

To find the total number of teeth, all the figures are added together and multiplied by two. For an adult human this is 32. Our first set of teeth, or milk teeth, has no molars, so, a child will have a dental formula of $\frac{2120}{2120}$ and a total of 20 teeth.

or, more simply: $\frac{2123}{2123}$

Teeth

Teeth are used for cutting and grinding food before swallowing. The teeth of mammals come in various shapes and sizes, depending on what the animal eats. However, they all have the same basic structure as seen in this section of a human **incisor**.

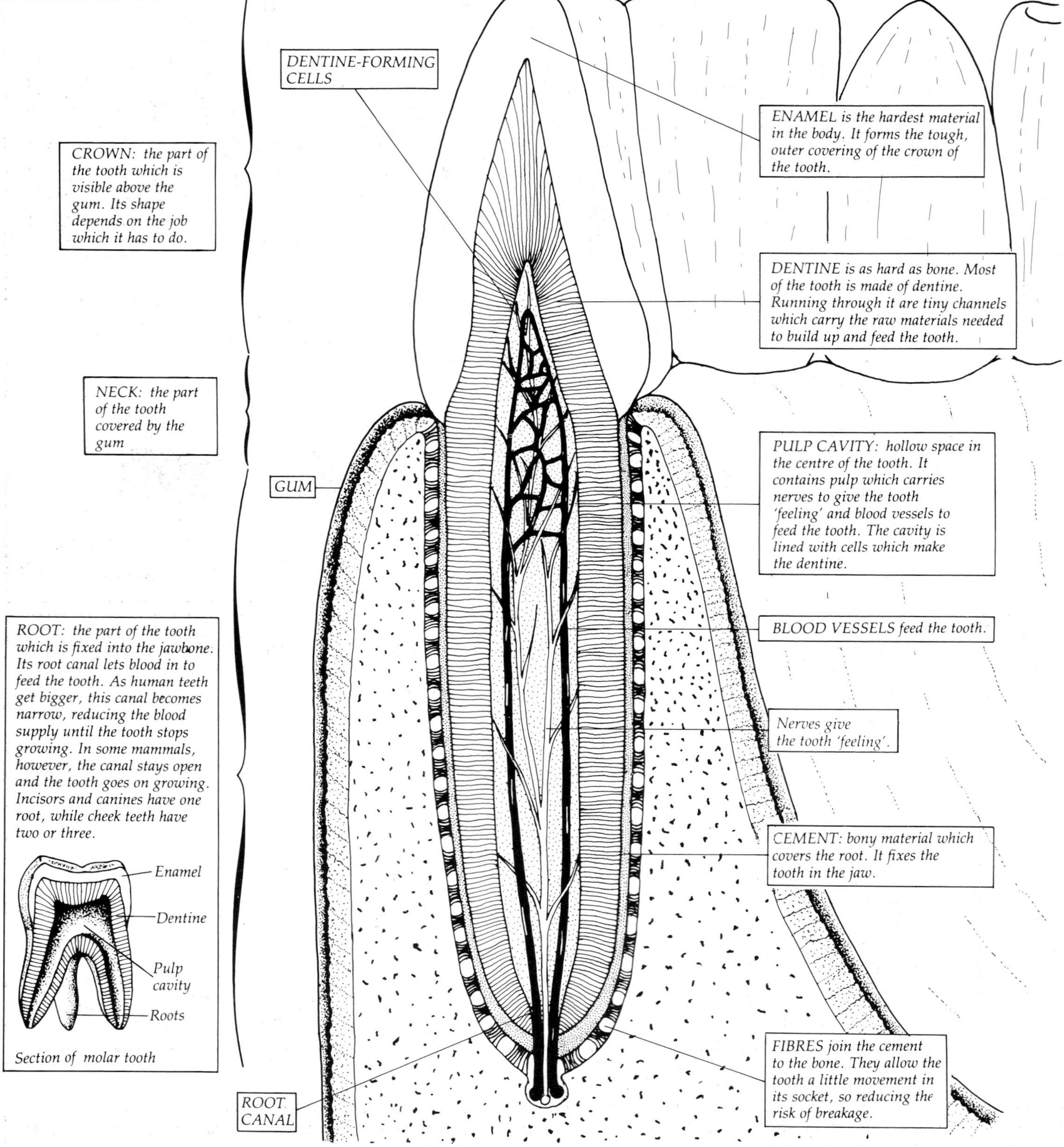

DENTINE-FORMING CELLS

ENAMEL is the hardest material in the body. It forms the tough, outer covering of the crown of the tooth.

CROWN: the part of the tooth which is visible above the gum. Its shape depends on the job which it has to do.

DENTINE is as hard as bone. Most of the tooth is made of dentine. Running through it are tiny channels which carry the raw materials needed to build up and feed the tooth.

NECK: the part of the tooth covered by the gum

PULP CAVITY: hollow space in the centre of the tooth. It contains pulp which carries nerves to give the tooth 'feeling' and blood vessels to feed the tooth. The cavity is lined with cells which make the dentine.

GUM

BLOOD VESSELS feed the tooth.

ROOT: the part of the tooth which is fixed into the jawbone. Its root canal lets blood in to feed the tooth. As human teeth get bigger, this canal becomes narrow, reducing the blood supply until the tooth stops growing. In some mammals, however, the canal stays open and the tooth goes on growing. Incisors and canines have one root, while cheek teeth have two or three.

Nerves give the tooth 'feeling'.

CEMENT: bony material which covers the root. It fixes the tooth in the jaw.

Enamel

Dentine

Pulp cavity

Roots

Section of molar tooth

ROOT CANAL

FIBRES join the cement to the bone. They allow the tooth a little movement in its socket, so reducing the risk of breakage.

TOOTH DECAY, that is teeth going bad, is caused by a layer of germs on the teeth called **plaque**. When we eat sugar, the plaque turns it into **acid**.

The acid dissolves the tooth, making holes called **caries**. If a hole gets deep enough, it lets the germs into the pulp where they cause infection and toothache.

PLAQUE + SUGAR ➡ ACID ➡ DECAY

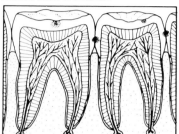

Plaque and sugar on teeth produce acid. Enamel starts to dissolve.

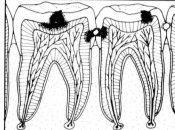

Acid reaches softer dentine. Decay speeds up. There is occasional pain.

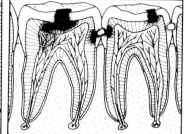

Germs invade pulp cavity. Toothache starts.

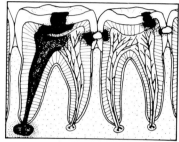

Infection spreads through pulp into gum, causing severe toothache.

If plaque doesn't get sugar, it can't cause tooth decay. Therefore, it is a good idea not to eat sweet things between meals and to brush the teeth after meals. Brushing helps in two ways. Firstly, it removes plaque. Secondly, it removes scraps of food which are stuck to the teeth. These scraps (and most plaque) tend to get between teeth down at the gum, or else on the flat tops of cheek teeth. It is these bits of the teeth which go bad first. Using the toothbrush correctly makes sure that these areas are kept thoroughly clean.

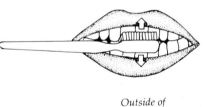

Outside of front teeth

Inside of front teeth

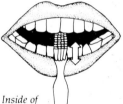

Inside of cheek teeth

Top surfaces of cheek teeth

Outside of cheek teeth

FLUORIDE is a mineral which is found in the public water supply. Some years ago, it was discovered that in areas where the water contained a lot of fluoride, children had fewer bad teeth than children from places where the water contained little fluoride.

The ideal concentration is about one part per million (ppm), that is, one gram of fluoride dissolved in every million grams of water. This amount gives good protection from decay with no mottling.

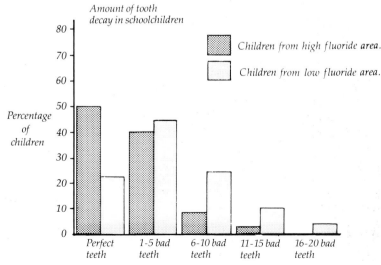

Amount of tooth decay in schoolchildren

Children from high fluoride **area**.

Children from low fluoride **area**.

Percentage of children

Perfect teeth | *1-5 bad teeth* | *6-10 bad teeth* | *11-15 bad teeth* | *16-20 bad teeth*

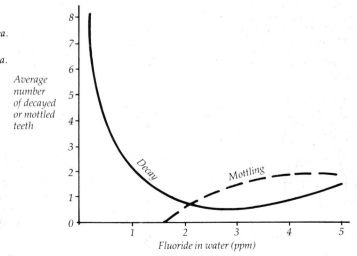

Average number of decayed or mottled teeth

Decay

Mottling

Fluoride in water (ppm)

Fluoride toughens tooth enamel and this reduces decay. However, if there is too much fluoride in the water, although the teeth are stronger, they also have an unpleasant appearance known as **mottling**.

Many places add fluoride to their water supply to reduce decay in their area. Where this does not happen, fluoride in toothpaste or pills will make teeth stronger.

Feeding in herbivores

A **herbivore** is an animal which eats only plant food. Plant material, especially the **cellulose** of plant cell walls, is very tough, so herbivores have to grind their food very thoroughly before it can be digested. Those mammals which are herbivores have teeth specially adapted to cut bits off plants and grind them before swallowing. The front teeth do the cutting and the cheek teeth do the grinding. The sheep's teeth, for example, are perfect for dealing with the grass which they eat.

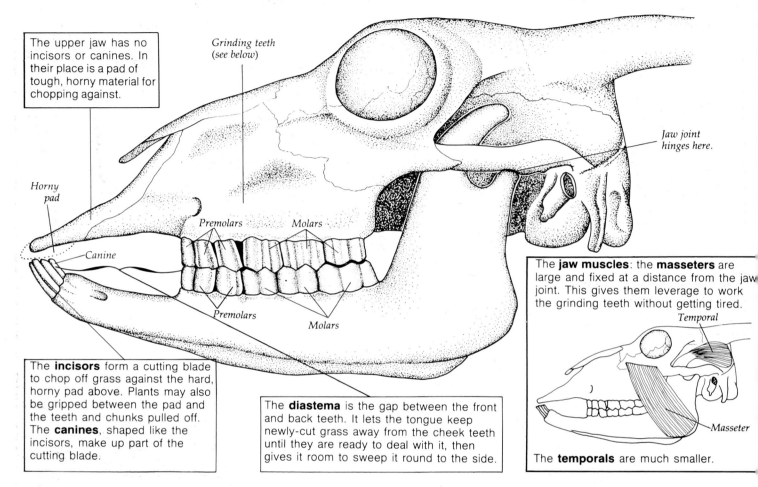

The upper jaw has no incisors or canines. In their place is a pad of tough, horny material for chopping against.

Grinding teeth (see below)

Jaw joint hinges here.

Horny pad

Premolars *Molars*

Canine

Premolars

Molars

The **incisors** form a cutting blade to chop off grass against the hard, horny pad above. Plants may also be gripped between the pad and the teeth and chunks pulled off. The **canines**, shaped like the incisors, make up part of the cutting blade.

The **diastema** is the gap between the front and back teeth. It lets the tongue keep newly-cut grass away from the cheek teeth until they are ready to deal with it, then gives it room to sweep it round to the side.

The **jaw muscles**: the **masseters** are large and fixed at a distance from the jaw joint. This gives them leverage to work the grinding teeth without getting tired.

Temporal

Masseter

The **temporals** are much smaller.

The cow, which has a diet very similar to that of the sheep, has very similar teeth and even the same dental formula. However, when a herbivore's diet is different, its dentition will also be different. Rabbits, for example, as well as eating grass also gnaw at hard material like bark and roots. They have sharp **incisors** to do this job.

The **dental formula** of a sheep is:

$$i\frac{0}{3} \quad c\frac{0}{1} \quad pm\frac{3}{3} \quad m\frac{3}{3}$$

First set: 20 teeth; adult set: 32 teeth.

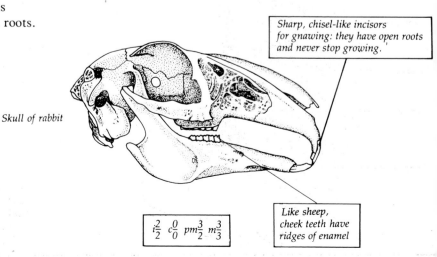

Sharp, chisel-like incisors for gnawing: they have open roots and never stop growing.

Skull of rabbit

$$i\frac{2}{2} \quad c\frac{0}{0} \quad pm\frac{3}{2} \quad m\frac{3}{3}$$

Like sheep, cheek teeth have ridges of enamel

The **premolars** and **molars** in the cheeks have broad, rough surfaces with upper and lower sets fitting closely together. Grass is placed between these and, with a side-to-side action, the lower teeth are scraped across the upper, so grinding and tearing the food to a mushy pulp before swallowing.

Scraping the cheek teeth together like this wears them down very quickly. However, the hard enamel wears down more slowly than the rest of the tooth and ridges of enamel are left sticking up. These enamel ridges make the teeth surfaces like the blades of a file, ideal for grinding up tough food. So that the teeth don't wear out completely, their **root canals** stay wide to let in a good blood supply and keep the tooth growing.

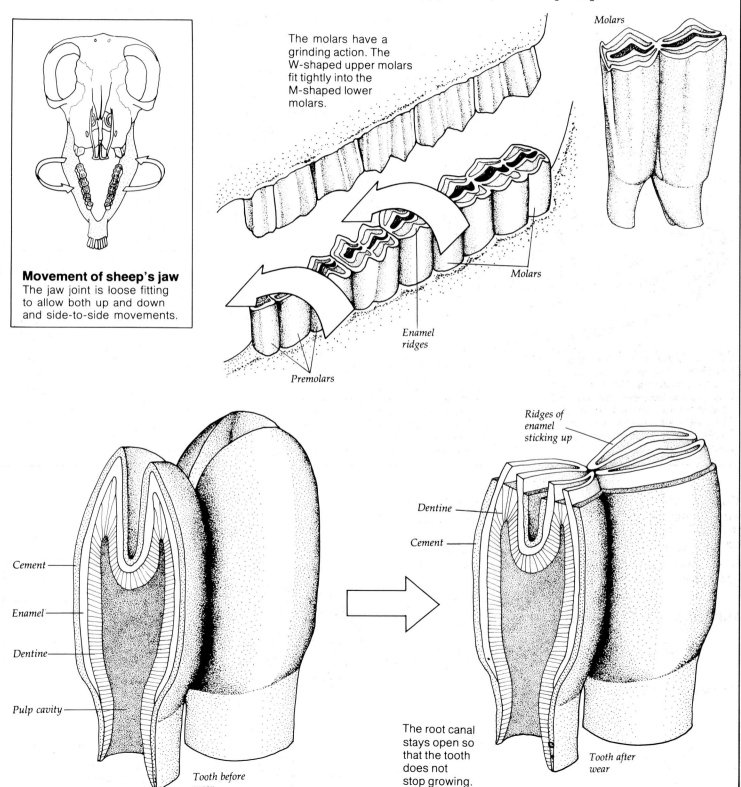

Movement of sheep's jaw
The jaw joint is loose fitting to allow both up and down and side-to-side movements.

The molars have a grinding action. The W-shaped upper molars fit tightly into the M-shaped lower molars.

Molars

Molars

Premolars

Enamel ridges

Ridges of enamel sticking up

Dentine

Cement

Cement

Enamel

Dentine

Pulp cavity

Tooth before wear

The root canal stays open so that the tooth does not stop growing.

Tooth after wear

Feeding in carnivores

A **carnivore** is an animal which eats flesh. It has to be able to catch and kill its prey. It must then be able to take the tough, raw body of its victim and cut it into pieces small enough to swallow. Those mammals which are carnivores have specially shaped teeth to carry out these jobs. The dog is an example.

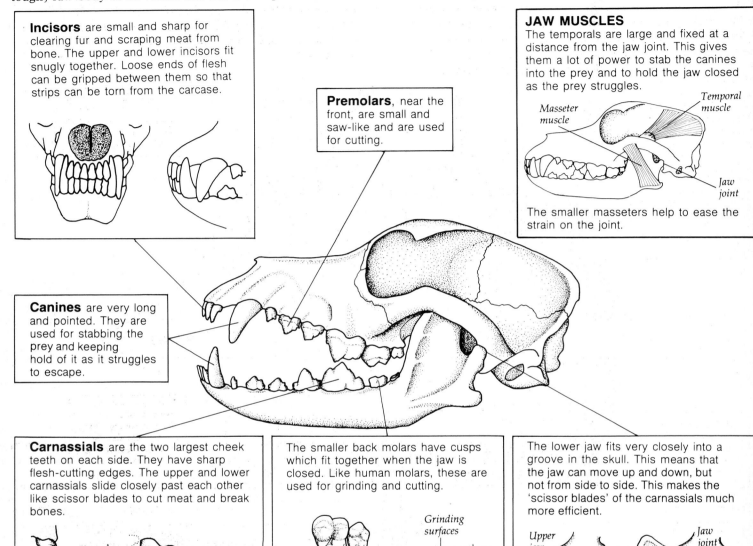

Incisors are small and sharp for clearing fur and scraping meat from bone. The upper and lower incisors fit snugly together. Loose ends of flesh can be gripped between them so that strips can be torn from the carcase.

Premolars, near the front, are small and saw-like and are used for cutting.

JAW MUSCLES
The temporals are large and fixed at a distance from the jaw joint. This gives them a lot of power to stab the canines into the prey and to hold the jaw closed as the prey struggles.

Masseter muscle

Temporal muscle

Jaw joint

The smaller masseters help to ease the strain on the joint.

Canines are very long and pointed. They are used for stabbing the prey and keeping hold of it as it struggles to escape.

Carnassials are the two largest cheek teeth on each side. They have sharp flesh-cutting edges. The upper and lower carnassials slide closely past each other like scissor blades to cut meat and break bones.

The smaller back molars have cusps which fit together when the jaw is closed. Like human molars, these are used for grinding and cutting.

Cusps

Grinding surfaces

The lower jaw fits very closely into a groove in the skull. This means that the jaw can move up and down, but not from side to side. This makes the 'scissor blades' of the carnassials much more efficient.

Upper jaw

Jaw joint

Lower jaw

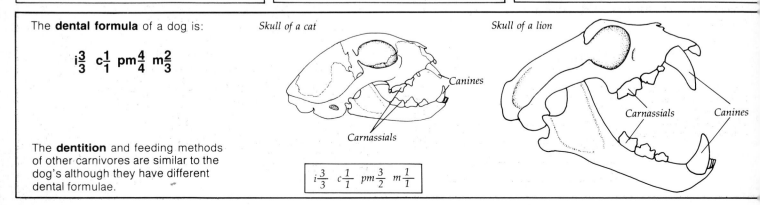

The **dental formula** of a dog is:

$$i\frac{3}{3} \quad c\frac{1}{1} \quad pm\frac{4}{4} \quad m\frac{2}{3}$$

The **dentition** and feeding methods of other carnivores are similar to the dog's although they have different dental formulae.

Skull of a cat

Canines

Carnassials

$$i\frac{3}{3} \quad c\frac{1}{1} \quad pm\frac{3}{2} \quad m\frac{1}{1}$$

Skull of a lion

Carnassials

Canines

Digestion

The food materials which our cells need for their **metabolism** (see page 62) are carried to them dissolved in the blood. However, most of the food we eat consists of very large molecules which do not dissolve. Before they can be **absorbed** (taken in) by the bloodstream, they must first be broken down into the smaller, soluble units of which they are made. This breaking-down process is called **digestion**. Digestion takes place in the **digestive system** which is a long tube through which the food is passed. As the food goes along the tube, a number of **digestive juices** are mixed with it. These juices contain the **digestive enzymes** which digest the food. The small, soluble molecules formed can then pass easily through the walls of the tube into the blood, which can then carry them to every cell in the body.

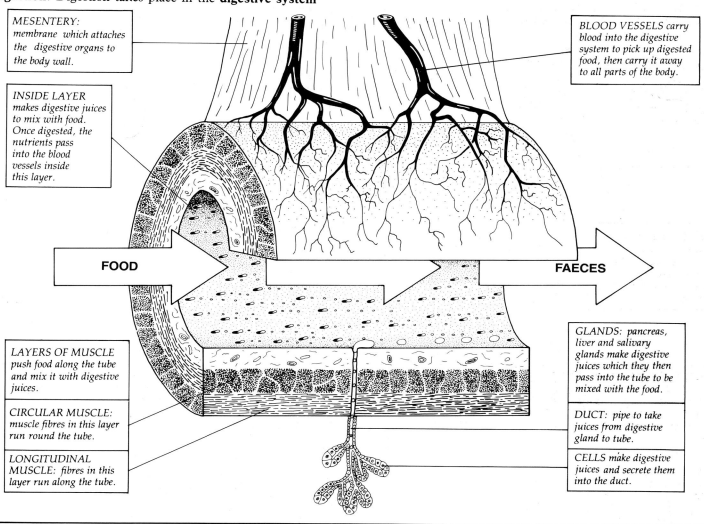

MESENTERY: membrane which attaches the digestive organs to the body wall.

INSIDE LAYER makes digestive juices to mix with food. Once digested, the nutrients pass into the blood vessels inside this layer.

BLOOD VESSELS carry blood into the digestive system to pick up digested food, then carry it away to all parts of the body.

FOOD

FAECES

LAYERS OF MUSCLE push food along the tube and mix it with digestive juices.

CIRCULAR MUSCLE: muscle fibres in this layer run round the tube.

LONGITUDINAL MUSCLE: fibres in this layer run along the tube.

GLANDS: pancreas, liver and salivary glands make digestive juices which they then pass into the tube to be mixed with the food.

DUCT: pipe to take juices from digestive gland to tube.

CELLS make digestive juices and secrete them into the duct.

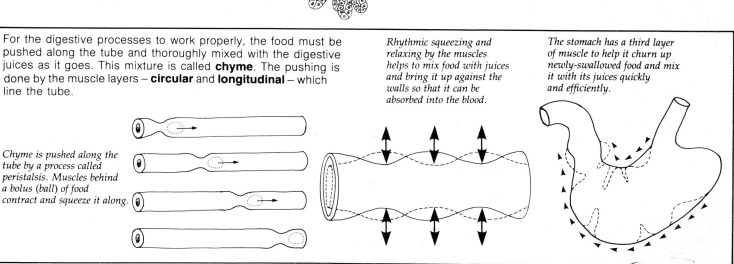

For the digestive processes to work properly, the food must be pushed along the tube and thoroughly mixed with the digestive juices as it goes. This mixture is called **chyme**. The pushing is done by the muscle layers – **circular** and **longitudinal** – which line the tube.

Rhythmic squeezing and relaxing by the muscles helps to mix food with juices and bring it up against the walls so that it can be absorbed into the blood.

The stomach has a third layer of muscle to help it churn up newly-swallowed food and mix it with its juices quickly and efficiently.

Chyme is pushed along the tube by a process called peristalsis. Muscles behind a bolus (ball) of food contract and squeeze it along.

The digestive enzymes

The process of **digestion** involves splitting up large food molecules into the smaller units of which they are made. This is important because only small food molecules can pass through the walls of the **digestive system** into the blood and only small molecules can later pass out of the bloodstream to feed the cells of the body. To digest (break down) large food molecules, the digestive system makes a number of **digestive enzymes**.

PROTEASES are enzymes which break down large protein molecules into the small **amino acids** of which they are made. The first protease to be mixed with food is **pepsin**. Pepsin is made by the stomach and starts the digestion of protein there. Pepsin splits proteins into smaller chains of amino acids called **peptides**. Pepsin has a low optimum pH and so can work well in the acid conditions of the stomach. When the food leaves the stomach, pepsin stops working and other proteases take over. **Trypsin**, made by the **pancreas**, carries on the digestion of proteins and the process is completed by **peptidase** made by the small intestine. This leaves the small, soluble amino acids which are able to pass into the blood.

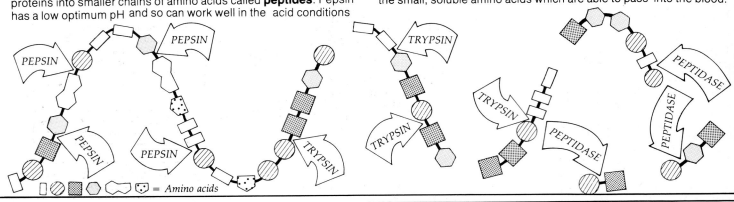

CARBOHYDRASES are enzymes which break down large carbohydrate molecules, like starch, into the small sugars of which they are made. The first carbohydrase to be mixed with food is **salivary amylase** (also called **ptyalin**) made by the salivary glands in the mouth. This begins starch digestion. Salivary amylase splits starch up into 'double sugars' called maltose. However, it cannot do much, since stomach acid stops it working. The next carbohydrase the food meets is **pancreatic amylase**. This is made by the pancreas and put into the duodenum where it changes all the starch to maltose. Other enzymes, made by the walls of the small intestine, split all the 'double sugars' like maltose and sucrose into 'single sugars' like glucose which are able to pass into the blood.

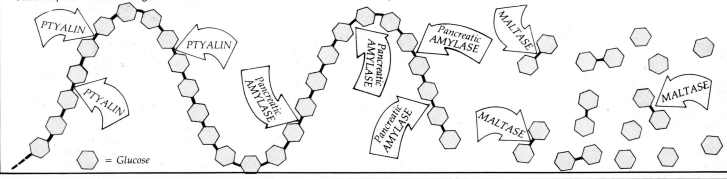

LIPASES are proteins which break down large fat molecules into the smaller **glycerol** and **fatty acids** of which they are made. The main lipase is made by the pancreas. This is put into the **duodenum** where it completes fat digestion, leaving fatty acids and glycerol. However, fats cannot mix with the watery pancreatic juice which contains the lipase. So, when we eat fatty food, **bile**, which is made by the liver, though stored in the **gall bladder** until needed, is squirted into the duodenum. This breaks the fats into small droplets which can then mix with the juices, forming an emulsion, and the enzyme can get to work. After digestion, the products do not enter the blood, but go instead into the **lymphatic system** (see pages 132–3).

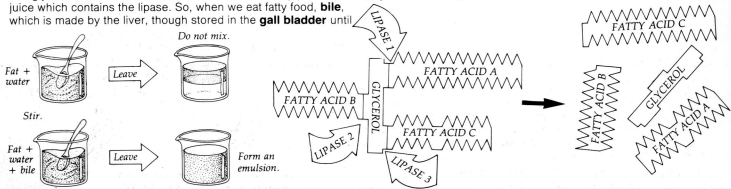

The digestive system

The **digestive system** consists of a long tube called the **alimentary canal** and a number of **glands** which are attached to it. The glands and some of the cells which line the canal make **digestive juices**. These are mixed with the food in the canal to make a liquid called **chyme**. The juices contain the **digestive enzymes** (see page 76) which break down large food molecules into smaller pieces which then can pass easily through the walls of the canal into the bloodstream. The lining cells also secrete a greasy fluid called **mucus** to lubricate the food and to protect the canal from its own digestive enzymes. When all the goodness has been taken out of the food, the indigestible solid waste which is left behind is expelled through the **anus** at the end of the tube. This waste is called **faeces**.

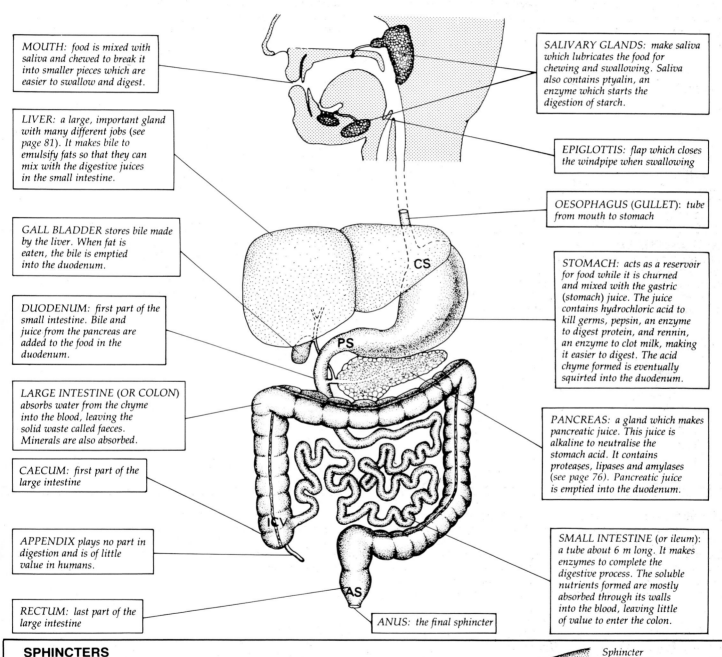

MOUTH: *food is mixed with saliva and chewed to break it into smaller pieces which are easier to swallow and digest.*

LIVER: *a large, important gland with many different jobs (see page 81). It makes bile to emulsify fats so that they can mix with the digestive juices in the small intestine.*

GALL BLADDER *stores bile made by the liver. When fat is eaten, the bile is emptied into the duodenum.*

DUODENUM: *first part of the small intestine. Bile and juice from the pancreas are added to the food in the duodenum.*

LARGE INTESTINE (OR COLON) *absorbs water from the chyme into the blood, leaving the solid waste called faeces. Minerals are also absorbed.*

CAECUM: *first part of the large intestine*

APPENDIX *plays no part in digestion and is of little value in humans.*

RECTUM: *last part of the large intestine*

SALIVARY GLANDS: *make saliva which lubricates the food for chewing and swallowing. Saliva also contains ptyalin, an enzyme which starts the digestion of starch.*

EPIGLOTTIS: *flap which closes the windpipe when swallowing*

OESOPHAGUS (GULLET): *tube from mouth to stomach*

STOMACH: *acts as a reservoir for food while it is churned and mixed with the gastric (stomach) juice. The juice contains hydrochloric acid to kill germs, pepsin, an enzyme to digest protein, and rennin, an enzyme to clot milk, making it easier to digest. The acid chyme formed is eventually squirted into the duodenum.*

PANCREAS: *a gland which makes pancreatic juice. This juice is alkaline to neutralise the stomach acid. It contains proteases, lipases and amylases (see page 76). Pancreatic juice is emptied into the duodenum.*

SMALL INTESTINE (or ileum): *a tube about 6 m long. It makes enzymes to complete the digestive process. The soluble nutrients formed are mostly absorbed through its walls into the blood, leaving little of value to enter the colon.*

ANUS: *the final sphincter*

SPHINCTERS

At a number of places along the alimentary canal, its muscular walls are thickened to form rings of muscle called sphincters. These rings of muscle can, when necessary, contract to close the tube and relax to open it. The sphincters at each end of the stomach, for example, can either hold food in the stomach or let it pass out of the stomach. The main sphincters are marked in the diagram above:

CS – cardiac sphincter   PS – pyloric sphincter
ICV – ilio-caecal valve   AS – anal sphincter

Sphincter

Muscle contracted, sphincter closed   *Muscle relaxed, sphincter open*

After digestion: absorption

By the time food has passed through the **duodenum**, the process of digestion is almost finished. However, the nutrients are still inside the gut – a long way from the cells which need them. They must now pass through the walls of the gut into the body so that they can be carried to every cell which requires them. This process is called **absorption**. The whole idea of digestion has been to break down large food molecules into smaller pieces – **amino acids, sugars, fatty acids** and **glycerol** – which can be absorbed easily through the inner surface of the gut into the body. To do this efficiently, there has to be a lot of surface available. Most food is absorbed into the body through the wall of the **small intestine**. This is a tube, about six metres long, with a special inside lining which has a very large area of absorbing surface. Amino acids and sugars (mainly glucose) pass through this into the bloodstream. Fatty acids and glycerol pass through it to enter the **lymphatic system**. They are then carried throughout the body.

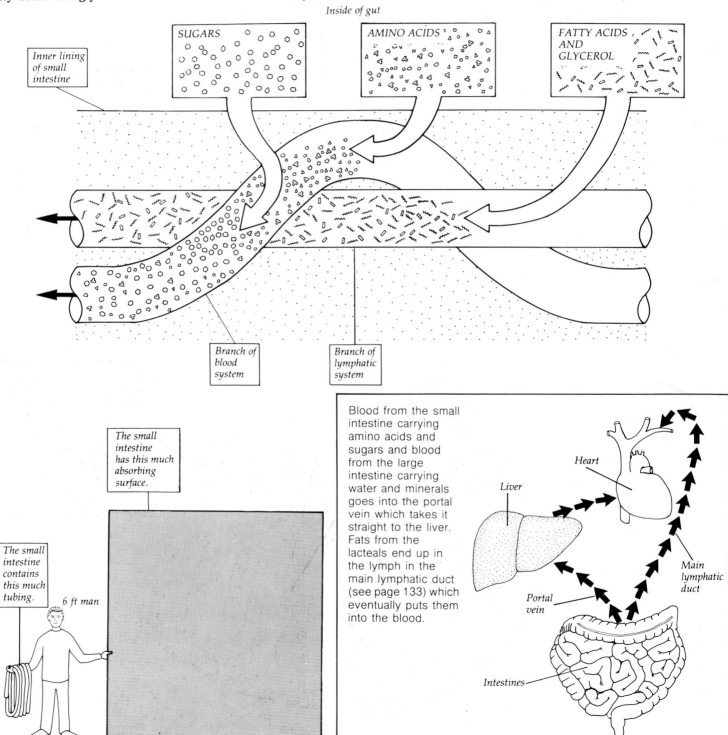

Inside of gut

SUGARS

AMINO ACIDS

FATTY ACIDS AND GLYCEROL

Inner lining of small intestine

Branch of blood system

Branch of lymphatic system

The small intestine has this much absorbing surface.

The small intestine contains this much tubing.

6 ft man

Blood from the small intestine carrying amino acids and sugars and blood from the large intestine carrying water and minerals goes into the portal vein which takes it straight to the liver. Fats from the lacteals end up in the lymph in the main lymphatic duct (see page 133) which eventually puts them into the blood.

Liver

Heart

Main lymphatic duct

Portal vein

Intestines

To give it the huge surface it needs to do its job, the inside lining of the small intestine has lots of folds in it. It is also covered with millions of tiny 'fingers' called **villi** (sing: *villus*) which wave about in the digested food, absorbing the nutrients.

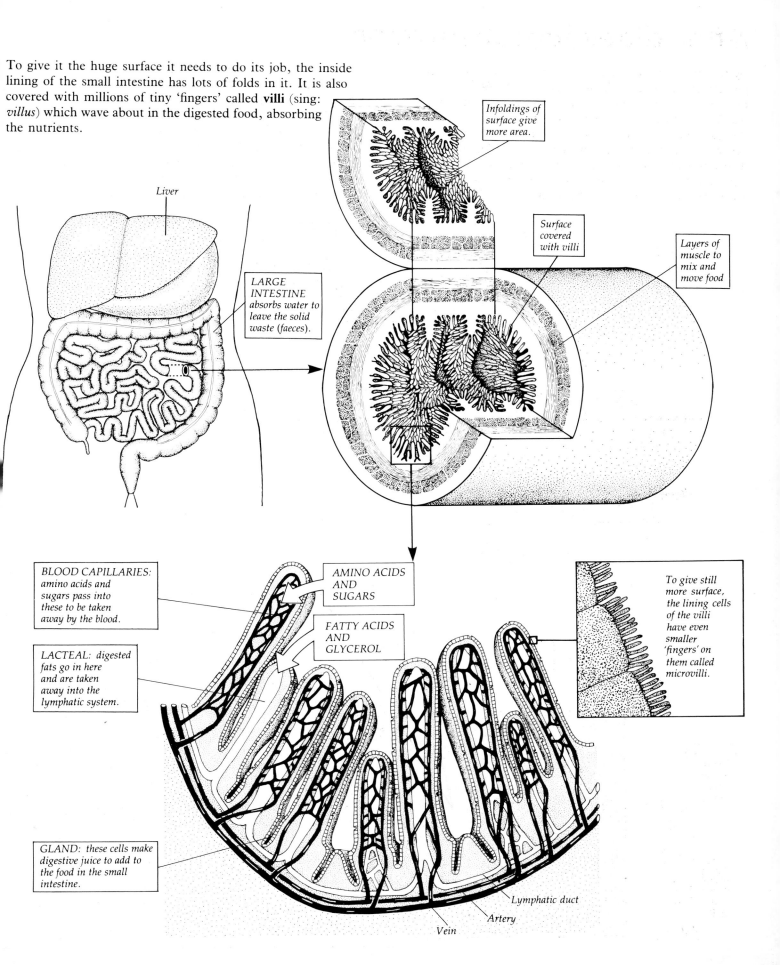

Liver

Infoldings of surface give more area.

Surface covered with villi

Layers of muscle to mix and move food

LARGE INTESTINE absorbs water to leave the solid waste (faeces).

BLOOD CAPILLARIES: amino acids and sugars pass into these to be taken away by the blood.

AMINO ACIDS AND SUGARS

FATTY ACIDS AND GLYCEROL

To give still more surface, the lining cells of the villi have even smaller 'fingers' on them called microvilli.

LACTEAL: digested fats go in here and are taken away into the lymphatic system.

GLAND: these cells make digestive juice to add to the food in the small intestine.

Lymphatic duct

Artery

Vein

Using absorbed food

After digestion, food has been converted to **glucose, amino acids, fatty acids** and **glycerol**. These soluble nutrients are absorbed from the **alimentary canal** by the **circulatory system**. They are then carried round the body to be used by those cells which need them.

GLUCOSE is used by cells to provide them with energy when they need it. The glucose level in the blood needs to be kept fairly steady. After a meal, if it gets too high, the liver takes the extra glucose out of the blood and stores it as **glycogen** (animal starch). Glycogen is simply hundreds of glucose molecules joined together. Some glycogen is also stored in the muscles. The liver stores glucose as glycogen when 'ordered' to do so by a hormone called **insulin** (see page 197). Insulin is made in the pancreas by patches of cells called **islets of Langerhans**. The rest of the pancreas makes digestive juice. The insulin is put straight into the blood which carries it to the liver. **Diabetes** is an illness caused by the pancreas being unable to make enough insulin.

Sometimes, perhaps when danger threatens, the cells need a sudden supply of glucose for extra energy. This is provided when another hormone called **adrenalin** 'orders' the liver to break down some glycogen into glucose. Adrenalin is made by the **adrenal glands** (see page 197).

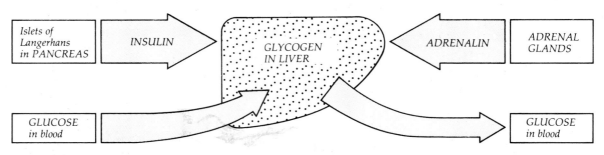

If we eat more carbohydrate than we need, the extra is converted to fat and stored.

AMINO ACIDS are used by cells to make the many different kinds of proteins that they need – enzymes, etc. After absorption from the digestive system, the amino acids are carried around in the blood and taken out by those cells which need them. However, the body cannot store surplus amino acids. So, many extra amino acids are broken down by the liver, leaving a substance called **urea**. Urea is removed from the blood by the kidneys and expelled in the urine. This process of amino acid breakdown is called **deamination**.

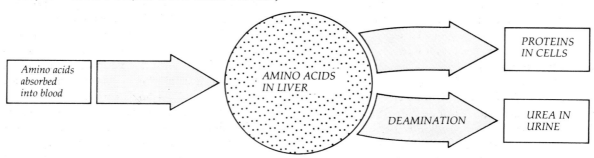

FATTY ACIDS AND GLYCEROL are absorbed into the **lacteals** (see pages 78–9) in the centre of the **villi** in the small intestine. From these, they enter the **lymphatic system** (see pages 132–3), which eventually empties them into the bloodstream near the heart. They are used by the cells to provide energy and any extra are stored as fat. Fat-storing tissue is called **adipose tissue**. Fats are also used by the cells to help make certain cell materials such as cell membranes.

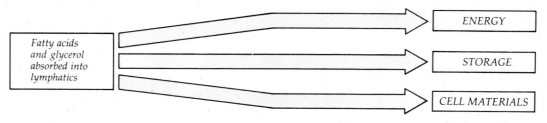

The liver

The liver is the largest organ in the body. It is tucked under the diaphragm on the right-hand side of the body and partly covers the stomach. It is divided into a number of sections called **lobes**. The liver carries out a number of duties which are absolutely essential to life and health. For this reason it is supplied with more blood than any other part of the body. It receives this blood from two sources. Part of it comes from the heart along the **hepatic artery**. The rest, rich in absorbed food, comes from the digestive system along the **portal vein**.

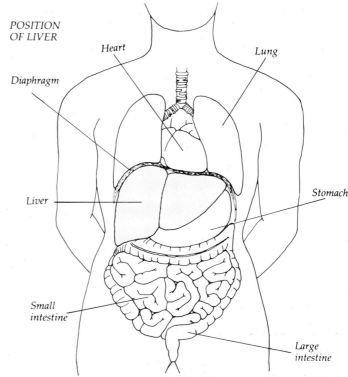

LIVER AND HEART SEEN FROM BEHIND

AORTA: main artery taking blood from the heart to the rest of the body

VENA CAVA takes blood back to the heart.

HEPATIC VEIN takes blood away from the liver back to the heart.

Heart

HEPATIC ARTERY takes blood from the heart to the liver.

Left lobe of liver

Right lobe of liver

GALL BLADDER stores bile made by the liver.

PORTAL VEIN takes blood loaded with nutrients from the digestive system to the liver.

BILE DUCT takes bile from the gall bladder to the duodenum.

POSITION OF LIVER

Heart

Lung

Diaphragm

Liver

Stomach

Small intestine

Large intestine

Here are some of the most important jobs the liver does.

1 **The liver makes bile**. Bile breaks down fatty foods into small droplets so that they mix more easily with the watery digestive juices. Bile is stored in the **gall bladder** until it is needed. It is then squirted into the **duodenum**.

2 **The liver controls blood sugar**. The level of glucose (sugar) in the blood must be kept fairly steady at about 0.1%. When it gets too high after a meal, the liver removes the extra and stores it as **glycogen** (animal starch). If it gets too low, the liver converts some of its glycogen into glucose and puts it back into the blood. This is an example of **homeostasis** (see pages 198–9). However, the liver does not do this automatically. These activities are controlled by the hormones **insulin** and **adrenalin** (see pages 196–7).

3 **The liver deaminates amino acids**. The body cannot store excess amino acids, so any unwanted amino acids are changed by the liver into ammonia (NH_3) and carbohydrate. The poisonous ammonia is immediately changed into **urea** which is got rid of by the kidneys (see page 118). The carbohydrate is used to produce energy. This is called **deamination**.

4 **The liver organises fats**. The liver changes fats to make these suitable either for producing energy or for being stored in the body's fat-storing tissues.

5 **The liver destroys poisons**. Many poisonous substances find their way into the blood. Some of these are waste products from chemical reactions going on inside the body. Others, such as alcohol or drugs, come from outside the body. As the blood flows through the liver, these poisons are made harmless. This is called **detoxification**.

6 **The liver stores iron**. The liver breaks down millions of old, worn out red blood cells every day. It takes the iron from their **haemoglobin** (see page 132) and stores it until it is needed to make new red blood cells.

7 **The liver stores vitamins**. Several vitamins, such as vitamin A and vitamin D, are stored in the liver until they are needed by the body.

8 **The liver makes plasma proteins**. Many of the important proteins, called plasma proteins, which are found in the blood, are made by the liver. These include **fibrinogen**, which is essential for blood clotting.

9 **The liver makes heat**. All the chemical reactions going on in the body make up its **metabolism**. Much of this metabolism is carried out by the liver, which is like a large chemical factory. All of these chemical reactions generate heat, and this heat produced by the liver is essential for keeping the body at the correct temperature.

```
Unwanted
amino    →  Ammonia  →  Urea
acids
         →  Carbohydrate  →  Energy
```

Digestion in herbivores

As a source of food, plant material is very tough and difficult to digest. **Herbivores** can use their special grinding teeth (see pages 72–3) to break open the plant cells and get at the nourishment inside. However, in many plants, for example grass, most of the food value is in the **cell walls**. Plant cell walls are made mainly of **cellulose** and mammals cannot produce the **enzymes** to digest this. In humans, for example, cellulose makes up the **roughage** in the diet. Roughage has no food value, though it does help the muscles of the digestive system to work properly. Some mammals, however, like the rabbit and the cow, can make use of cellulose. Although they cannot make the necessary enzymes themselves, in certain parts of the gut they have micro-organisms, mainly bacteria, which can. The bacteria digest the cell walls, and the sugars and fatty acids they produce are absorbed by the animal. This is an example of **mutualism** (see page 86). The animal supplies the bacteria with food and the bacteria digest it for the animal's benefit. Even with such help, these herbivores need a very long digestive system and their food has to spend a much longer time in it than food does in the digestive systems of omnivores and carnivores.

DIGESTION IN THE RABBIT

The rabbit has a very long intestine to carry out the slow, difficult job of digesting and absorbing its food. It also has a very large **caecum** and **appendix**. In the caecum and appendix are the **mutualistic bacteria** which it relies upon to digest its cellulose. When food has passed once through the rabbit's digestive system, the remains are expelled as soft, moist pellets. Later on, the rabbit eats these pellets, so that the food goes through the gut a second time. In this way, it makes sure the food has been completely digested and that the nutrients have been absorbed into the blood. The final rabbit droppings, or faeces, are in the form of the hard, dry pellets it leaves outside its burrow.

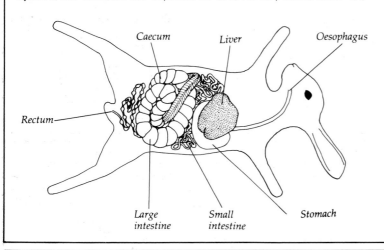

Caecum · Liver · Oesophagus · Rectum · Large intestine · Small intestine · Stomach

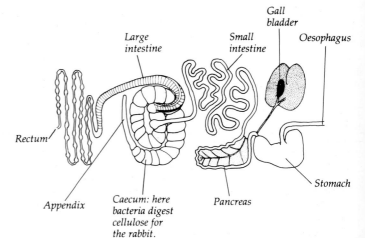

Gall bladder · Large intestine · Small intestine · Oesophagus · Rectum · Appendix · Caecum: here bacteria digest cellulose for the rabbit. · Pancreas · Stomach

DIGESTION IN HERBIVORES

Herbivores such as cattle and sheep are known as **ruminants**. A ruminant's stomach is divided into four chambers, the largest of which is called the **rumen**. When a cow, or other ruminant, swallows its food, the food goes down into the rumen. Bacteria in the rumen digest the cellulose. Later, balls of this digesting food are taken back up into the mouth and thoroughly ground up by the molars. This is called chewing the cud. The food is then swallowed for a second time and goes into the rest of the digestive system for digestion and absorption to be completed. This long, slow process requires a very long small intestine – the cow's is about 40 metres long. Like the rabbit, ruminants have a very large caecum and appendix, but most cellulose digestion takes place in the rumen.

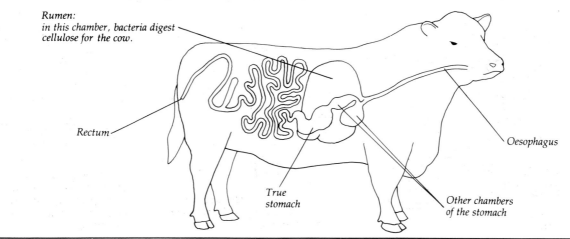

Rumen: in this chamber, bacteria digest cellulose for the cow. · Rectum · Oesophagus · True stomach · Other chambers of the stomach

Feeding in insects

Insects eat many different things, ranging from the blood of animals to fresh green leaves. They have special mouthparts designed to deal with the kind of food they prefer.

Basically, these mouthparts are suited either to biting or sucking their food.

BITING INSECTS are those with mouthparts that can cut off a piece of food and then crunch it up before swallowing. They include insects like the locust which eat leaves.

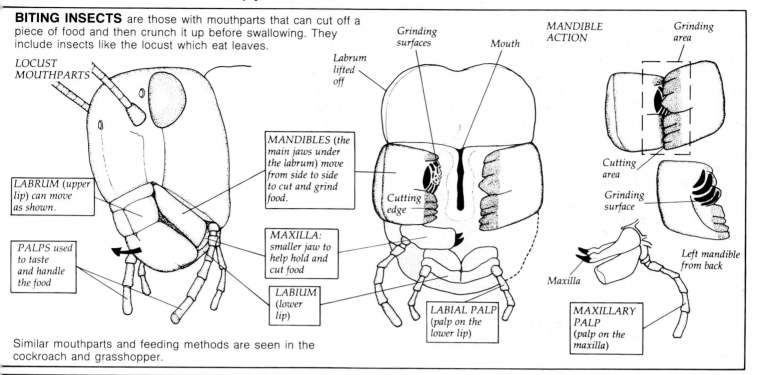

LOCUST MOUTHPARTS

LABRUM (upper lip) can move as shown.

PALPS used to taste and handle the food

MANDIBLES (the main jaws under the labrum) move from side to side to cut and grind food.

MAXILLA: smaller jaw to help hold and cut food

LABIUM (lower lip)

Grinding surfaces

Mouth

Labrum lifted off

Cutting edge

LABIAL PALP (palp on the lower lip)

MANDIBLE ACTION

Grinding area

Cutting area

Grinding surface

Maxilla

Left mandible from back

MAXILLARY PALP (palp on the maxilla)

Similar mouthparts and feeding methods are seen in the cockroach and grasshopper.

SUCKING INSECTS take only liquid food Many, like the butterfly, suck the sweet nectar from flowers. Some suck the juice out of other organisms. The mosquito, for example, sucks blood from animals, while the aphid (greenfly) sucks the sap from plants. The housefly has to dissolve its food with saliva before it can suck it up.

The housefly's mouthparts are in the form of a feeding tube called a **proboscis** which ends in a fleshy pad. Saliva is pumped down this on to the food. This starts to digest the solid food and the liquid it forms is sucked into the pad, up the proboscis and then into the gut:

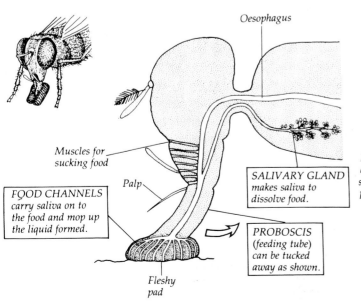

Oesophagus

Muscles for sucking food

Palp

FOOD CHANNELS carry saliva on to the food and mop up the liquid formed.

SALIVARY GLAND makes saliva to dissolve food.

PROBOSCIS (feeding tube) can be tucked away as shown.

Fleshy pad

The housefly's saliva contains germs which it picks up in dustbins, manure, etc. and it can spread these on to human food while it feeds and so cause disease in humans.

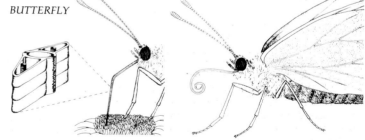

BUTTERFLY

The butterfly's proboscis is like a long straw which it pushes into flowers to reach and suck up the nectar. It can be coiled up when it is not being used.

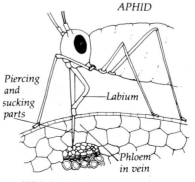

APHID

Piercing and sucking parts

Labium

Phloem in vein

With its proboscis the aphid can pierce a plant's skin and suck up the sap.

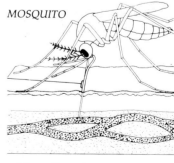

MOSQUITO

Mosquitos pierce an animal's skin, inject a liquid to stop the animal's blood clotting, then suck up the blood.

Eating tiny food

Drifting in the waters of lakes and seas is a very valuable, yet almost invisible, source of food for many animals. This is **plankton**, tiny organisms, mostly too small to be seen without a microscope. Plankton consists of microscopic plants called **phytoplankton** (*phyto*: plant) and tiny animals called **zooplankton** (*zoo*: animal). Two common ways in which animals feed on such tiny organisms are by **phagocytosis** and by **filter feeding**.

PHAGOCYTOSIS means 'cell-eating'. Amoeba is a typical phagocyte. It is a single-celled animal which moves by flowing along, changing its shape as it goes. When it comes across a piece of food – usually a single-celled plant – it flows round it and takes it into its **cytoplasm**. It then digests it. This is known as **intracellular digestion** (*intra*: within).

The Amoeba flows towards a food particle.	The cytoplasm flows round the food and forms a cup.	The food is taken into the cytoplasm and trapped inside a food vacuole.	Digestive enzymes are added to the food in the food vacuole.	The food is digested and absorbed into the surrounding cytoplasm.	The Amoeba leaves the waste behind as it flows away from it.

FILTER FEEDING is a widely-used method of catching plankton. A current of water is passed through the body in some way and the plankton it contains is kept behind. By filtering huge quantities of water, some very large animals such as the blue whale can live on plankton. Among the great variety of water animals which are filter feeders are the mussel and the herring.

The mussel is a **bivalve mollusc**, that is, a mollusc with two shells (*bi*: two). Mussels are found, often in large bunches, tied to rocks on the seashore. When covered by the tide, they filter food from the water. Water is drawn in through a tube called the **inhalent siphon** and passed over the four flat gills. A layer of sticky mucus on the gills catches any suitable food particles. The water and any unwanted material such as sand grains are moved through the gills and out of the **exhalent siphon**. The water current is actually caused by the beating of millions of tiny cilia (hairs) which cover the gill surfaces. Cilia can also move the mucus, together with the food it carries, to the mouth. It is scraped off by the **palps** and swallowed.

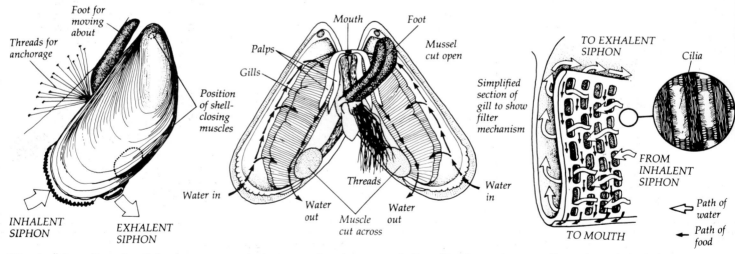

The herring, like other fish, passes a constant stream of water over its gills. The gill filaments absorb dissolved oxygen from the water and add carbon dioxide to it. Each gill also has a row of comb-like **gill rakers**. As water filters through the rakers, the plankton is caught and swallowed.

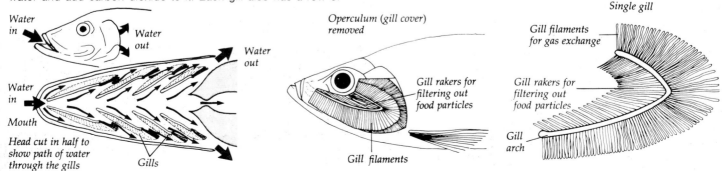

Heterotrophic plants

Most plants are **autotrophs**. Autotrophs can make their own food from simple substances by the process of **photosynthesis** (see pages 88–9). There are some plants, however, which must get all or part of their food in other ways. These plants are **heterotrophs**. Some heterotrophic plants are **parasites**. They feed on other organisms called **hosts** while these organisms are still alive, and can cause harm to them. A number of parasitic flowering plants are described below.

DODDER shoots spread along the ground until they reach a suitable plant. Suckers from the dodder pierce the host's stem to take food from its veins. The young dodder's roots can then just wither away.

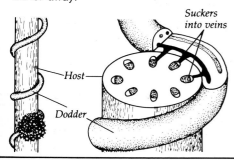

Suckers into veins
Host
Dodder

TOOTHWORT sends out roots from its underground stem. These pierce the roots of trees such as the hazel and take food from its veins.

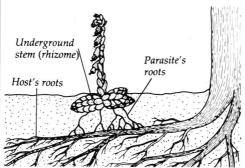

Underground stem (rhizome)
Parasite's roots
Host's roots

MISTLETOE's sticky seeds get left by birds on the bark of trees. They penetrate into the wood. From this they get water and mineral salts. Mistletoe's green leaves can carry out photosynthesis, so it is not a complete parasite.

Green leaves
Woody (xylem) tissue
Apple branch

There are a small number of plants which eat insects. These are called **insectivorous plants**. Actually, they get most of their food from photosynthesis, but since they normally grow in marshy soils, which are low in nitrogen, they trap insects and digest them to get the nitrogen they require. In Britain there are only three kinds of insectivorous plants: butterwort, bladderwort and sundew.

BUTTERWORT leaves are covered with a sticky yellow substance to catch insects. The leaves curl round any stuck insect, leaf **enzymes** digest it and the plant then absorbs all the nitrogen.

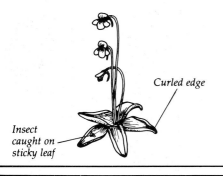

Curled edge
Insect caught on sticky leaf

BLADDERWORT has underwater bladders. If insects touch the hairs at the entrance to one of these, they get sucked inside. They are then digested.

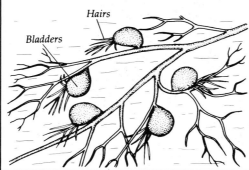

Hairs
Bladders

SUNDEW leaves are covered with tentacles, each tipped with a drop of 'glue'. When an insect gets stuck on these, they curl round to hold the insect until it is digested.

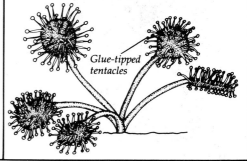

Glue-tipped tentacles

FUNGI (sing: *fungus*) are a group of plants which, since they have no **chlorophyll**, cannot make their own food by photosynthesis. The body of a fungus is called the **mycelium**. It is made of tiny threads called **hyphae** (sing: *hypha*). These threads spread into the food and put out digestive juices into it. The enzymes in the juices dissolve the food. This can then diffuse back into the hyphae to feed the fungus.

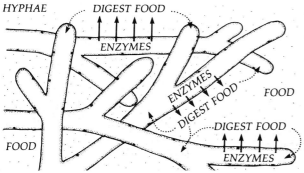

HYPHAE
DIGEST FOOD
ENZYMES
ENZYMES
DIGEST FOOD
FOOD
DIGEST FOOD
DIGEST FOOD
ENZYMES
FOOD

SAPROPHYTIC FUNGUS

Hyphae spread into log, absorbing it.
Cup fungus on log

If a fungus feeds on dead material, it is called a **saprophyte**. Saprophytes do a useful job in breaking down dead organisms.

PARASITIC FUNGUS

Polyporous on living oak

If a fungus feeds on living organisms, it is called a **parasite**. These fungi cause disease.

Symbiosis: living together

All species of organism form relationships of one kind or another with other species. However, many organisms are found living together in unusually close and special relationships with members of completely different species.

This is called **symbiosis**. There are many kinds of these **symbiotic** relationships, some closer than others, but there are three main categories: **mutualism, commensalism** and **parasitism**.

MUTUALISM is a relationship between two species from which both partners get some benefit. They may be unable to live separately:

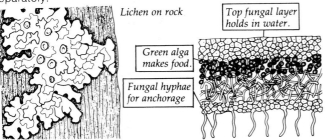

Lichen on rock

Top fungal layer holds in water.

Green alga makes food.

Fungal hyphae for anchorage

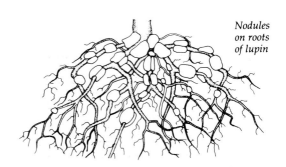

Nodules on roots of lupin

Lichens are plants which can grow on bare rocks and other hostile places. In fact, lichens consist of two organisms – an **alga** and a **fungus** – joined closely together. The alga makes food for the fungus by photosynthesis, while, in return, the fungus gives the alga moisture and anchorage.

Root nodules are lumps which appear on the roots of leguminous plants like peas, beans, clover and lupins. They contain bacteria called **Rhizobium** which can take nitrogen gas from the air and change it into a form the plant can use to help it to grow. In return, the Rhizobium gets food from the plant.

COMMENSALISM is a relationship between two species in which one partner, called the **commensal**, gets some benefit, while the other, called the **host**, neither gains nor loses:

Sea anemone (commensal)

Hermit crab (host)

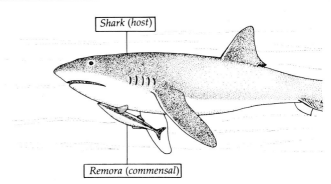

Shark (host)

Remora (commensal)

Hermit crabs occupy the empty shells of dead animals such as whelks in order to get protection for their soft, vulnerable bodies. Sea anemones and other animals attach themselves to this shell so that they can get transport and scraps of food from the crab. In return, the crab usually gets very little of value.

Remora is a small fish which can attach itself to a shark by using a sucker on the top of its head. In this way, it gets carried around by the shark with its mouth free to catch bits of food which the shark may drop. The shark appears to be completely unaffected by this.

PARASITISM is a relationship between two species in which one, called the **parasite**, gets food and shelter from the other, called the **host**, while causing some degree of harm to it – perhaps eventually killing it:

from being digested themselves. Segments full of ripe eggs are passed in the person's faeces to spread the infection.

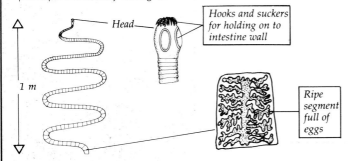

Head

Hooks and suckers for holding on to intestine wall

1 m

Ripe segment full of eggs

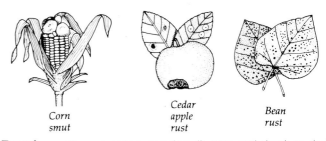

Corn smut

Cedar apple rust

Bean rust

Tapeworms live in the intestines of people who have eaten infected meat. Their long (up to 6 m) flat bodies absorb the person's digested food, while special chemicals keep the worms

Fungi are often parasites, causing disease and death to their hosts – mainly plants. Spores land on the plant and germinate. The fungal **hyphae** spread through the plant tissues, feeding on the cells and killing them. The fungus then produces more spores to spread the disease to other plants.

SECTION 8

Making Food

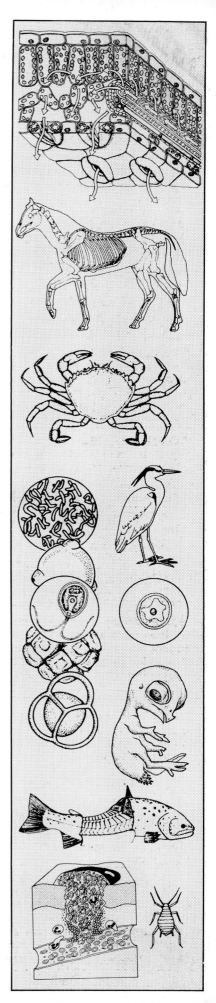

Photosynthesis: how plants make food

All living things need food to supply them with the energy they need to stay alive and the building materials they need for growth. All animals and some plants must obtain their food in the form of large 'readymade' food molecules such as **carbohydrates**, **proteins** and **fats**. They get these by feeding on other organisms. For this reason, they are known as **heterotrophs** (*hetero*: other; *troph*: food). Green plants, however, can make their own food. Since they can make their own food, they are known as **autotrophs** (*auto*: self; *troph*: food). The process by which green plants make food is called **photosynthesis**. In photosynthesis green plants take carbon dioxide gas and combine it with water to make glucose (the basic sugar). This process needs **light energy**. Oxygen gas is given off as waste. It is a very complicated chemical process, but it can be summarised like this:

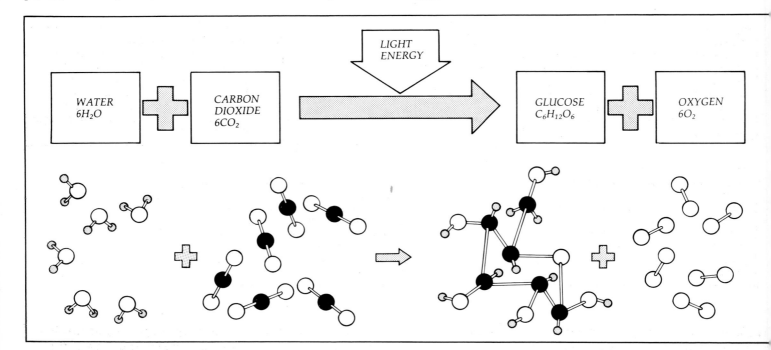

In photosynthesis, light energy from the sun has been changed into the chemical energy which holds the glucose molecule together. In **respiration** (see page 94) animals and plants can release this energy and use it to keep themselves alive. Photosynthesis is really a way of harvesting the energy of the sun to power life on Earth.

To gather the sun's energy, plants contain a green substance called **chlorophyll**. Chlorophyll absorbs light energy and changes it into chemical energy. The chemical energy is then used to split water into hydrogen and oxygen. The oxygen is given off as waste and more chemical energy is used to join the hydrogen to carbon dioxide to make glucose.

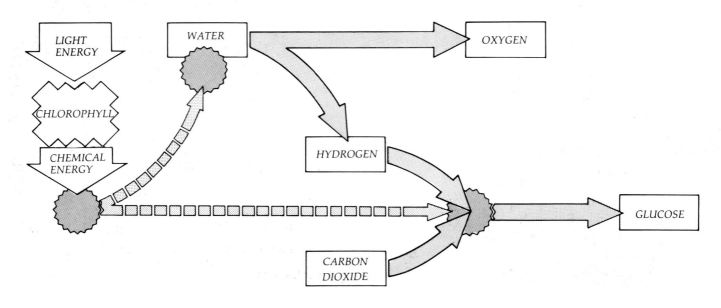

Once a plant has made glucose and other sugars by photosynthesis, a number of things can be done with them:

Sugar

Translocation
The leaves of a plant make more sugar than they need. The surplus is transported to other parts of the plant, e.g. the roots, to supply their needs. This is called translocation.

Respiration
Like animals, plants need a non-stop supply of energy in order to stay alive. They get this by oxidising some food in the process called respiration (see pages 94–5). This converts the food back into water and carbon dioxide, releasing its energy.

Making other cell materials
From sugar can be made the other materials – proteins, fats, etc. – which the plant needs. However, for some things, other ingredients are required. For example, nitrogen is needed to make protein. These are obtained as minerals which the plant absorbs from the soil.

Conversion to starch
In good light, sugar is made in a leaf faster than it can be taken away. The extra is stored as starch so that the water balance of the cells is not upset. So, in daytime, most leaves contain starch. At night it is reconverted to sugar and transported out of the leaf.

Storage
Plants must store some food for the next generation. It may be stored in the cotyledons or endosperms of seeds or in storage organs such as tubers or bulbs. For storage, sugar is converted to either starch or fat.

The green chemical chlorophyll is essential for making food by photosynthesis. If we look at plant cells under a microscope, we find that all the chlorophyll is inside tiny green bodies. These are called **chloroplasts**. Chloroplasts, are the tiny 'food factories' of the cell. Any part of a plant which is green will be able to carry out photosynthesis, but the cells of the leaves, especially those near the top of the plant, contain the most chloroplasts, so it is the leaves which make most of a plant's food.

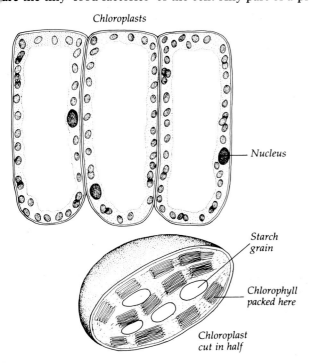

Chloroplasts

Nucleus

Starch grain

Chlorophyll packed here

Chloroplast cut in half

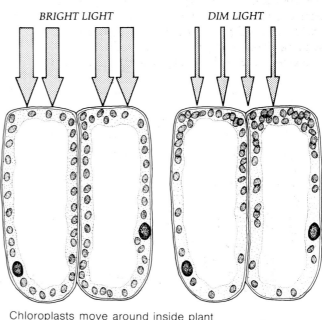

BRIGHT LIGHT   *DIM LIGHT*

Chloroplasts move around inside plant cells to get into the best position to catch the light

The rate of photosynthesis

Photosynthesis is the process by which plants make food. On this food all other life depends. It is important, therefore, to know which conditions are best for photosynthesis. To make food by photosynthesis, plants need light (and the chlorophyll to absorb it), carbon dioxide and water. Oxygen is given off as waste. In the laboratory we can measure how fast photosynthesis is going by measuring how much oxygen a plant is giving off. The higher the plant's **rate of photosynthesis**, the more oxygen is produced. If we test plants under different conditions, we can come to a number of conclusions about the factors which affect the rate of photosynthesis.

LIGHT INTENSITY AFFECTS PHOTOSYNTHESIS

The brightness of light is called **light intensity**. Increasing the light intensity on a plant will speed up its photosynthesis, but only up to a certain point. Beyond this, extra light makes no difference whatsoever, usually because the plant cannot absorb carbon dioxide fast enough. We say that carbon dioxide is **limiting** the process.

Some plants can grow in very shady places, perhaps on a forest floor where the trees block out the sun. These plants have the ability to carry out photosynthesis quite efficiently at light intensities which would be too low for most other plants to survive. In Nature, light intensity changes throughout the day and so, therefore, does the amount of photosynthesis.

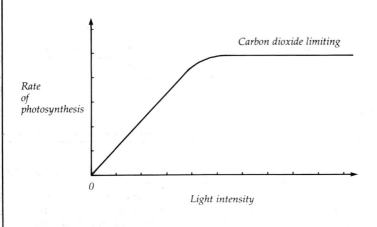

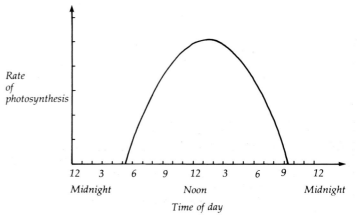

CARBON DIOXIDE AFFECTS PHOTOSYNTHESIS

As the concentration of carbon dioxide round a plant goes up, so does its rate of photosynthesis, but only up to a certain point. Beyond this, more carbon dioxide makes no difference, usually because there is not enough light to cope with it. Light is said to be the limiting factor.

In Nature, the amount of carbon dioxide in the air stays steady at about 0.03%. It can be increased artificially in greenhouses to get better crops.

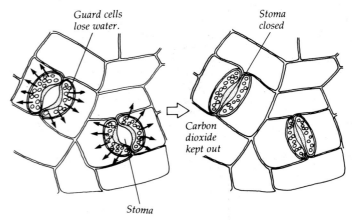

Water is essential for photosynthesis. However, lack of water is itself seldom a problem. If a plant is short of water, the first effect is to close the **stomata** (air pores) on the leaf. This stops carbon dioxide getting into the leaf. So, it is really lack of carbon dioxide, not lack of water, which cuts down photosynthesis.

TEMPERATURE AFFECTS PHOTOSYNTHESIS

As the temperature increases, so does the rate of photosynthesis, up to about 30°C. Above this it stops. This is because the enzymes which control the process have become denatured.

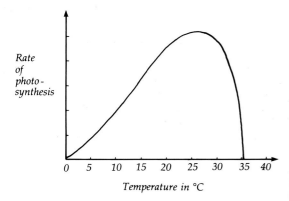

Rate of photo-synthesis

Temperature in °C

Most plants grow best between 20°C and 30°C. In hot climates or in warm greenhouses plants can grow very fast.

LIMITING FACTORS

Photosynthesis takes place in a number of steps. The speed of such a process depends, not on the fastest step, but on the slowest. The slowest step holds up the whole process. It is called the **limiting factor**. Consider this bucket brigade. The amount of water put on the fire depends on how fast the slowest member of the chain can work. He or she is the limiting factor.

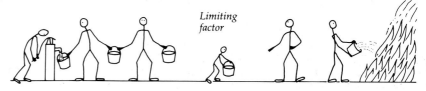

Limiting factor

In photosynthesis, if we increase the limiting factor, the rate of photosynthesis increases until it is limited again.

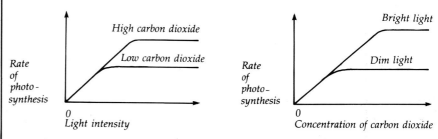

Rate of photo-synthesis — 0 — Light intensity

High carbon dioxide — Low carbon dioxide

Rate of photo-synthesis — 0 — Concentration of carbon dioxide

Bright light — Dim light

ISOTOPES IN THE STUDY OF PHOTOSYNTHESIS

Most elements exist in several different forms called **isotopes**. All the isotopes of an element behave the same in chemical reactions. However, they have slightly different 'weights', or atomic masses. For example, the common form of carbon has an atomic mass of 12 units. It is known as carbon-12 (^{12}C). An isotope exists, however, with an atomic mass of 14 (^{14}C). Oxygen, too, has several isotopes. The common form is ^{16}O, but a heavier isotope, ^{18}O, has been found.

Some isotopes, such as ^{14}C, are radioactive and their presence can be detected using a **geiger counter**. ^{18}O, on the other hand, is not radioactive, but it can be located using a machine called a **mass spectrometer**.

These isotopes have been very useful in the study of photosynthesis. If compounds are prepared using the isotopes, then their presence can be located and their progress followed. This technique is known as **labelling**.

For example, oxygen gas is given off in photosynthesis. But does this come from water (H_2O) or carbon dioxide (CO_2)? To find out, a single-celled green alga called Chlorella was used. This was grown in water labelled with $^{18}O(H_2{}^{18}O)$. When the oxygen given off was analysed, it was found to contain $^{18}O(^{18}O_2)$. When the alga was grown in normal water and given labelled carbon dioxide ($C^{18}O_2$), no ^{18}O was given off.

So, all the oxygen given off in photosynthesis must come from the splitting of water and not from carbon dioxide.

The radioactive isotope ^{14}C has been used to find out what happens to carbon atoms from carbon dioxide when they are absorbed by plants during photosynthesis. To do this, Chlorella was given carbon dioxide labelled with $^{14}C(^{14}CO_2)$ then short bursts of light. It was then analysed to find out where the ^{14}C had got to. In this way, it was found that the carbon is first used to make small carbohydrates. These are then converted to sugars, then starches, and eventually to proteins, fats and other cell materials.

Carbon-14 has also been used to follow what happens to sugars once they have been made. If a leaf of a growing plant is exposed to glucose labelled with ^{14}C, it is then possible using a geiger counter to follow the route taken by the glucose as it is translocated through the plant. If a section is made of the stem, then placed in darkness on a piece of photographic film, the radioactivity will show up as white areas on the developed film. This is known as making an **autoradiograph**. Careful examination of such autoradiographs shows that the labelled glucose is actually being transported through the phloem tissue of the plant.

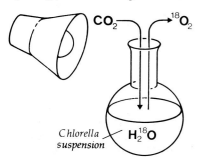

CO_2 → $^{18}O_2$

Chlorella suspension — $H_2{}^{18}O$

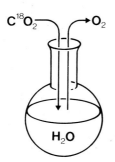

$C^{18}O_2$ → O_2

H_2O

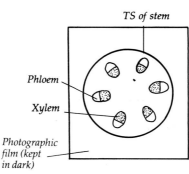

TS of stem

Phloem
Xylem
Photographic film (kept in dark)

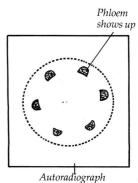

Phloem shows up

Autoradiograph

Leaves: the food makers

Green plants make food by the process called **photosynthesis**. During photosynthesis, light energy is absorbed by the green substance **chlorophyll**. This light energy is then used to convert water and carbon dioxide gas into sugar, with oxygen being produced as waste. Most of a plant's photosynthesis is carried on by its leaves. There are a number of ways in which leaves are organised so that they do this efficiently. These are described below.

LIGHT

Leaves are flat to catch as much light as possible. There are also various ways in which they can be arranged on the plant so that they don't get shaded too much from the sun by the other leaves (diagram 1). The leaves contain most of the plant's chlorophyll. This is found inside their cells in tiny 'blobs' called **chloroplasts**. So, it is the chloroplasts which actually carry out photosynthesis for the cell. They can move around the cell to catch as much light as possible. Starch grains made during photosynthesis are often to be seen inside the chloroplasts (diagram 2).

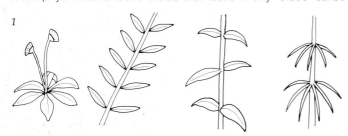

1

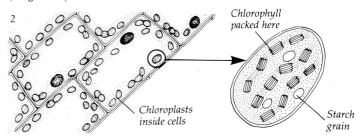

2

Chlorophyll packed here

Chloroplasts inside cells

Starch grain

TRANSPORT

Leaves have veins running through them. These carry in water for photosynthesis and carry out the sugars produced. They also help to support the leaf so it stays flat to catch the light.

In **monocotyledons** (see page 7) the veins run parallel to each other, while in **dicotyledons** they form a branching network.

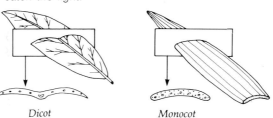

Dicot   Monocot

GAS EXCHANGE

Leaves must be able to take in carbon dioxide for photosynthesis and get rid of the oxygen which is produced. To do this, they have lots of tiny pores on their surfaces. These are called **stomata** (sing: *stoma*). However, with the heat of the sun, water can evaporate out of these pores and cause the plant to wilt. To reduce this, there are usually less stomata on the hotter, top surface of a leaf than on the lower, cool one.

A **transverse section** (slice across) of a leaf, seen under a microscope, shows some of the above features in more detail:

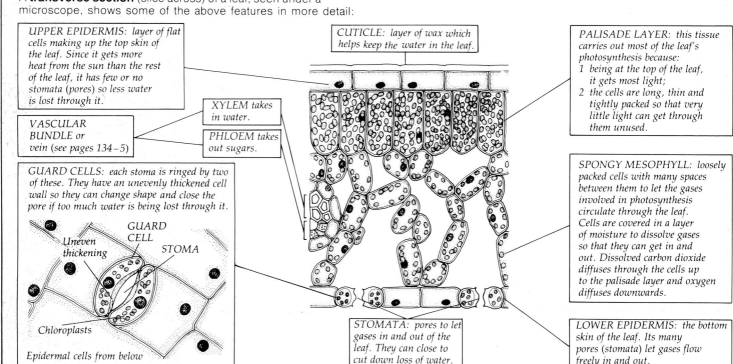

UPPER EPIDERMIS: *layer of flat cells making up the top skin of the leaf. Since it gets more heat from the sun than the rest of the leaf, it has few or no stomata (pores) so less water is lost through it.*

CUTICLE: *layer of wax which helps keep the water in the leaf.*

PALISADE LAYER: *this tissue carries out most of the leaf's photosynthesis because:*
1 *being at the top of the leaf, it gets most light;*
2 *the cells are long, thin and tightly packed so that very little light can get through them unused.*

VASCULAR BUNDLE or vein (see pages 134–5)

XYLEM *takes in water.*

PHLOEM *takes out sugars.*

GUARD CELLS: *each stoma is ringed by two of these. They have an unevenly thickened cell wall so they can change shape and close the pore if too much water is being lost through it.*

GUARD CELL

Uneven thickening

STOMA

Chloroplasts

Epidermal cells from below

SPONGY MESOPHYLL: *loosely packed cells with many spaces between them to let the gases involved in photosynthesis circulate through the leaf. Cells are covered in a layer of moisture to dissolve gases so that they can get in and out. Dissolved carbon dioxide diffuses through the cells up to the palisade layer and oxygen diffuses downwards.*

STOMATA: *pores to let gases in and out of the leaf. They can close to cut down loss of water.*

LOWER EPIDERMIS: *the bottom skin of the leaf. Its many pores (stomata) let gases flow freely in and out.*

Getting Energy from Food

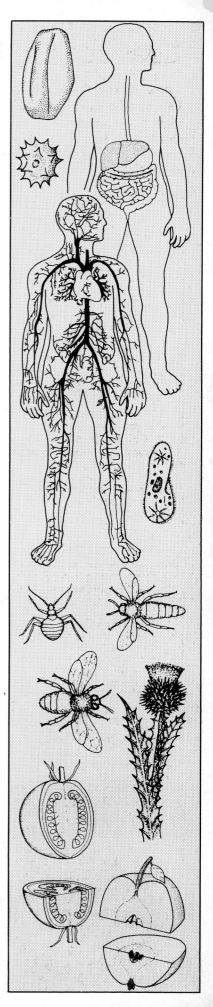

Respiration

Without energy, life is impossible. All organisms, be they plant or animal, need a non-stop supply of energy to stay alive. To get this energy, they must have food. Plants are luckier than animals in this respect, since they can make their own food by **photosynthesis** (see pages 88–9), often more than they need. Animals must have their food readymade.

Food contains chemical energy 'locked' inside it. Each cell must process its food so that it gives up its energy in forms which the cell can use. The process by which living things release energy from their food is called **respiration**.

Note: the word 'respiration' is often taken to mean simply breathing. For this reason, the energy-producing respiration is sometimes called **tissue** or **cellular respiration**.

Through respiration, proteins, fats and carbohydrates can all be processed to produce energy. The most convenient and most used energy source, however, is the sugar called glucose.

For the most efficient type of respiration, that is the type which makes available the greatest amount of energy, oxygen is needed. This is called **aerobic respiration**. The aerobic respiration of glucose is summed up below.

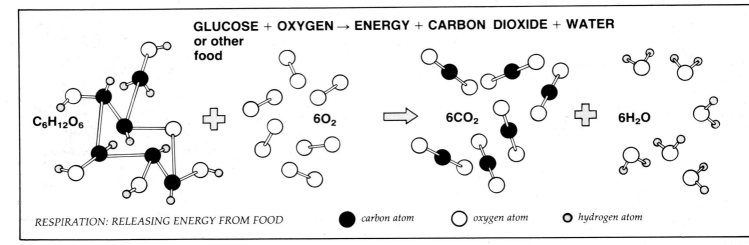

GLUCOSE + OXYGEN → ENERGY + CARBON DIOXIDE + WATER
or other food

$C_6H_{12}O_6$ + $6O_2$ ⟹ $6CO_2$ + $6H_2O$

RESPIRATION: RELEASING ENERGY FROM FOOD   ● *carbon atom*   ○ *oxygen atom*   ◉ *hydrogen atom*

At first sight, aerobic respiration resembles what happens when glucose is burned in a jar of pure, dry oxygen. The oxygen is consumed, carbon dioxide and water are produced and energy is released as the heat and light of the flames.

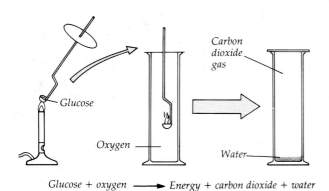

Glucose
Oxygen
Carbon dioxide gas
Water

Glucose + oxygen ⟶ Energy + carbon dioxide + water

In both cases, certainly, extra oxygen atoms are added to the glucose as it splits apart to release its energy. This type of chemical reaction is called **oxidation**. Respiration and burning, therefore, both involve the oxidation of glucose. However, the two oxidations are brought about in very different ways.

Before glucose will burn, it must be heated strongly. Its energy is then released violently and fast. Such conditions would be lethal to any living thing. The oxidation inside a cell is much more gentle. The glucose is taken apart bit by bit, in more than thirty small steps. Its energy is released in safe, usable amounts. Each small change (or chemical reaction) is made possible and carefully controlled by its own special **enzyme** (see pages 54–5). These **respiratory enzymes** allow glucose and other foods to yield up their energy in the mild, watery environment of a living cell.

Metabolism and metabolic rate

With the help of enzymes, cells can carry out hundreds of different chemical reactions quickly and efficiently. These reactions make possible all the activities of a living organism. The sum total of all the reactions taking place in an organism makes up its **metabolism**. The level at which an organism's metabolism is operating is called its **metabolic rate**. During sleep, for example, the metabolic rate is low, while during exercise it is high.

Respiration provides the energy to drive the metabolism. Therefore, the respiration rate and the metabolic rate are very closely connected. In fact, the metabolic rate can be defined as the rate at which an organism uses energy. Anything which can be used to measure the rate of respiration in an organism can also be taken as a measure of its metabolic rate. Oxygen consumption and heat production, for example, which are both caused by respiration, are commonly used as measures of metabolic rate.

Respiration: the signs to look for

How can we tell when respiration is taking place? With animals it is often easy enough. We may see them moving around, using energy which came from respiration. However, it is not always so simple. What about plants and micro-organisms, for example? All organisms, plants just as much as animals, must carry out respiration if they are to stay alive. When they are respiring, it should be possible to observe one or more of the five signs which are outlined below.

1 Weight loss

During respiration, food materials such as carbohydrate and fat are used up. They are converted to carbon dioxide and water and are then excreted by the organism. If the missing food is not replaced, the organism's weight should decrease. This effect is clearly seen in an animal suffering from starvation. Its body becomes lighter and thinner as its tissues are consumed in order to provide energy to keep it alive.

Respiration also causes weight loss in plants. This is best seen in germinating seeds. As they start to grow, they use up the food stored in their endosperm or cotyledons (see page 190). To follow what happens, we can plant a large number of seeds. Then, every few days, some should be taken, dried in an oven and weighed. We can now calculate the average **dry weight** of the seeds at different stages in the germination process. This graph shows what happens:

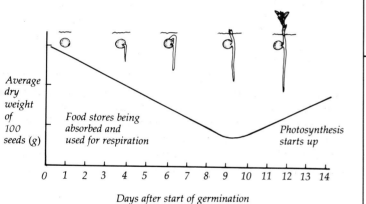

Days after start of germination

The dry weight of the seeds falls rapidly as they use up their food store to provide energy for growth. This goes on until the first leaves have opened out. The seedlings now begin to make more food by photosynthesis than they are consuming through respiration. Their dry weight starts to rise.

Note: we must concentrate on the dry weight in this study, since the seeds absorb so much water that their overall weight actually rises. Also, since the drying process kills the seeds, we must germinate a large number.

2 Oxygen consumption

If we keep an organism in an enclosed space for a while and then analyse the air which it has used, we find that it contains less oxygen than it did to start with. This happens with plants, too, although they do not use much oxygen. Plants must be kept in darkness throughout, otherwise, the oxygen produced by photosynthesis will mask the result.

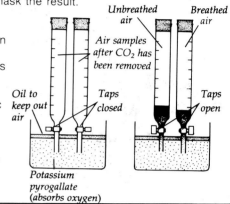

The rate at which an organism uses oxygen can be taken as an indirect measure of its **metabolic rate**, for example, we could express the metabolic rate of an average-sized man lying completely at rest as being about 350 litres of oxygen per day.

3 Carbon dioxide production

Carbon dioxide is a useful sign that respiration is taking place, since it is easy to detect. It turns lime water from clear to cloudy and it turns bicarbonate indicator from red to yellow. The tests are simple to do, for example:

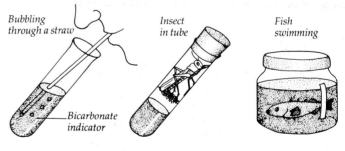

Bicarbonate indicator can be used to show that plants, too, produce carbon dioxide by respiration. However, they must be tested in darkness. In light, plants tend to absorb more carbon dioxide (for photosynthesis) than they are producing.

4 Water vapour

There is no doubt that plants and animals give off water vapour. On a cold day, for instance, we can clearly see the water in our breath. Plants lose large amounts of water through **transpiration** from their leaves. Water produced by respiration, though – what we call **metabolic water** – makes up only a fraction of this. However, by using radioactive **isotopes** (see page 89), scientists have definitely proved that some of the water vapour coming from organisms has been formed by the respiration of food.

For some desert organisms, such as the kangaroo rat, this water is of vital importance. Holding on to their metabolic water allows them to survive in very dry conditions.

5 Heat production

During respiration, the chemical energy of food is released and converted into the other forms of energy which the organism needs. Some of it is always turned into heat energy, so the production of heat is always a good indicator that respiration is going on. The amount of heat produced depends on the organism. Animals produce more heat than plants, and warm-blooded animals produce the most heat of all.

Eventually, all the other forms of energy derived from respiration are converted into heat energy also. The amount of heat given off by an organism in a certain time can be used therefore as a measure of its metabolic rate. A resting man will produce about 7000 kJ of heat energy per day.

Anaerobic respiration

All cells, and therefore all organisms, need energy to keep going. The way in which they usually get this energy is by the **aerobic respiration** of glucose. To do this, of course, they need oxygen. In the human body, the lungs and the heart together have the job of delivering the oxygen. The lungs absorb oxygen from the air and pass it into the blood, and the heart pumps the **oxygenated** (oxygen-rich) blood round the body.

Most of the time, this system is perfectly adequate. Sometimes, though, the heart and lungs, even working flat out, cannot supply all the oxygen the body needs. When we run fast our muscles use up a lot of energy, much more than they can get from aerobic respiration alone. They must be able, therefore, to produce some energy without using oxygen to do it. The process by which cells release energy from food without using oxygen is called **anaerobic respiration** (*an*: no; *aero*: air). During anaerobic respiration,

cells break down glucose to form a substance called **lactic acid**. This releases energy from the glucose and allows the muscles to do their work.

Anaerobic respiration has two drawbacks. Firstly, the glucose is only partly broken down and so only a small part of its stored energy is released. In fact, anaerobic respiration will yield less than 1 kJ of energy from every gram of glucose, whereas aerobic respiration would supply about 16 kJ from the same amount. The second problem is the end product, lactic acid. This is harmful and if too much of it builds up in a muscle, it causes **cramp**. The muscle then stops working. Also, when a bout of exercise is over, the body has to go on absorbing large amounts of oxygen in order to remove the lactic acid from the blood. This is known as 'paying off an **oxygen debt**'. To illustrate these processes, shown below is what happens before, during and after a few minutes of strenuous exercise.

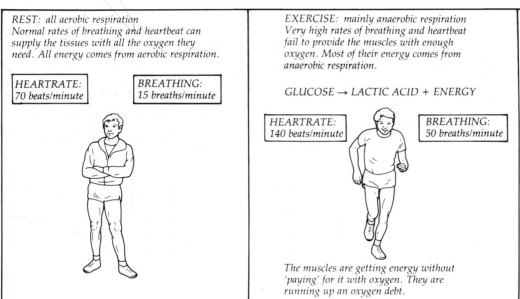

REST: *all aerobic respiration*
Normal rates of breathing and heartbeat can supply the tissues with all the oxygen they need. All energy comes from aerobic respiration.

HEARTRATE:
70 beats/minute

BREATHING:
15 breaths/minute

EXERCISE: *mainly anaerobic respiration*
Very high rates of breathing and heartbeat fail to provide the muscles with enough oxygen. Most of their energy comes from anaerobic respiration.

GLUCOSE → LACTIC ACID + ENERGY

HEARTRATE:
140 beats/minute

BREATHING:
50 breaths/minute

The muscles are getting energy without 'paying' for it with oxygen. They are running up an oxygen debt.

RECOVERY: *paying off the oxygen debt.*
For some time, the breathing and heartbeat remain high, even though the muscles are at rest. The extra oxygen now being taken in is used to convert the lactic acid into carbon dioxide and water. This is called 'paying off the oxygen debt'.

HEARTRATE:
140 beats/minute
falling to normal after some minutes

BREATHING:
50 breaths/minute
falling to normal after some minutes

Panting and rapid heartbeat continue until the lactic acid has been removed. Physically fit people can recover fastest.

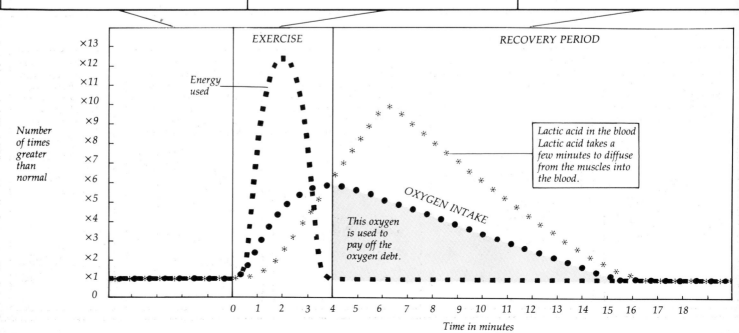

EXERCISE — RECOVERY PERIOD

Number of times greater than normal

×13 ×12 ×11 ×10 ×9 ×8 ×7 ×6 ×5 ×4 ×3 ×2 ×1 0

Energy used

Lactic acid in the blood
Lactic acid takes a few minutes to diffuse from the muscles into the blood.

OXYGEN INTAKE

This oxygen is used to pay off the oxygen debt.

Time in minutes
0 1 2 3 4 5 6 7 8 9 10 11 12 13 14 15 16 17 18

Alcoholic fermentation

Anaerobic respiration is very common in plants and micro-organisms (see page 96). In fact, many micro-organisms known as **anaerobes**, use anaerobic respiration much, or even all of the time. In these cases, the process is often referred to as fermentation. There are various kinds of fermentation, but the best-known is the alcoholic fermentation carried out by the single-celled fungus yeast (see page 169). If yeast is added to sugar solution, in the absence of oxygen, it will convert the sugar to carbon dioxide gas and **ethanol**, a type of alcohol. We can sum it up like this:

$$\textbf{Sugar} \longrightarrow \textbf{Ethanol} + \textbf{Carbon} + \textbf{Energy}$$
$$\textbf{(alcohol)} \quad \textbf{dioxide}$$

In this way, the yeast obtains the energy it needs to stay alive without having to use oxygen. The process, however, is much less efficient than aerobic respiration – the ethanol still contains a lot of unused energy. Also, ethanol is itself harmful to the yeast, which must excrete it into the surrounding liquid. Even then, if the ethanol concentration gets too high (about 14% is enough), the yeast is killed and fermentation stops.

People have used this type of fermentation for thousands of years to make alcoholic drinks such as wine and beer. Wine is made by allowing yeast to ferment the sugars in grape juice. One method of beer making is outlined below, as also is another important use of yeast – the making of bread.

The same kind of fermentation process is used by plants to see them through tricky situations. When soil is waterlogged and contains very little oxygen, plants can switch to anaerobic respiration and go on living for several weeks. Germinating seeds, too, in the absence of oxygen, can produce carbon dioxide and ethanol.

BREWING BEER

1 Malt, which is made from germinating barley, and hops are boiled together. The malt will provide malt sugar for the brew. The hops will give the beer its flavour.

2 The malt/hop extract is strained and added to the correct amount of water. Yeast and extra sugar are stirred in and the brewing bin is lightly covered and put in a warm place. Over the next few days, the yeast converts the sugar into alcohol and carbon dioxide. The escaping gas helps keep out air and harmful bacteria. When the sugar is used up, fermentation stops.

3 The beer, which is completely flat is siphoned into strong bottles. A small amount of sugar is put into each bottle and they are tightly stoppered.

4 A second fermentation takes place inside the bottle. This time the carbon dioxide cannot escape.
It dissolves in the beer, making it fizzy and giving it 'a head'. So, dissolved in the final beer are both products of fermentation: alcohol and carbon dioxide.

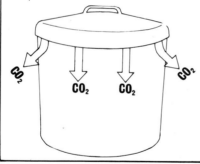

MAKING BREAD

1 Yeast and sugar are mixed with a little warm water. The mixture is left in a warm place until it froths. This shows that the yeast cells are becoming active.

2 The yeast liquid is mixed with flour, salt and more warm water to make dough.

3 The dough is kneaded for about 10 minutes by folding and pushing on it with the hands. This makes sure that the yeast and other ingredients are thoroughly mixed. Otherwise, the bread will have large holes in it.

4 The dough is left in a warm place. Fermentation by the yeast produces alcohol and carbon dioxide gas. The gas causes the dough to rise. After about an hour, the dough should have doubled in size.

5 The dough is baked in a hot oven which kills off the yeast. The 'pores' left in the bread by the carbon dioxide bubbles give it its light, spongy texture. The alcohol is evaporated, but still gives the newly-baked bread its aroma.

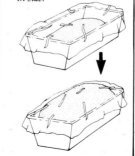

ATP: energy money

To function properly, living cells must be able to perform a large number of different chemical reactions. Some of these, chiefly the reactions of respiration, produce energy. Others must be given energy before they will go. A single chemical substance links these two types of reaction. This substance is called **adenosine triphosphate**, **ATP** for short. ATP consists of a large molecule called **adenosine** with three (*tri*: three) smaller **phosphate** groups joined to it, something like this:

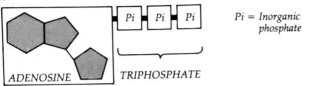

Pi = Inorganic phosphate

ATP is found in all living cells and all living cells can make it. They do this by taking a similar substance called **adenosine diphosphate**, or **ADP**, and adding a third phosphate to it. Energy is needed for this.

$$ADP + Pi + ENERGY \rightarrow ATP$$

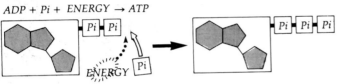

This, in fact, is what a cell does with the energy it sets free in respiration. It uses it to make ATP. This energy is not lost. It is safely stored inside the ATP molecule. There it stays until the cell needs it. As soon as the energy is required, perhaps to power a particular chemical reaction, the process is instantly reversed and the energy is made available (see below).

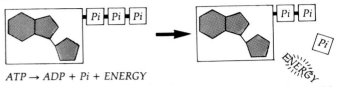

$$ATP \rightarrow ADP + Pi + ENERGY$$

Thus, the energy-releasing reactions inside the cell, working through ATP, drive the energy-requiring processes. ATP is continually being made up and broken down again. The whole system forms a sort of ATP/ADP cycle as shown in the diagram below.

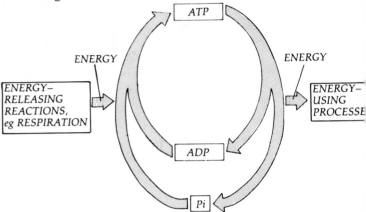

RESPIRATION AND ATP

One advantage of the ATP system is that its energy is released in one quick step. Compare this with respiration where about 30 steps, some aerobic and some anaerobic, are involved:

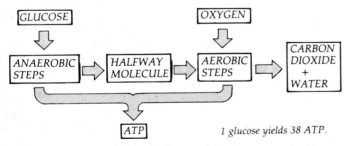

1 glucose yields 38 ATP.

When oxygen is scarce, only the aerobic steps operate. Very little ATP is made and the process is much less efficient.

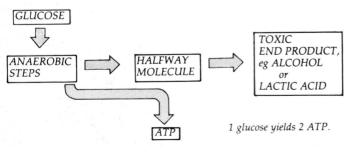

1 glucose yields 2 ATP.

Either way, the energy of the glucose is released in small, safe steps and transferred to the ATP. The ATP is then able to dispense the energy in small amounts, exactly as it is needed, anywhere in the cell, with the minimum of waste.

ATP AT WORK

ATP is like 'energy money' which the cell can use to 'pay for' a whole range of different processes, for example:

1. When making proteins, essential for growth, one molecule of ATP is needed each time an amino acid is added to the protein chain:

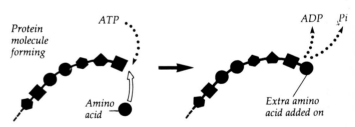

2. ATP provides the energy for muscles to contract so that animals can move. Even a piece of meat will contract if ATP is dropped on it.

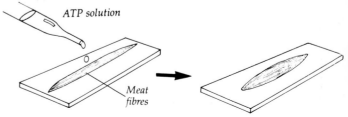

When a muscle is overworked, it runs short of ATP and begins to feel tired. When allowed to rest, it converts ADP and phosphate back to ATP and is ready to start again.

Food Chains, Food Webs, Ecosystems

Food chains and food webs

The place where an organism, be it plant or animal, lives is called its **habitat**. All habitats support a number of different species of plants and animals. All the plants and animals found in a particular habitat are known as a **community**. The community's power supply is the sun. The green plants in the community absorb the sun's light energy and use it to make food. This food is then passed along **food chains** to provide the rest of the community with energy and materials for growth.

A FOOD CHAIN

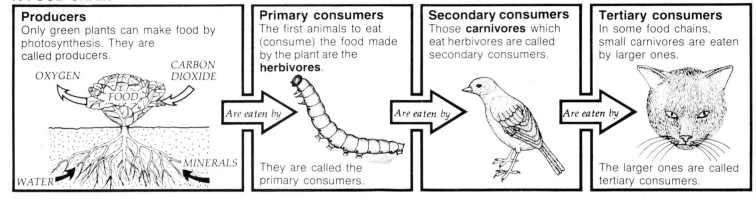

Producers
Only green plants can make food by photosynthesis. They are called producers.

OXYGEN   FOOD   CARBON DIOXIDE
WATER   MINERALS

Are eaten by

Primary consumers
The first animals to eat (consume) the food made by the plant are the **herbivores**.

They are called the primary consumers.

Are eaten by

Secondary consumers
Those **carnivores** which eat herbivores are called secondary consumers.

Are eaten by

Tertiary consumers
In some food chains, small carnivores are eaten by larger ones.

The larger ones are called tertiary consumers.

Most food chains have only three links, though many have five or even more. Here are a few food chains from different habitats:

Farmland
Grass → Cow → Man

Sea
Plant plankton → Animal plankton → Barnacle larva → Arrow worm → Herring → Gull

Fresh water
Algae → Water plants → Sticklebacks

Woodland
Plants → Rabbit → Fox

The food chains above, where each organism is killed and eaten by the next in the chain, are called **predator food chains**. However, certain organisms in a habitat get their food without killing. They feed on the remains of other organisms. These are the scavengers and decomposers.

Insect larvae   *Earthworm*   *Dung beetle*

Scavengers feed on the flesh of dead animals or on dead bits of plants. Some feed on animal droppings. They do a valuable job keeping the environment clean. They may be eaten by carnivores.

Meadow mushroom   *Cup fungus on log*   *Mariasmus on pine needles*

Decomposers are the **saprophytic fungi** and **bacteria** which cause dead things to decay. When they have finished, all that is left are inorganic minerals which they return to the soil. Thus, decomposers do a vital job in recycling the minerals which plants need for healthy growth.

Most organisms feed on more than one kind of food. This means they must belong to more than one food chain. If we look at all the food chains in a habitat, we can join them together to give an overall picture called a **food web**.

A FOOD WEB

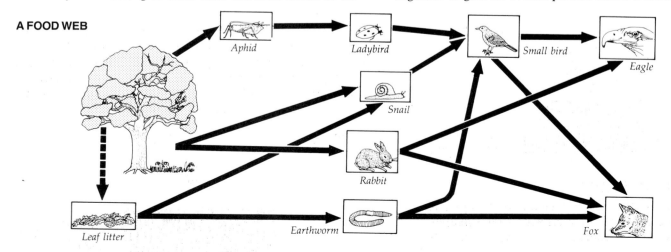

Aphid   *Ladybird*   *Snail*   *Rabbit*   *Small bird*   *Eagle*   *Leaf litter*   *Earthworm*   *Fox*

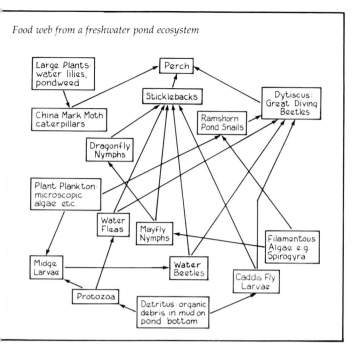

Food web from a freshwater pond ecosystem

Pyramid of numbers

At each link in a predator food chain, the tissues of the prey are eaten and used to build up the tissues of the predator. Since each predator is bigger than its prey, there must be fewer predators. At the end of the food chain will be just one or two **top carnivores**. We could represent the situation like this:

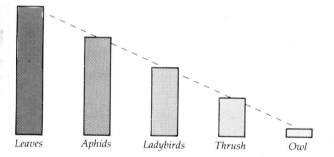

In fact this 'graph' is usually put on to its side. It is then known as a **pyramid of numbers**.

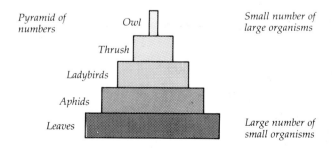

Pyramid of numbers — *Small number of large organisms*

Owl

Thrush

Ladybirds

Aphids

Leaves — *Large number of small organisms*

Population changes

In a balanced **ecosystem**, the numbers in each population stay fairly constant. Losses are replaced by **reproduction**. Sometimes, however, a population may change drastically.

It might be almost killed off by disease, for example, or bumper food supplies might cause a **population explosion**. In either case, the effects will ripple through the food chain and the food web of which it is part.

The graph below shows how the population of a predator and its prey might change over a period of years, if the numbers of prey animals suddenly increased.

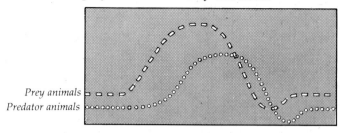

Prey animals

Predator animals

At first, the number of predators also rises because of the improved food supply. This puts added pressure on the prey population which begins to decline. There is not now enough food to support all the extra predators and many of them starve. Eventually, the balance is restored.

Pyramid of biomass

A pyramid of numbers tells only part of the story. At each level in the food chain some food is lost. Fur, bones, etc. may not be eaten. Some may not be digested and end up in the **faeces** (solid waste) of the animal. Much of it will be used to produce energy by **respiration** (see page 94). The losses at each stage may be as high as 90% or more. 1000 kg of cattle feed, for example, might yield around 120 kg of cattle flesh. Eaten by a growing child, this, in turn, might produce only 5 or 6 kg of human tissue. This is why food chains usually have no more than two or three different **consumers** in them. By the end of the chain there is very little food left.

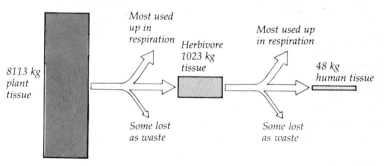

8113 kg plant tissue — Most used up in respiration — Herbivore 1023 kg tissue — Most used up in respiration — 48 kg human tissue — Some lost as waste — Some lost as waste

For this reason, it is often more useful to calculate the dry weight, known as the **biomass**, for each member of the food chain. From these, a **pyramid of biomass**, like the one below, can be constructed. A pyramid of biomass is often quite different from the pyramid of numbers for the same food chain. It is not usually as steep.

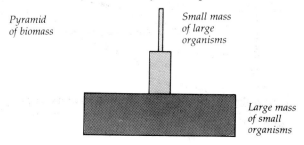

Pyramid of biomass — *Small mass of large organisms* — *Large mass of small organisms*

Ecosystems

The place where an organism lives is called its **habitat**. All the organisms which live in a habitat make up its **community**. Each habitat provides its community with certain living conditions – the **environment**. The environment has two components: the **physical** (non-living) environment and the **biotic** (biological) environment.

The physical environment

Conditions which are not caused by other organisms form the physical environment of the habitat. The physical environment affects the community in many ways. It includes water supply, light, temperature and pH.

The availability of water

Water is essential for life (see pages 114–5). Its availability is obviously more of a problem for **terrestrial** (land) organisms than for **aquatic** (water) organisms. Some ways in which animals have adapted to cope with their water supply are described on pages 120–1.

Most land plants thrive in moist but not waterlogged soils. Water lost by **transpiration** from the leaves can be quickly replaced with water absorbed by the roots (see pages 122–3). Where soil is too wet or too dry, fewer plants and soil organisms will be able to grow in it. Some plants, known as **xerophytes**, can live in very dry conditions. Various adaptations such as those shown opposite allow them to make the most of what little water there is.

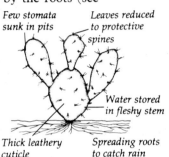

Few stomata sunk in pits

Leaves reduced to protective spines

Water stored in fleshy stem

Thick leathery cuticle

Spreading roots to catch rain

Light

Light is the original source of energy for all habitats. Plants need light to make food by **photosynthesis**. This food allows them to grow and so provide nourishment for the whole community. In general, habitats which are well-lit support most life. The bright sunshine of the tropics, for example, allows the growth of dense vegetation, while, nearer home, the long days of summer are times of plenty in countryside and garden. On the other hand, growth is poor in dim light. Cave-dwelling animals must venture outside to find food. Some plants can tolerate fairly shady conditions. The seedlings of woodland trees can grow in the shade of their relatives, until they, too, are tall enough to enjoy the best light.

Light also affects behaviour. The longer days of spring cause the reproductive organs of many animals to start growing. This brings on their **breeding season**. Thus, the young are born by summer when there is plenty of food for them. Plants, too, react to the number of hours of daylight. Many plants flower only when the days reach a certain number of hours. The number required varies from species to species so that all plants don't produce their flowers at the same time of year.

Finally, it is the autumn decrease in daylight hours which triggers the **migration** of many animals, especially birds.

Behaviour which is controlled by the number of hours of daylight is called **photoperiodism**.

Temperature

An organism's choice of home is limited by the temperatures which it can tolerate. Plants, for example, seldom do well more than 160 kilometres north or south of their natural habitat. Even a far-flying insect like the migratory locust never ventures too far north. Young organisms of all kinds are especially sensitive to temperature.

The problems are greatest on land. Water temperatures do not vary much, but on land there may be wide fluctuations between day and night, winter and summer. To survive, each organism must be able to cope with the extremes of temperature which occur in its habitat. Thick fur, feathers, or layers of body fat help mammals and birds to keep warm. The camel can survive its body temperature climbing to as much as 40°C during the day, then falling to 34°C at night. This is very unusual for a mammal. The resting stages of plants such as seeds, tubers and bulbs are much more resistant to the cold than growing plants are.

Behaviour, too, is important. Desert rats sleep through the dangerous heat of the day, coming out only at night to feed. Reptiles warm their blood by basking in the heat of the sun, then seek the shade when they become too hot. We ourselves wear clothes to keep us warm, while many animals avoid the worst of the winter by **hibernating**.

Plant growth, on which the food supply of the community depends, is affected by temperature. Warm, steady temperatures, such as those of the tropics, are best. Elsewhere, growth may be slowed or even stopped as the temperature changes.

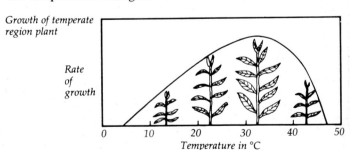

Growth of temperate region plant

Rate of growth

Temperature in °C

Plant development is also subject to temperature. Most seeds cannot **germinate** until they have been kept cold for several months. This ensures that the vulnerable seedlings cannot sprout until they have been exposed to a winter's cold. This gives them a chance of a season's growth before they must devote their resources to flower production.

pH

The pH of a soil affects the type of plants, and to some extent, the animals which live there. Most species prefer a fairly neutral pH, around 7, though some are tolerant of **acid** or **alkaline** soils.

pH affects aquatic organisms also. Freshwater fish do well in waters of pH 5 to 9. Above or below these limits their survival becomes more difficult.

The biotic environment

The biotic environment of an organism consists of all the other organisms which share its habitat. This includes members of its own species, since each habitat will house a number of individuals of the same type. Such a group is called a **population**.

The organisms in a community do not live separate lives. They **interact** with others in various ways. Some provide food for others (see page 68). Some form very close, or **symbiotic**, relationships with other species (see page 86). Some of them, such as trees, provide others with shelter. In fact, in many ways the biotic environment has a bigger impact on an organism's life than its physical environment. The scientific study of organisms in their natural environment is called **ecology**.

Ecosystems

The members of a community interact with each other and with their non-living environment. When all the many and complex interactions result in a balanced, stable unit, that unit is called an **ecosystem**. An ecosystem, therefore, consists of the balanced interactions between a community and its habitat. Some of the features of a woodland ecosystem are outlined below.

In an ecosystem every organism has its own part to play. This is called its **niche**. Its niche is mainly where it rests and what it eats. The aphid's niche, for example, is dwelling on oak leaves sucking their sap, while the caterpillar's niche is on the oak leaves, but eating them. When two organisms try to occupy the same niche, they are said to be in **competition** and one will eventually lose out. Competition may occur between members of the same species or between members of different, usually closely-related species.

AN OAK WOODLAND ECOSYSTEM

In this ecosystem, the most important species is the oak tree. It is said to be the **dominant species**. It affects the community in many ways. As well as providing many of them with food and shelter, it also affects their physical environment. Its leaves form a covering or canopy over the ecosystem. This blocks the light so that only shade-tolerant plants can grow beneath it. It also reduces the amount of rainwater which reaches the ground. It keeps the temperature below more regular by making it cooler by day and warmer by night, so, woodland organisms are protected from extremes of temperature. It also keeps out the wind. This makes the air more humid (moist) with the result that plants need less water.

In winter, the scene changes. Being a **deciduous** tree, the

oak sheds its leaves. Evergreen bushes like holly can now make up for lost time. Other plants, too, get a chance to grow, flower and produce seed in the spring before the oak trees have restored the leaf canopy. Leaf litter from oak and other plants provides shelter for many ground organisms. Eventually, it rots down to form a rich **humus** (see pages 218–9) in the soil. From this, the living plants obtain valuable minerals.

This ecosystem is usually thought of as being divided into the five layers shown in the diagram below. The many interactions between the community and the environment produce a stable, balanced unit. A few members of this community and the niches they occupy in the ecosystem are mentioned below.

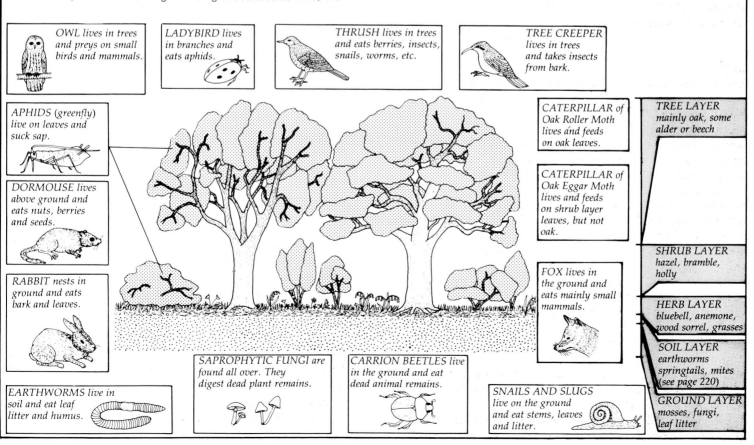

OWL lives in trees and preys on small birds and mammals.

LADYBIRD lives in branches and eats aphids.

THRUSH lives in trees and eats berries, insects, snails, worms, etc.

TREE CREEPER lives in trees and takes insects from bark.

APHIDS (greenfly) live on leaves and suck sap.

DORMOUSE lives above ground and eats nuts, berries and seeds.

RABBIT nests in ground and eats bark and leaves.

CATERPILLAR of Oak Roller Moth lives and feeds on oak leaves.

CATERPILLAR of Oak Eggar Moth lives and feeds on shrub layer leaves, but not oak.

FOX lives in the ground and eats mainly small mammals.

EARTHWORMS live in soil and eat leaf litter and humus.

SAPROPHYTIC FUNGI are found all over. They digest dead plant remains.

CARRION BEETLES live in the ground and eat dead animal remains.

SNAILS AND SLUGS live on the ground and eat stems, leaves and litter.

TREE LAYER mainly oak, some alder or beech

SHRUB LAYER hazel, bramble, holly

HERB LAYER bluebell, anemone, wood sorrel, grasses

SOIL LAYER earthworms springtails, mites (see page 220)

GROUND LAYER mosses, fungi, leaf litter

SECTION 11

Gas Exchange

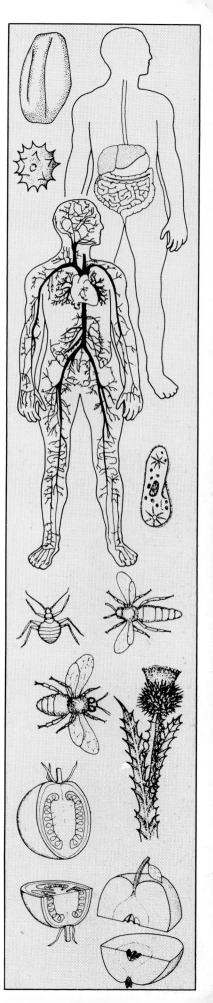

Gas exchange

Respiration is the process which keeps things alive. Living things use respiration to get out the energy which is 'locked up' in their food. Since living things, both plant and animal, need a non-stop supply of energy, both day and night, their cells must carry out respiration at all times. To do this they need a supply of oxygen to 'burn' their food. This releases the energy they need to stay alive, but it also produces carbon dioxide gas and water vapour as waste products.

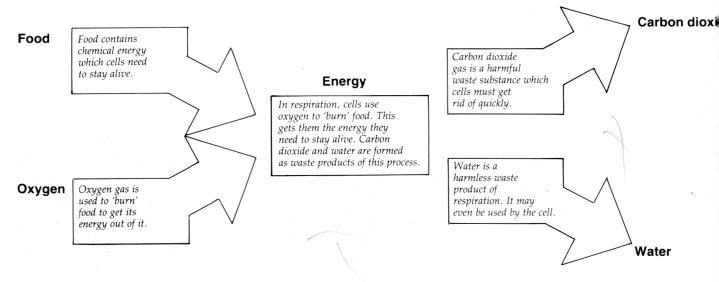

Food

Food contains chemical energy which cells need to stay alive.

Oxygen

Oxygen gas is used to 'burn' food to get its energy out of it.

Energy

In respiration, cells use oxygen to 'burn' food. This gets them the energy they need to stay alive. Carbon dioxide and water are formed as waste products of this process.

Carbon dioxi

Carbon dioxide gas is a harmful waste substance which cells must get rid of quickly.

Water is a harmless waste product of respiration. It may even be used by the cell.

Water

To stay alive, organisms must be able to take oxygen *from* the air and get rid of their carbon dioxide *into* the air. Swapping oxygen for carbon dioxide like this is called **gas exchange**. Organisms carry out gas exchange in many different ways, but all their gas exchange systems have certain things in common.

1 The gases pass in or out of an organism through a **gas exchange surface**. The amount of surface an organism needs for this depends on how active it is. If it is very active, it will use up a lot of energy and so will need a very large area of gas exchange surface.

2 Inside cells the gases are always dissolved in water, so the gas exchange surface must always be kept moist.

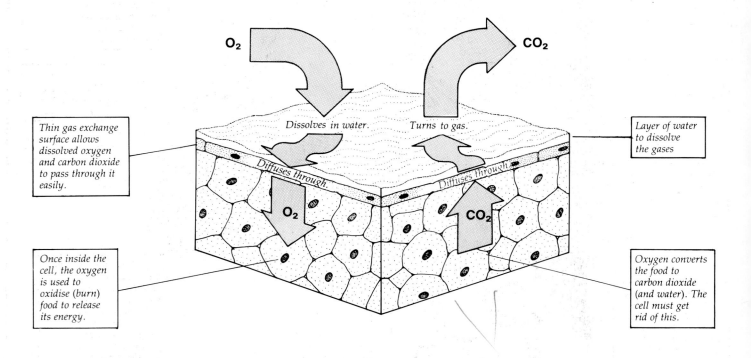

O_2 CO_2

Dissolves in water.   *Turns to gas.*

Thin gas exchange surface allows dissolved oxygen and carbon dioxide to pass through it easily.

Layer of water to dissolve the gases

Diffuses through.   *Diffuses through.*

O_2 CO_2

Once inside the cell, the oxygen is used to oxidise (burn) food to release its energy.

Oxygen converts the food to carbon dioxide (and water). The cell must get rid of this.

Gas exchange in mammals

Mammals are very active, warm-blooded animals which use up a lot of energy. To supply this they need a very efficient **gas exchange system**. Mammals have two special gas exchange organs called **lungs**. The lungs, together with the heart, are inside the **thorax** or chest.

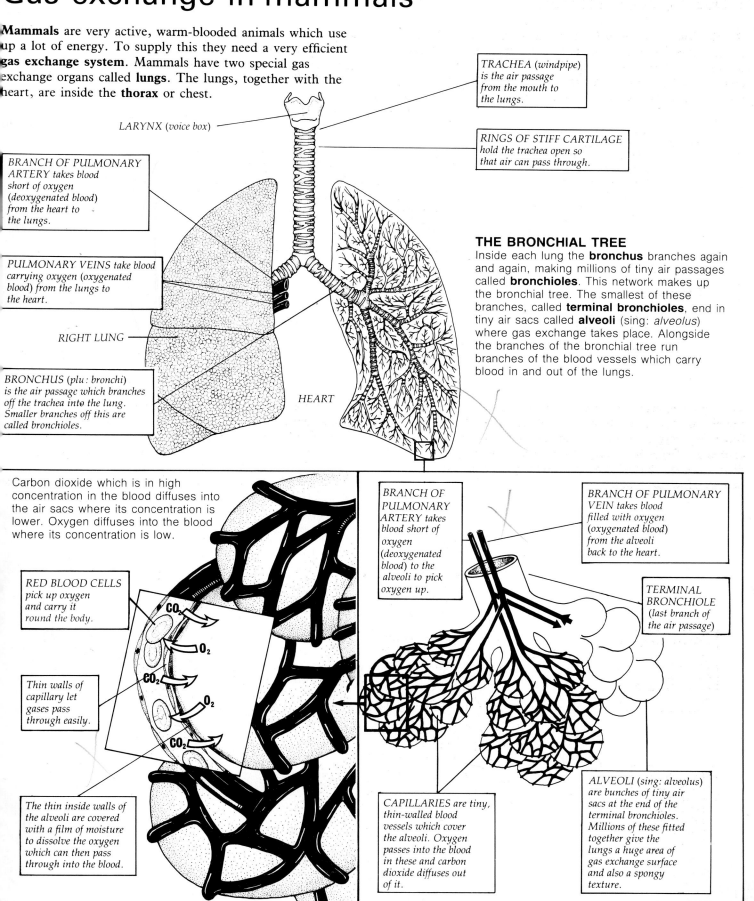

LARYNX (voice box)

TRACHEA (windpipe) is the air passage from the mouth to the lungs.

RINGS OF STIFF CARTILAGE hold the trachea open so that air can pass through.

BRANCH OF PULMONARY ARTERY takes blood short of oxygen (deoxygenated blood) from the heart to the lungs.

PULMONARY VEINS take blood carrying oxygen (oxygenated blood) from the lungs to the heart.

RIGHT LUNG

BRONCHUS (plu: bronchi) is the air passage which branches off the trachea into the lung. Smaller branches off this are called bronchioles.

HEART

THE BRONCHIAL TREE

Inside each lung the **bronchus** branches again and again, making millions of tiny air passages called **bronchioles**. This network makes up the bronchial tree. The smallest of these branches, called **terminal bronchioles**, end in tiny air sacs called **alveoli** (sing: *alveolus*) where gas exchange takes place. Alongside the branches of the bronchial tree run branches of the blood vessels which carry blood in and out of the lungs.

Carbon dioxide which is in high concentration in the blood diffuses into the air sacs where its concentration is lower. Oxygen diffuses into the blood where its concentration is low.

RED BLOOD CELLS pick up oxygen and carry it round the body.

Thin walls of capillary let gases pass through easily.

The thin inside walls of the alveoli are covered with a film of moisture to dissolve the oxygen which can then pass through into the blood.

CO_2

O_2

CO_2

O_2

CO_2

BRANCH OF PULMONARY ARTERY takes blood short of oxygen (deoxygenated blood) to the alveoli to pick oxygen up.

BRANCH OF PULMONARY VEIN takes blood filled with oxygen (oxygenated blood) from the alveoli back to the heart.

TERMINAL BRONCHIOLE (last branch of the air passage)

CAPILLARIES are tiny, thin-walled blood vessels which cover the alveoli. Oxygen passes into the blood in these and carbon dioxide diffuses out of it.

ALVEOLI (sing: alveolus) are bunches of tiny air sacs at the end of the terminal bronchioles. Millions of these fitted together give the lungs a huge area of gas exchange surface and also a spongy texture.

Breathing in mammals

The lungs and the heart of mammals are inside a chamber called the **thorax** or chest. This chamber is made by the ribs, the breastbone and the backbone. The floor of the chamber is a large sheet of muscle called the **diaphragm**. Running diagonally between the ribs are the **intercostal muscles**. The only way air can get in or out of the thorax to fill and empty the lungs is through the **trachea** or windpipe, which is kept open by rings of stiff **cartilage**.

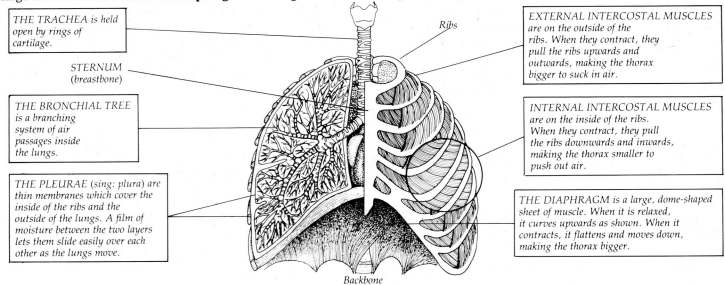

THE TRACHEA is held open by rings of cartilage.

STERNUM (breastbone)

THE BRONCHIAL TREE is a branching system of air passages inside the lungs.

THE PLEURAE (sing: plura) are thin membranes which cover the inside of the ribs and the outside of the lungs. A film of moisture between the two layers lets them slide easily over each other as the lungs move.

Ribs

EXTERNAL INTERCOSTAL MUSCLES are on the outside of the ribs. When they contract, they pull the ribs upwards and outwards, making the thorax bigger to suck in air.

INTERNAL INTERCOSTAL MUSCLES are on the inside of the ribs. When they contract, they pull the ribs downwards and inwards, making the thorax smaller to push out air.

THE DIAPHRAGM is a large, dome-shaped sheet of muscle. When it is relaxed, it curves upwards as shown. When it contracts, it flattens and moves down, making the thorax bigger.

Backbone

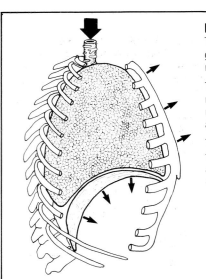

INSPIRATION

The diaphragm contracts, gets flatter and moves downwards.

The external intercostal muscles contract and pull the ribs and sternum upwards and outwards.

These two actions increase the space in the thorax and air gets sucked in to fill the extra space.

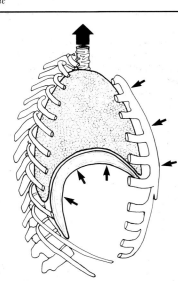

EXPIRATION

The diaphragm relaxes and curves upwards into the thorax.

The internal intercostal muscles contract and pull the sternum and ribs downwards.

These two actions reduce the space in the thorax and push out the air.

Artificial respiration

Sometimes, due to accident or illness, a person's breathing may stop. Artificial respiration is used to get oxygen into their blood before it is too late. In mouth-to-mouth respiration, exhaled breath, which still contains 17% oxygen, is breathed into the person's lungs, which are then allowed to empty by themselves.

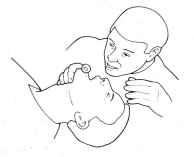

The lungs at work

The lungs have two tasks. First, they must obtain oxygen from the air so that it can be carried by the blood to every cell in the body. The absorption and transport of oxygen is made ten times more efficient by the red protein called **haemoglobin** which is contained in red blood cells. Haemoglobin has a strong attraction for oxygen and as the blood flows through the lungs, oxygen combines rapidly with it to form **oxyhaemoglobin**. When this blood reaches the body tissues, the lower oxygen concentration there causes oxygen to split away from haemoglobin and diffuse out of the blood into the surrounding cells.

The lungs' second task is **excretion**. During **tissue respiration** carbon dioxide is produced. This must be excreted (removed) from the body, since it makes the body fluids too acid. It diffuses out of the cells and into the **blood plasma** where its concentration is lower. There it dissolves to form **bicarbonate ions** (see page 53). These are carried to the lungs, converted to carbon dioxide gas and excreted in the breath. These processes could be summed up like this:

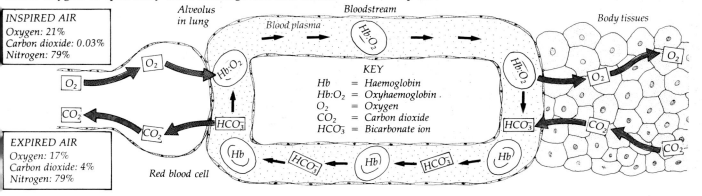

INSPIRED AIR
Oxygen: 21%
Carbon dioxide: 0.03%
Nitrogen: 79%

EXPIRED AIR
Oxygen: 17%
Carbon dioxide: 4%
Nitrogen: 79%

Alveolus in lung — *Bloodstream* — *Blood plasma* — *Body tissues* — *Red blood cell*

KEY
Hb	= Haemoglobin
$Hb{:}O_2$	= Oxyhaemoglobin
O_2	= Oxygen
CO_2	= Carbon dioxide
HCO_3^-	= Bicarbonate ion

LUNG CAPACITIES

The lungs of an average man can hold about 5500 ml of air. This lung capacity is not always in use, however. In quiet breathing, only about 500 ml of air are breathed in and out each time. This is called the **tidal volume**. The maximum volume of air which can be breathed in and out at one time is called the **vital capacity** of the lungs. This is about 4000 ml. No matter how hard we try to breathe out, it is impossible to empty the lungs completely. Some **residual air** – about 1500 ml on average – is always left behind. This air is not stale. Fresh air mixes with it each time we inhale.

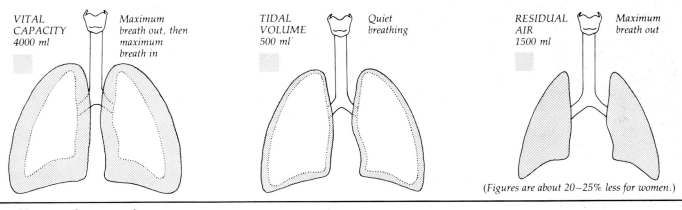

VITAL CAPACITY 4000 ml — Maximum breath out, then maximum breath in

TIDAL VOLUME 500 ml — Quiet breathing

RESIDUAL AIR 1500 ml — Maximum breath out

(Figures are about 20–25% less for women.)

The effect of exercise

At rest, the average person might take about 16 breaths each minute, delivering about 8 litres of air. During exercise, this is not enough. The muscles need more oxygen to release extra energy and the increased carbon dioxide they produce must be excreted. This is reflected in the composition of expired (breathed out) air during exercise.

	BEFORE EXERCISE	DURING EXERCISE
Oxygen	17%	12%
Carbon dioxide	4%	9%
Nitrogen	79%	79%

Both the number and the volume of breaths must be increased to meet the increased demands. Breathing rate could rise to 50 breaths per minute, with each breath supplying 4 litres of air.

Thus, air intake could rise from 8 litres to as much as 200 litres per minute. At the same time, the heart has to work harder. It must carry away the extra oxygen and also return carbon dioxide quickly for excretion. It might have to double its rate from, say, 70 to 140 beats per minute.

Even with all this increased breathing and heart rate, the oxygen supply may not be enough to meet the needs of the muscles. To fill the gap, they are forced to obtain some energy by a process called **anaerobic respiration** (see page 96), which does not use up oxygen. This causes a build up of **lactic acid** in the body. Because of this, breathing and heart rate have to remain high for some time after the exercise has stopped. The extra oxygen this supplies is now needed to remove the lactic acid. This is called 'paying off the **oxygen debt**'.

The lungs under attack

Gas exchange actually takes place in the millions of tiny **alveoli** (air sacs) in the lungs. These are very delicate. Their thin walls, which are essential if gases are to pass through them, are easily damaged. Yet, with every breath, we draw in more than just air. Dust and dirt, pollen, spores, germs and other harmful substances are also taken in. To prevent damage to the alveoli, all the air passages from the nose to the tiniest **bronchioles**, have a special **epithelium** (lining). The cells of this epithelium are designed to trap and remove unwanted particles so that the air which we finally receive is clean and germ free. This kind of lining is known as a **ciliated epithelium**. The types of cell which make it up and the way in which they work are shown opposite.

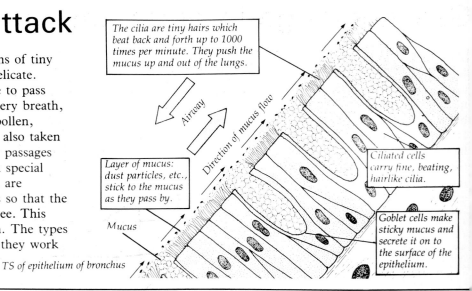

The cilia are tiny hairs which beat back and forth up to 1000 times per minute. They push the mucus up and out of the lungs.

Airway

Direction of mucus flow

Layer of mucus: dust particles, etc., stick to the mucus as they pass by.

Mucus

Ciliated cells carry fine, beating, hairlike cilia.

Goblet cells make sticky mucus and secrete it on to the surface of the epithelium.

TS of epithelium of bronchus

THE EFFECTS OF SMOKING

Cigarette smoke contains hundreds of different chemicals. Some of these are **irritants**, substances which annoy the lungs. Others are **carcinogens**, substances which cause cancer.

When cigarette smoke is inhaled into the lungs, it affects the epithelium in two ways. Firstly, it irritates the goblet cells, making them produce more mucus. Secondly, it slows down, or even stops, the beating of the cilia so that they can no longer 'sweep out' that mucus. The build-up of mucus in the lungs can only be cleared by coughing. This is commonly known as 'smoker's cough'.

If the lungs are exposed to cigarette smoke over a long period of time, a number of serious, and often fatal, diseases may arise. Among these are bronchitis, emphysema and lung cancer.

Bronchitis results as damage to the epithelium gets worse. Germs and irritants penetrate deeper into the lungs. The body's defence cells move in to attack them. Their remains, along with the mucus, make up **phlegm** which must be coughed up and spat out every day. Bronchitis is an unpleasant and disabling disease. More work days are lost due to it than to any other cause and the death toll from bronchitis runs into thousands each year.

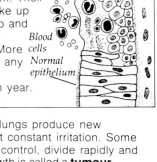

Cilia destroyed

Blood cells

Normal epithelium

Emphysema occurs when many of the delicate walls between the alveoli become torn and broken, while those that are left become thicker. This leaves the lungs with much less surface available for gas exchange – perhaps less than a quarter of normal. The sufferer coughs and wheezes and struggles for breath. This leads to permanent disability and eventually death.

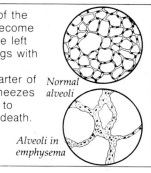

Normal alveoli

Alveoli in emphysema

Lung cancer may develop as the lungs produce new tissues to defend themselves against constant irritation. Some cells in these tissues may go out of control, divide rapidly and invade the surrounding lung. This growth is called a **tumour** or cancer. The tumour spreads through the lung, destroying the normal lung tissue. Some cancer cells may be carried by the blood to elsewhere in the body where they grow into secondary tumours. Lung cancer can be treated in its early stages, though, in most cases, it is detected too late and the victim dies. The connection between cigarette smoking and lung cancer is well established as these graphs show:

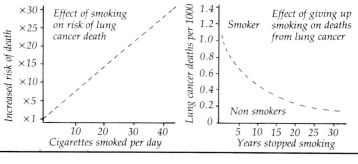

Effect of smoking on risk of lung cancer death

Increased risk of death

Cigarettes smoked per day

Effect of giving up smoking on deaths from lung cancer

Lung cancer deaths per 1000

Smoker

Non smokers

Years stopped smoking

Other lung diseases

Pneumonia

This disease occurs when the alveoli become filled with fluid and cell debris. Large areas of the lungs can become useless and **oxygen starvation** results. Pneumonia is usually caused by bacterial or virus infections. It can also be brought on by other diseases such as bronchitis or TB.

Tuberculosis

Tuberculosis is commonly called TB. It is caused by a **bacillus** (see pages 228–9). The TB infection may be breathed in or caught from drinking infected cow's milk. In many cases, the germ does little harm. Sometimes, however, it can spread through the lungs, causing severe damage. TB used to kill more people than most other diseases, including cancer. Nowadays, TB is much less of a threat. This is because of better housing conditions, milk being pasteurised, mass X-ray campaigns to find people at risk and BCG **vaccination**. TB can also be treated with **antibiotics**.

Dust diseases

Dust diseases are caused by breathing in large amounts of dust at work. Over long periods of time the lungs may become badly damaged, leading to disability and early death. Stone cutters, for example, may get **silicosis**, miners **pneumoconiosis** (black lung) and asbestos workers may catch **asbestosis**. Special precautions can prevent such diseases, but, once caught, they are incurable.

Gas exchange in other animals

INSECTS have a row of air holes called **spiracles** along both sides of their bodies. The spiracles lead into a system of branching air tubes called **tracheae** (sing: *trachea*). Air diffuses along these to all parts of the insect's body. The tiniest branches of the tracheae, called **tracheoles**, are filled with water. The water dissolves oxygen so that it can enter the cells. Carbon dioxide diffuses the other way.

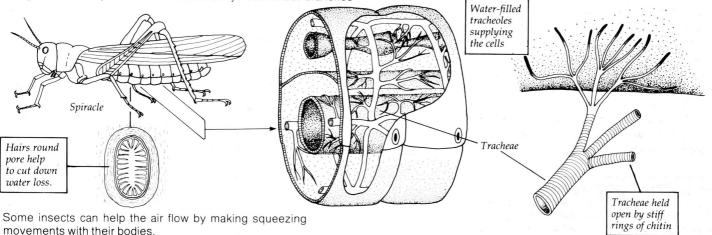

Spiracle

Hairs round pore help to cut down water loss.

Water-filled tracheoles supplying the cells

Tracheae

Tracheae held open by stiff rings of chitin

Some insects can help the air flow by making squeezing movements with their bodies.

FISH have gills, four on each side of the head, which get dissolved oxygen from the water and pass it into their blood. Carbon dioxide passes in the other direction. To do this, fish take a stream of water into their mouths, pass it over the gills, then out of the side of their heads under the **operculum** or gill cover.

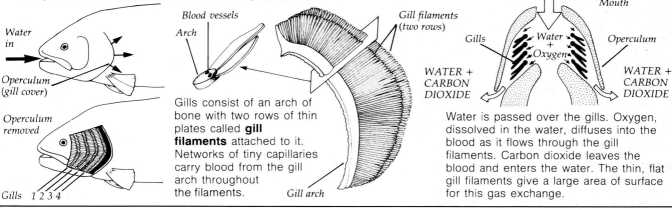

Water in

Operculum (gill cover)

Operculum removed

Gills 1 2 3 4

Blood vessels

Arch

Gill filaments (two rows)

Gills consist of an arch of bone with two rows of thin plates called **gill filaments** attached to it. Networks of tiny capillaries carry blood from the gill arch throughout the filaments.

Gill arch

Mouth

Gills

Water + Oxygen

Operculum

WATER + CARBON DIOXIDE

WATER + CARBON DIOXIDE

Water is passed over the gills. Oxygen, dissolved in the water, diffuses into the blood as it flows through the gill filaments. Carbon dioxide leaves the blood and enters the water. The thin, flat gill filaments give a large area of surface for this gas exchange.

GAS EXCHANGE THROUGH THE SKIN

Small animals have more skin, in proportion to their size, than large ones. If the animal is small enough, it may be able to absorb all the oxygen it needs through its skin. To do this, the skin must be kept moist to dissolve the gas. Examples of this are given below.

Flatworms absorb oxygen from the water around them through their skins. They are so thin that the gas can be easily diffused throughout their bodies.

Planarian: a flatworm

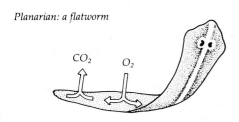

CO_2 O_2

Carbon dioxide diffuses out of the cells into the water.

Earthworms keep their skins moist with a layer of mucus. This dissolves oxygen which can then diffuse into the blood vessels which carry it round the body.

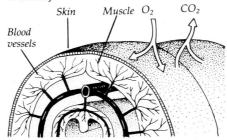

Skin *Muscle* O_2 CO_2

Blood vessels

Carbon dioxide in the blood diffuses out of the skin.

Frogs, when not active, for example in winter, can get all their oxygen through the skin. The skin is kept moist, dissolving oxygen which diffuses into capillaries under the skin.

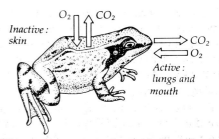

O_2 CO_2

Inactive: skin

CO_2
O_2

Active: lungs and mouth

When active, gas exchange in frogs is mainly by lungs or mouth.

Gas exchange in plants

Like animals, plants need oxygen to stay alive. However, since plants use very little energy, they do not need much oxygen. So, for these plant tissues which do not carry out photosynthesis, gas exchange is very simple, for example:

ROOTS
Oxygen diffuses from air spaces in the soil into the **root hair cells** and then to the other cells. Carbon dioxide goes the other way.

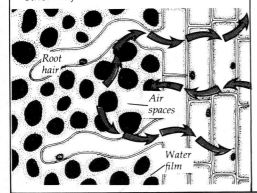

STEMS
The bark of woody stems is airproof. **Lenticels** are breaks in the bark to allow gas exchange with the living cells underneath it.

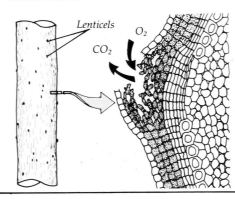

FUNGI
The fungal threads (**hyphae**) are only one cell thick so gases just diffuse in and out. The hyphae may pass oxygen along to the fruiting bodies.

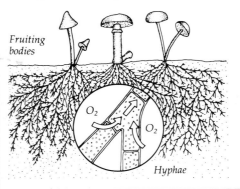

GREEN PLANTS also need to take in oxygen and get rid of carbon dioxide. However, when they are making food by photosynthesis, they also *use* carbon dioxide and *produce* oxygen. In good light, their main gas exchange problem is getting the carbon dioxide they need for photosynthesis and removing the oxygen it makes.

Small green plants, like the mosses, can do this by simple diffusion. Large green plants, like the flowering plants, have special cells and tissues in their leaves to absorb lots of carbon dioxide and get rid of lots of oxygen very efficiently.

The UPPER EPIDERMIS is the top skin of the leaf. The top of a leaf gets hotter than the bottom and there is a danger that too much water could evaporate through it. To stop this, there are few or no pores and the epidermis is covered with an airproof, waxy layer called the cuticle. So, little gas exchange occurs at the top of a leaf and this is used for respiration and not photosynthesis.

Upper epidermis from above

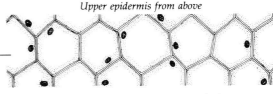

CUTICLE *(airproof layer of wax)*

UPPER EPIDERMIS *(top skin of the leaf)*

Leaf cut across (transverse section)

The PALISADE LAYER consists of tightly packed cells filled with chloroplasts. This layer is at the top of the leaf to get the most light. It is the main food-making tissue of the leaf.

SPONGY MESOPHYLL is the gas exchange tissue of the leaf. The spaces between its loosely packed cells let air flow around. Carbon dioxide dissolves on their moist surfaces. It can then diffuse to the palisade layer for photosynthesis. Oxygen diffuses out the other way.

The LOWER EPIDERMIS is the bottom skin of the leaf. It has lots of pores called stomata (sing: stoma) to let carbon dioxide into the leaf and oxygen out.

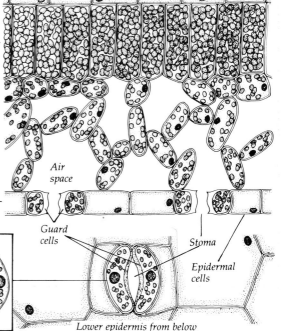

Air space

Guard cells

Stoma

Epidermal cells

Lower epidermis from below

Each stoma is edged by two guard cells. They are sausage-shaped with an unevenly-thickened wall. Unlike other epidermal cells, they have chloroplasts. In the light the chloroplasts make sugar. This draws in water by osmosis, changing the shape of the guard cells and opening the pore, letting in carbon dioxide for photosynthesis.

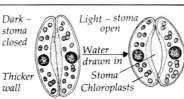

Dark – stoma closed

Light – stoma open

Water drawn in

Thicker wall

Stoma

Chloroplasts

SECTION 12

Water and Living Things

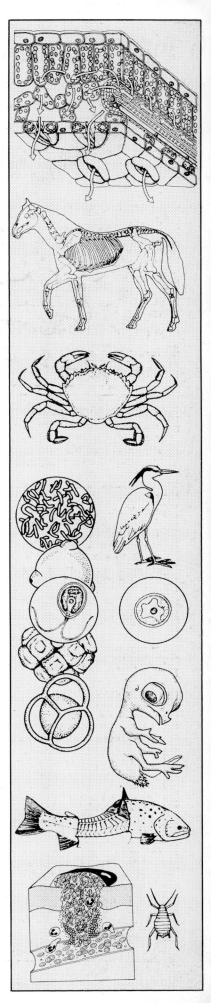

Water and living things

Living cells are made of many different substances, some of which are very large and complex molecules, but the most abundant and most important substance of all is also one of the simplest. That substance is water. A water molecule consists of just one oxygen atom with two hydrogen atoms attached to it. Its chemical formula is H_2O.

Anything between 60% and 95% of the weight of a living organism is water, thus most organisms can withstand very little water loss. Human beings (65% water), for example, can survive for months without food, but for only about two weeks without water. There is no part of life in which water is not involved. Listed below are some of its more important functions.

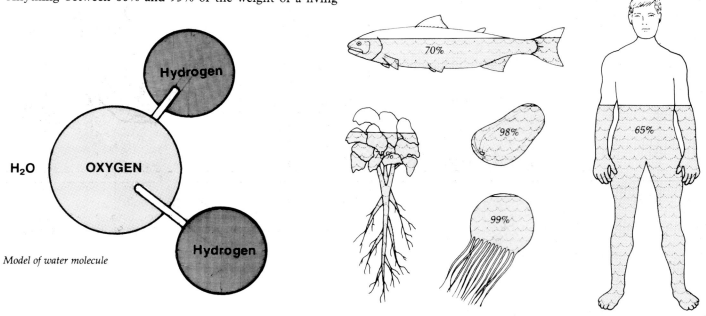

H_2O

Model of water molecule

A SOLVENT

Water is the best solvent known. This means that more things can dissolve in water than in any other liquid. When a substance dissolves, its particles become evenly spread among the water molecules. If two substances are to react chemically with each other, they must first be thoroughly mixed together. Dissolving them both in water makes mixing them together very easy. For this reason, all of a cell's reactions are done in aqueous (water) solution. Gases like carbon dioxide and oxygen, which are very important to living things can also dissolve in water. Before these gases can be absorbed by an organism, they must first be dissolved in water. So, all gas exchange surfaces must be kept moist. Carbon dioxide is very soluble in water with which it forms an acid solution. Oxygen does not dissolve so well, but enough can dissolve to supply the needs of organisms like fish which live in water.

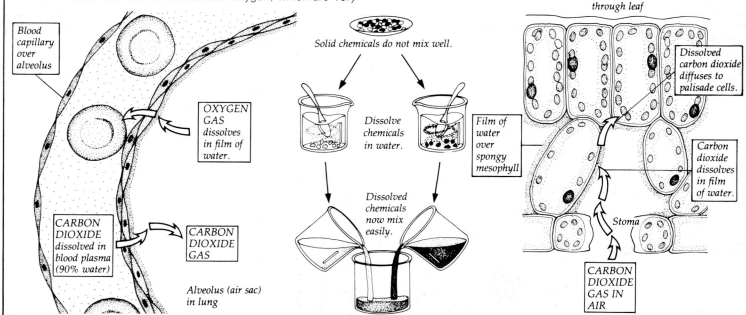

Blood capillary over alveolus

OXYGEN GAS dissolves in film of water.

CARBON DIOXIDE dissolved in blood plasma (90% water)

CARBON DIOXIDE GAS

Alveolus (air sac) in lung

Solid chemicals do not mix well.

Dissolve chemicals in water.

Dissolved chemicals now mix easily.

Section through leaf

Dissolved carbon dioxide diffuses to palisade cells.

Film of water over spongy mesophyll

Carbon dioxide dissolves in film of water.

Stoma

CARBON DIOXIDE GAS IN AIR

CONTROLLING TEMPERATURE

When warm-blooded animals get too hot, glands in their skin produce sweat which is mainly water. This helps to cool down the body. Also, unlike other liquids, when water gets very cold, it gets lighter. In winter, ice and cold water will stay at the top of a frozen lake or river, allowing water animals to survive in the warmer water below.

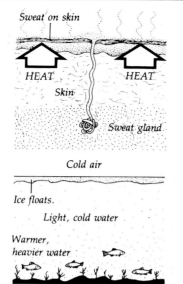

FOR SUPPORT

When the **vacuoles** of plant cells are full of water, they push against the cell walls, making the cells **turgid** (stiff). This helps to support the plant. When a plant is short of water, it wilts, unable to support itself. Water organisms rely on the uplift they get from the water to support them.

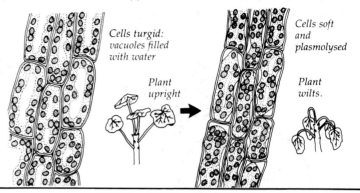

Cells turgid: vacuoles filled with water

Cells soft and plasmolysed

Plant upright

Plant wilts.

A RAW MATERIAL

As a solvent, water is essential for all of a cell's reactions. However, water molecules themselves take part in many reactions. The most important of these is photosynthesis – the food-making processes of green plants.

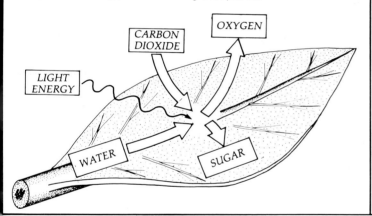

FOR SEXUAL REPRODUCTION

For all animals and for simple plants, eggs cannot be fertilised without water, since the male **gametes** (sperms) need water to swim to the female eggs.

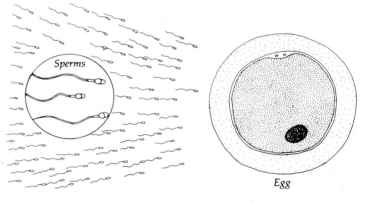

Sperms

Egg

FOR TRANSPORT

Since it is a good solvent, water is the ideal transport fluid for both animals and plants. Blood plasma (90% water) carries many dissolved substances around. It can also carry things like cells and proteins which are not dissolved.

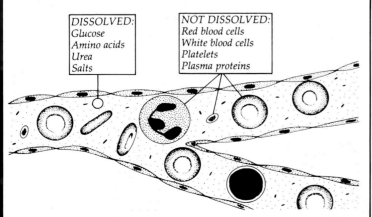

DISSOLVED:
Glucose
Amino acids
Urea
Salts

NOT DISSOLVED:
Red blood cells
White blood cells
Platelets
Plasma proteins

FOR LUBRICATION

In the bodies of animals, watery substances are used in many places to provide important lubrication.

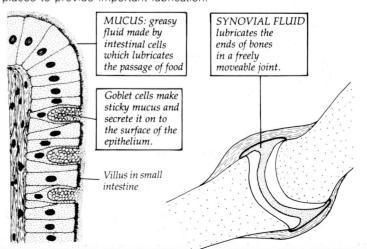

MUCUS: greasy fluid made by intestinal cells which lubricates the passage of food

SYNOVIAL FLUID lubricates the ends of bones in a freely moveable joint.

Goblet cells make sticky mucus and secrete it on to the surface of the epithelium.

Villus in small intestine

Diffusion and osmosis

Living cells must be able to transport water and other substances in and out. Two processes which are vital for this, in both animals and plants, are **diffusion** and **osmosis**.

DIFFUSION

The molecules of a gas or liquid are in continual motion. They move around haphazardly in all directions. If such molecules start off more concentrated in one region than in another, this movement will gradually spread them out until they are evenly concentrated all over. This process is called **diffusion**.

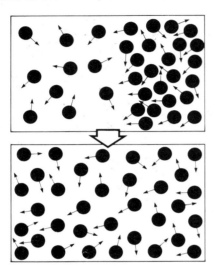

We say that diffusion takes place down a **concentration gradient**. This means that substances diffuse from areas of high concentration to areas of low concentration.

TRANSPORT BY DIFFUSION

Concentration gradients occur in all organisms. Where they do, the organism can use simple diffusion to transport things around. Nutrients being carried in the blood, for example, will diffuse into those cells which need them. Diffusion is also vital for getting oxygen into cells and carbon dioxide out of them, for example, in humans:

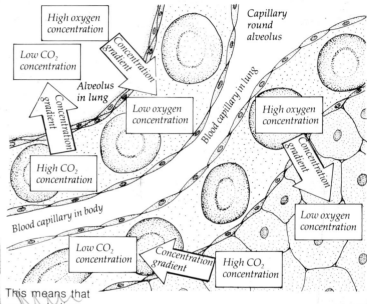

OSMOSIS

Water, like other substances, can come in different concentrations. Pure water is the most concentrated of all. When we dissolve something, for example sucrose, in water, the sucrose molecules push the water molecules apart, so making the water less concentrated. If we have a concentration gradient, with water being more concentrated in one part of a solution than another, the continuous movement of the water molecules will cause them to diffuse until the concentration is even all over. Of course, at the same time, the sucrose molecules will be diffusing in the opposite direction. **Osmosis** is a special case of the diffusion of water. Osmosis occurs when water diffuses across a **semi-permeable** membrane. A semi-permeable membrane is a thin skin which will let small molecules pass through it easily, but which will hold back larger molecules like sucrose. It acts as if it has tiny holes in it, too small for the larger molecules to squeeze through. Now, if the water on one side of a semi-permeable membrane is more concentrated than on the other side, water molecules will diffuse from high to low until the concentration on both sides is the same. However, if the substance, or substances, dissolved in the water is, like sucrose, too big to cross the membrane, then the concentration on both sides can never become the same and so the water will go on moving from one side to the other. Osmosis, therefore, is the diffusion of water across a semi-permeable membrane.

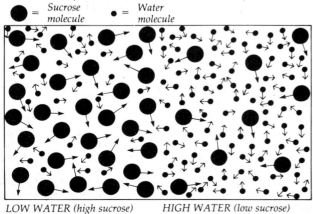

LOW WATER (high sucrose) CONCENTRATION   HIGH WATER (low sucrose) CONCENTRATION

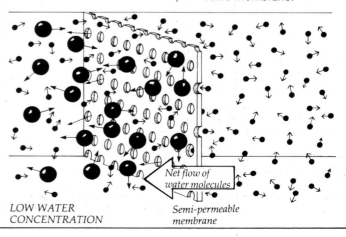

LOW WATER CONCENTRATION   Semi-permeable membrane

OSMOTIC EFFECTS

The membranes of cells are semi-permeable. This means that osmosis and its effects are of great importance to living things. Osmotic effects can be very useful to both plants and animals.

The root hairs of plants use osmosis to get water from the soil. Soil water is more concentrated than the water in root hair cells and so enters them by osmosis. Osmosis then takes it, cell by cell, across the root to the veins in the centre which carry it upwards to the rest of the plant.

When blood first enters a capillary, its very high pressure forces its watery part, the plasma, with its dissolved nutrients, through the capillary walls to bathe the surrounding cells. The plasma proteins, however, are too big to get out. Their presence keeps up a concentration gradient and further along the capillary, when the pressure is lower, this draws part of the water back into the blood by osmosis.

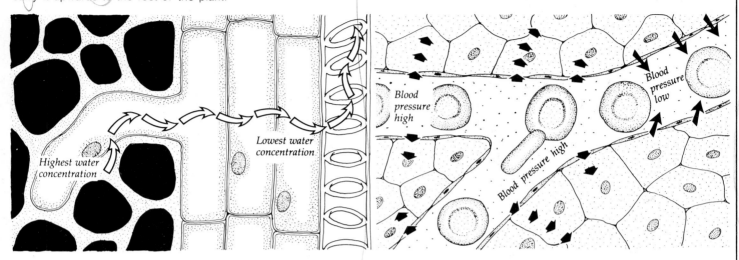

We can see the effects on cells if we bathe plant or animal cells in solutions of different water concentration and observe them under the microscope.

Ⓛ *Low water concentration*   Ⓜ *Medium water concentration*   Ⓗ *High water concentration*

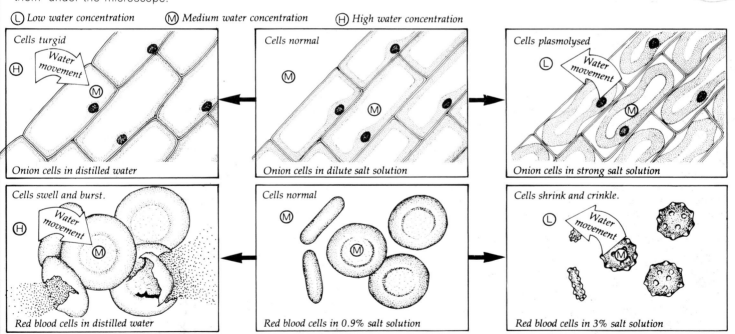

When water enters a cell by osmosis, a pressure builds up. This is known as **osmotic pressure**. This is useful to plants since the pressure pushes the cell contents against the tough cell wall, making the cell stiff or turgid. This **turgor** helps to support the plant. On the other hand, animal cells, having no cell wall, will burst like a balloon if the pressure gets too high. Whenever water leaves a cell by osmosis, the cell contents will shrivel up. In plant cells we can actually see the membrane coming away from the wall – a condition known as **plasmolysis**. A plasmolysed cell will recover if given water.

The osmotic pressure which a solution is capable of causing is called its **osmotic potential**. Thus, 20% sucrose solution has a higher osmotic potential than 5%. If two solutions with the same osmotic potential are separated by a semi-permeable membrane, no osmosis will take place. Organisms must control the osmotic potential of the liquids inside and outside of their cells to make sure that just the correct amount of osmosis takes place. The methods they use to achieve this are called **osmoregulation**.

The kidneys

As blood flows through the body, the cells empty their waste into it. This waste must be got rid of before it builds up and causes damage. The removal of waste from the body is called **excretion**. The body's main excretory organs are the lungs, skin and kidneys. The kidneys' job is to filter the blood which passes through them and to take out

nitrogenous waste such as **urea**, unwanted salts and excess water. The waste liquid which is formed is called **urine**. Urine leaves the kidneys and is stored in the bladder until it can be eliminated. The two kidneys, the bladder and their connected vessels make up the body's **urinary system**.

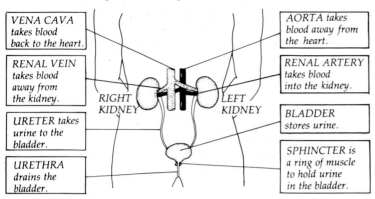

VENA CAVA takes blood back to the heart.

AORTA takes blood away from the heart.

RENAL VEIN takes blood away from the kidney.

RENAL ARTERY takes blood into the kidney.

RIGHT KIDNEY   LEFT KIDNEY

URETER takes urine to the bladder.

BLADDER stores urine.

URETHRA drains the bladder.

SPHINCTER is a ring of muscle to hold urine in the bladder.

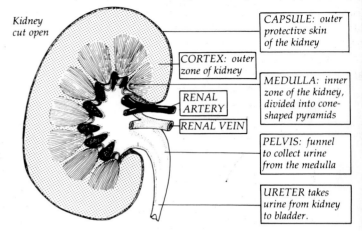

Kidney cut open

CAPSULE: outer protective skin of the kidney

CORTEX: outer zone of kidney

RENAL ARTERY

RENAL VEIN

MEDULLA: inner zone of the kidney, divided into cone-shaped pyramids

PELVIS: funnel to collect urine from the medulla

URETER takes urine from kidney to bladder.

BLOOD SUPPLY TO THE KIDNEYS
The renal arteries take blood from the aorta to the kidneys. There, they branch again and again, ending in tiny **arterioles** which supply each glomerulus. When it leaves the nephron, the purified blood is collected by a tiny **venule**. The venules lead it to the renal veins which return it to the heart. Each heartbeat sends about a quarter of the heart's blood to the kidneys.

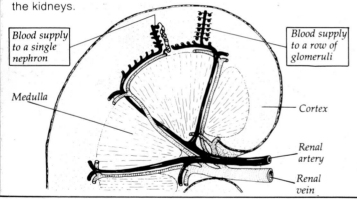

Blood supply to a single nephron

Blood supply to a row of glomeruli

Medulla

Cortex

Renal artery

Renal vein

A kidney consists mostly of about one million tiny kidney units called **nephrons**. Each nephron receives its own supply of blood, cleans it and discards the urine which is formed. This blood-cleaning process is done in two stages. First, there is **filtration**, which removes much of the water from the blood along with everything dissolved in it. Second, there is **reabsorption**, when most of the water and anything else of value is taken back into the blood. The structure of a nephron is illustrated below.

Collecting the urine
Urine flows from the kidney tubule into the collecting ducts. The ducts take it into the **pyramids of the medulla** and it drips from these into the pelvis. It is then moved by **peristalsis** (see page 75) down the ureters to the bladder. When convenient, the sphincter is opened and the bladder's muscular wall forces the urine out of the body through the urethra.

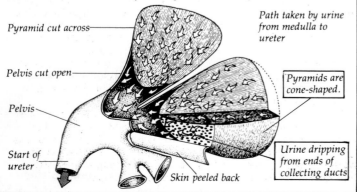

Pyramid cut across

Pelvis cut open

Pelvis

Start of ureter

Path taken by urine from medulla to ureter

Pyramids are cone-shaped.

Urine dripping from ends of collecting ducts

Skin peeled back

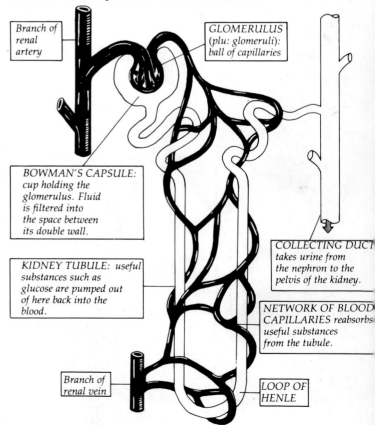

Branch of renal artery

GLOMERULUS (plu: glomeruli): ball of capillaries

BOWMAN'S CAPSULE: cup holding the glomerulus. Fluid is filtered into the space between its double wall.

KIDNEY TUBULE: useful substances such as glucose are pumped out of here back into the blood.

Branch of renal vein

COLLECTING DUCT takes urine from the nephron to the pelvis of the kidney.

NETWORK OF BLOOD CAPILLARIES reabsorbs useful substances from the tubule.

LOOP OF HENLE

How kidneys work

The kidneys have two vital jobs to do. Their first task is **excretion**. They purify the blood by removing waste substances from it. Their second job is **osmoregulation**. This means that they keep the concentration or **osmotic potential** (see pages 116–7) of the blood steady. To do this, they must control the amount of water and salts which the blood contains. Osmoregulation is one part of **homeostasis**, that is one of the ways in which the body cells are kept comfortable. Details of the kidneys' role in homeostasis are given on pages 198–9.

The tasks of excretion and osmoregulation are performed by the kidneys' million or so **nephrons**. A nephron does its work in two stages. The first is **filtration**. The blood is filtered to remove waste substances and excess water from it. However, at this stage, some valuable material such as glucose is also removed. The next stage, therefore, is the **reabsorption** back into the blood of anything which the body cannot afford to lose. The fluid which remains outside the blood after reabsorption is **urine**, the body's liquid waste. The tables below compare the composition of the three fluids involved in the process.

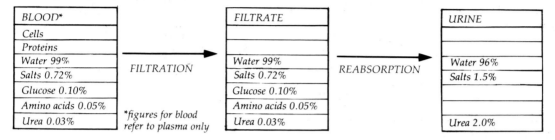

BLOOD*		FILTRATE		URINE
Cells				
Proteins				
Water 99%		Water 99%		Water 96%
Salts 0.72%	FILTRATION	Salts 0.72%	REABSORPTION	Salts 1.5%
Glucose 0.10%		Glucose 0.10%		
Amino acids 0.05%	*figures for blood	Amino acids 0.05%		
Urea 0.03%	refer to plasma only	Urea 0.03%		Urea 2.0%

PRESSURE FILTRATION

At the top of each nephron is a sort of hollow-walled cup called a **Bowman's capsule**. A ball of blood capillaries called a **glomerulus** (plu: *glomeruli*) fits inside each capsule. Blood enters the glomerulus by a wide **arteriole** (blood vessel), but has to leave through a narrow one. This makes the blood pressure in the glomerulus very high. This pressure forces fluid through the capillary walls into the Bowman's capsule. The liquid which has been filtered out of the blood in this way is known as **glomerular filtrate**. This liquid is very similar to blood plasma. Only blood cells and plasma proteins are missing from it, since they are too big to get out.

Thus, the blood is not just filtered, it is filtered under high pressure. This is called **pressure filtration**. It forces out of the blood not only waste such as urea, but other things such as glucose, amino acids and useful salts. As it is formed, the glomerular filtrate trickles out of the Bowman's capsule and along the kidney **tubule**.

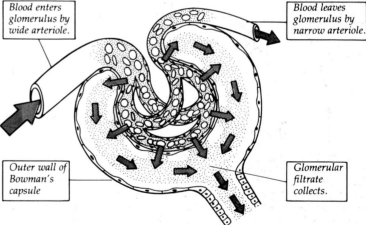

Blood enters glomerulus by wide arteriole.

Blood leaves glomerulus by narrow arteriole.

Outer wall of Bowman's capsule

Glomerular filtrate collects.

Reabsorption

Pressure filtration clears the blood of waste. Unfortunately, it also removes too much water and other valuable material. So, as the filtrate goes along the tubule, everything of value is passed back into the blood. This is called **reabsorption**. Most of the water and salts, along with all the glucose and amino acids, is reabsorbed by the blood. Urea and other waste, however, is not reabsorbed and ends up in the urine. Since most of the water is reabsorbed, the concentration of such waste is much higher in the urine than it was in the blood.

The tubule can vary the amount of water which is reabsorbed by the blood and so keep the concentration of the blood just right. This is the osmoregulation part of the kidney's job (see pages 116–7). It is controlled in this by a hormone called **anti-diuretic hormone** (ADH) made by the **pituitary gland**. High levels of this hormone in the blood cause increased reabsorption

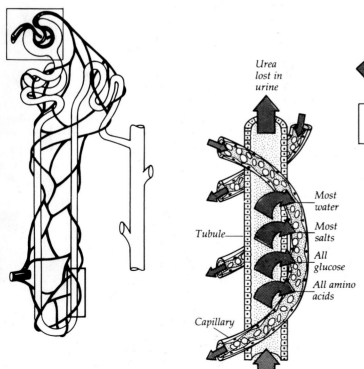

Urea lost in urine

Tubule

Capillary

Most water

Most salts

All glucose

All amino acids

Water balance in animals

Like all living things, animals must have water. However, too much water can be as harmful as too little. An animal's body, whether it is made of one cell or many millions of cells, must constantly strive to contain just the right amount of water. To do this, it must balance the water it loses with the water it gains. This is called **water balance**. Water may be lost in sweat, breath, faeces, urine, or by **osmosis** (see pages 116–7). It may be gained in food, drink, or by osmosis. In addition, the process of **respiration**, which gives organisms the energy they need to stay alive, also generates some water. It goes like this:

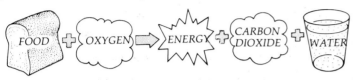

This is called **metabolic water**. There are some animals which could not survive without their supply of metabolic water.

By controlling its water balance, an animal is able, to some extent, to control the **osmotic potential** (concentration) of its body fluids. Such control is called **osmoregulation**. Osmoregulation, however, also involves controlling the amounts of soluble substances or **solutes** which are allowed to remain in the body. These include things like salts and glucose. Any changes in the concentration of these must be kept to a minimum.

Also important are the **nitrogenous wastes** produced by the body. These are formed from the breakdown of certain nitrogen compounds such as **amino acids**. The simplest of these waste substances is **ammonia**. This is highly poisonous and large amounts of water are needed to dilute it and flush it out of the system. If this water is not available, the nitrogen must be excreted in the form of less harmful substances such as **urea** or **uric acid**.

The problems of water balance and osmoregulation which an animal encounters depend on its habitat. Shown below are a few examples of these problems and of the ways in which they are overcome.

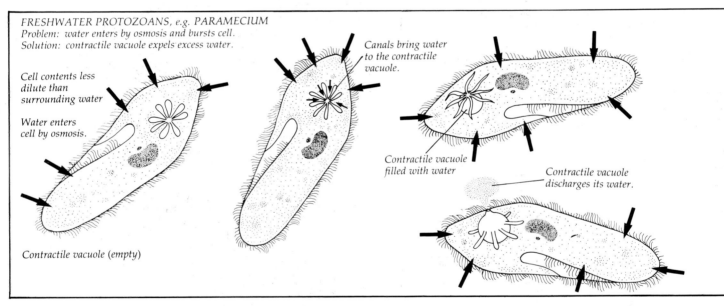

FRESHWATER PROTOZOANS, e.g. PARAMECIUM
Problem: water enters by osmosis and bursts cell.
Solution: contractile vacuole expels excess water.

Canals bring water to the contractile vacuole.

Cell contents less dilute than surrounding water

Water enters cell by osmosis.

Contractile vacuole filled with water

Contractile vacuole discharges its water.

Contractile vacuole (empty)

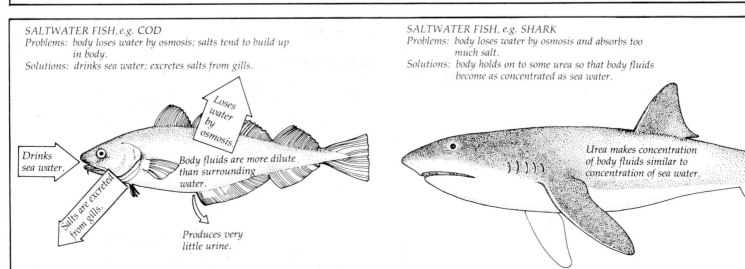

SALTWATER FISH, e.g. COD
Problems: body loses water by osmosis; salts tend to build up in body.
Solutions: drinks sea water; excretes salts from gills.

Loses water by osmosis

Drinks sea water.

Salts are excreted from gills.

Body fluids are more dilute than surrounding water.

Produces very little urine.

SALTWATER FISH, e.g. SHARK
Problems: body loses water by osmosis and absorbs too much salt.
Solutions: body holds on to some urea so that body fluids become as concentrated as sea water.

Urea makes concentration of body fluids similar to concentration of sea water.

FRESHWATER FISH, e.g. CARP
Problems: *water enters body by osmosis; salt level too low.*
Solutions: *large amount of urine produced; gills extract salts from the water.*

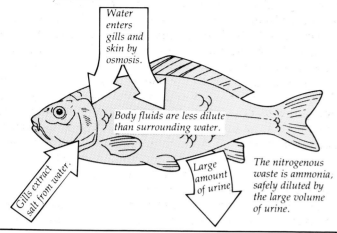

Water enters gills and skin by osmosis.

Body fluids are less dilute than surrounding water.

Gills extract salt from water.

Large amount of urine

The nitrogenous waste is ammonia, safely diluted by the large volume of urine.

MAMMAL, e.g. HUMAN
Problems: *water lost in sweat (for cooling), in breath, in faeces and in urine; salts eaten in food.*
Solutions: *water gained in food, in drink, and as metabolic water; kidneys excrete excess salts; the nitrogenous waste is urea which does not require as much water as ammonia for its removal.*

Average daily gains

Average daily losses

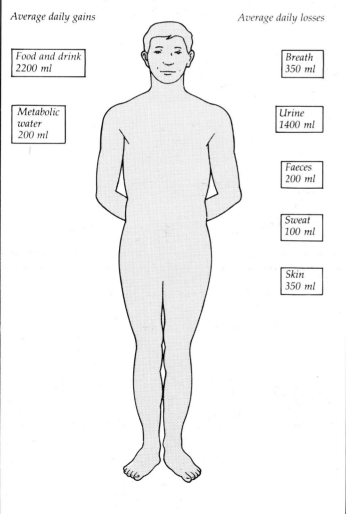

Food and drink
2200 ml

Metabolic water
200 ml

Breath
350 ml

Urine
1400 ml

Faeces
200 ml

Sweat
100 ml

Skin
350 ml

AMPHIBIANS, e.g. FROG
Problems: *water evaporates readily from thin, moist skin.*
Solutions: *lives in damp conditions; can absorb water through its skin; its nitrogenous waste is urea.*

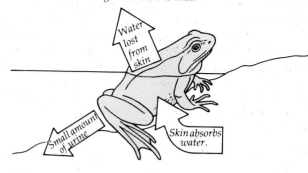

Water lost from skin

Small amount of urine

Skin absorbs water.

REPTILES, e.g. LIZARD
Problems: *water lost in breath, faeces and urine; salts eaten in food; lives in dry conditions.*
Solutions: *scaly, waterproof skin; water gained in food and drink; kidneys excrete surplus salts; nitrogenous waste is solid uric acid, so little water is needed to remove it.*

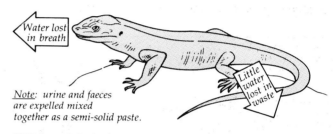

Water lost in breath

<u>Note</u>: urine and faeces are expelled mixed together as a semi-solid paste.

Little water lost in waste

BIRDS, e.g. PIGEON
Problems: *water lost in breath, through skin, in faeces and urine; salts eaten in food.*
Solutions: *skin covered by feathers; water gained in food and drink; kidneys excrete surplus salts; nitrogenous waste is uric acid.*

<u>Note</u>: urine and faeces are expelled mixed together as a semi-solid paste.

Water lost in breath as bird pants rapidly to keep cool

Little water lost in waste

DESERT MAMMAL, e.g. KANGAROO RAT
Problems: *lives in hot, dry areas where no drinking water is available; salts eaten in food.*
Solutions: *animal does not sweat; stays underground during the day; gets some water from food, but relies heavily on metabolic water; produces very little urine, containing a high concentration of salts and urea.*

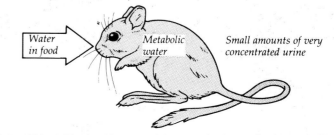

Water in food

Metabolic water

Small amounts of very concentrated urine

Water balance in plants

Plants, like animals, must be able to maintain a **water balance**. To do this, they must absorb enough water from the soil to meet their needs and to replace their losses. If they cannot obtain sufficient water, they wilt and may eventually die.

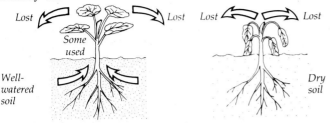

Plants need water for a variety of purposes. Firstly, plant cells, like all living cells, consist mainly of water. As a plant grows and produces more cells, water must be found for these. In fact, a plant cell's fastest growth occurs when its **vacuoles** are formed. These are filled with **cell sap** and this is largely water.

Secondly, when a plant cell has absorbed all the water it can, its contents press tightly against the tough, unstretching cell wall. This makes the cell very hard, or **turgid**. A similar thing happens when air is pumped into a bicycle tyre. The inner tube pushes against the rubber tyre, making it hard. In plants, the effect is to make the leaves and young stems firm and crisp. We can see how important this is when we look at a plant which is short of water. Its leaves and stems become soft and droopy, unable to support themselves. This is why wilting is a sure sign of a plant drying out.

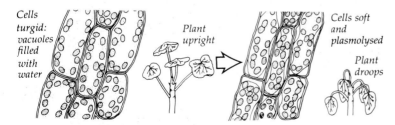

This method of support is only possible because of the presence of the cell wall. The cell wall has another advantage. Cells absorb water by **osmosis** (see page 116). As they do so, pressure builds up inside them. Cell walls can withstand this pressure and, once the cell is fully turgid, no more water can get in. Under the same conditions, animal cells, since they have no wall, will burst and die.

This is one water balance problem which plants do not have. Finally, plants use water as an ingredient or raw material in all sorts of plant processes. Among the most important of these is **photosynthesis** (see pages 88–9), the process by which they make their food:

Water + Carbon dioxide → Food + Oxygen

Transpiration

The biggest water balance problem which a plant faces is the ease with which water can be lost by **evaporation**. The evaporation of water from a plant is called **transpiration**. Most transpiration occurs through the leaves. There are two reasons for this. One reason is the large surface area which the leaves provide. The main reason, however, is the presence of millions of tiny air holes called **stomata** through which water vapour can escape. The diagram below shows how water moves into the cells of a leaf, and how a lot of it is quickly lost as water vapour out of the stomata.

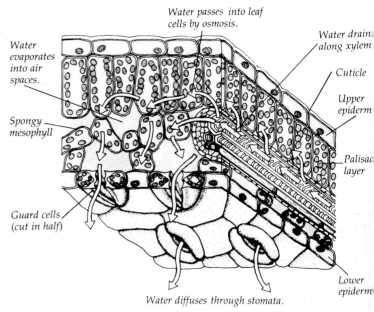

Water diffuses through stomata.

The main cause of the evaporation and loss of water from the leaves is the heat generated by the rays of the sun. Sometimes this increases transpiration so much that the plant wilts. Obviously, the upper surfaces of the leaves, which face the sun, will be most affected by this. The danger is reduced, however, by there being few or no stomata on the upper surfaces of leaves. Also, the **upper epidermis** (skin) of a leaf has a waxy layer called the **cuticle** which cuts down water loss.

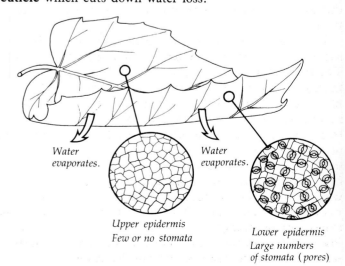

STOMATA (sing: *stoma*) are tiny holes in the epidermis of a leaf, visible only through a microscope. Their presence lets in the carbon dioxide which the leaf needs for photosynthesis and lets out the oxygen which is produced. Each stoma is ringed by two **guard cells**. These cells are quite different from the other cells of the epidermis which surround them. As the diagrams below indicate, these differences lead to the guard cells changing their shape so that the stomata are closed at night and open during the day. In this way, transpiration, and the water loss it causes, is reduced during the night. Of course, in the daytime, the stomata must be open, otherwise photosynthesis would be impossible. Unfortunately, this is also the time when the heat of the sun can make transpiration a real problem. On a very hot day, it may even cause the plant to wilt. Only when wilting has already set in do the stomata start to close up again.

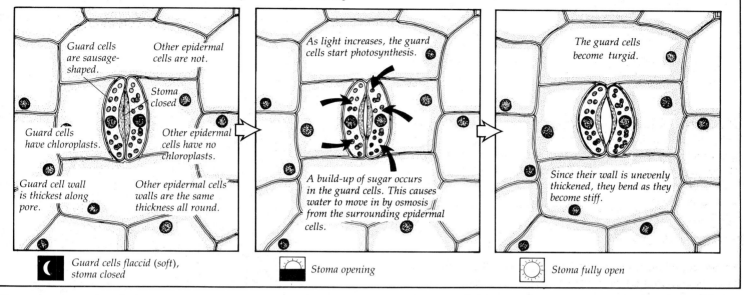

Guard cells are sausage-shaped. Other epidermal cells are not.
Stoma closed
Guard cells have chloroplasts. Other epidermal cells have no chloroplasts.
Guard cell wall is thickest along pore. Other epidermal cells walls are the same thickness all round.

Guard cells flaccid (soft), stoma closed

As light increases, the guard cells start photosynthesis.
A build-up of sugar occurs in the guard cells. This causes water to move in by osmosis from the surrounding epidermal cells.

Stoma opening

The guard cells become turgid.
Since their wall is unevenly thickened, they bend as they become stiff.

Stoma fully open

The transpiration stream

Water flows through a plant in an unbroken stream from the roots up to the leaves. This is called the **transpiration stream**. Two things seem to cause the transpiration stream. Firstly, water from the soil enters the roots by **osmosis**. This steady inward flow generates a pressure, called **root pressure**, strong enough to push water a short way up the stem. The second, and more important cause of water movement, though, is transpiration itself. As the leaf cells lose water by evaporation into the air, more is drawn out of the **xylem vessels**, by osmosis, to replace it. Water molecules tend to stick together and so they form a sort of queue. As the molecules at the head of the queue disappear, the ones behind move up to take their place. In this way, a continuous stream of water is drawn through the plant.

The transpiration stream is important to a plant. It supplies all its cells with water and minerals from the soil. The evaporation of water from the leaves may help to cool them down on hot days. The trouble is, however, that the plant has very little control over its rate of transpiration. A number of outside factors can increase a plant's transpiration and so cause it problems. The most important of these are:

light – opens the stomata;

heat – causes water to evaporate from the stomata;

wind – increases evaporation of water from the stomata;

dry air (low humidity) – allows water to evaporate from the stomata more quickly;

low air pressure such as mountain plants live in – allows water to evaporate more easily from the leaves.

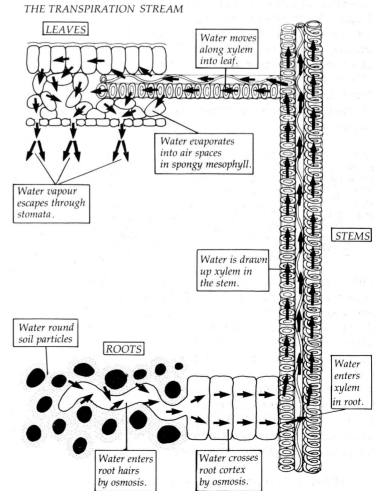

THE TRANSPIRATION STREAM

LEAVES
Water moves along xylem into leaf.
Water evaporates into air spaces in spongy mesophyll.
Water vapour escapes through stomata.

STEMS
Water is drawn up xylem in the stem.

ROOTS
Water round soil particles
Water enters xylem in root.
Water enters root hairs by osmosis.
Water crosses root cortex by osmosis.

Water cycle

The seas and oceans contain most of the Earth's water. In fact, they cover about two-thirds of the Earth's surface. Some of this water, however, is constantly being removed. The heat of the sun causes it to evaporate and it rises into the atmosphere as water vapour. In the sky it cools down and forms into clouds. Sooner or later the water droplets in the clouds fall to Earth as rain or snow. Some may fall straight back into the sea. Some may fall on land and find their way back to the sea at a later date. Either way, the water will have gone round in a circle. This is called the **water cycle**.

Even if there was no life on Earth there would still be a water cycle. However, since water is so important to living things, it is not surprising that they are involved in the use and recycling of water. Plants play the biggest part in this.

They absorb water in large quantities from the soil. Some of this is 'captured' in the process of **photosynthesis**, like this:

Water + Carbon dioxide → Food + Oxygen

Most of the water which plants absorb, though, is rapidly returned to the air as water vapour by **transpiration** (see pages 122–3). More water vapour is returned to the air by the **respiration** of plants and animals and the **combustion** of fossil fuels. These processes can be summarised like this:

Carbon compounds + Oxygen → Carbon dioxide + Water

Some of the factors involved in the water cycle are shown below.

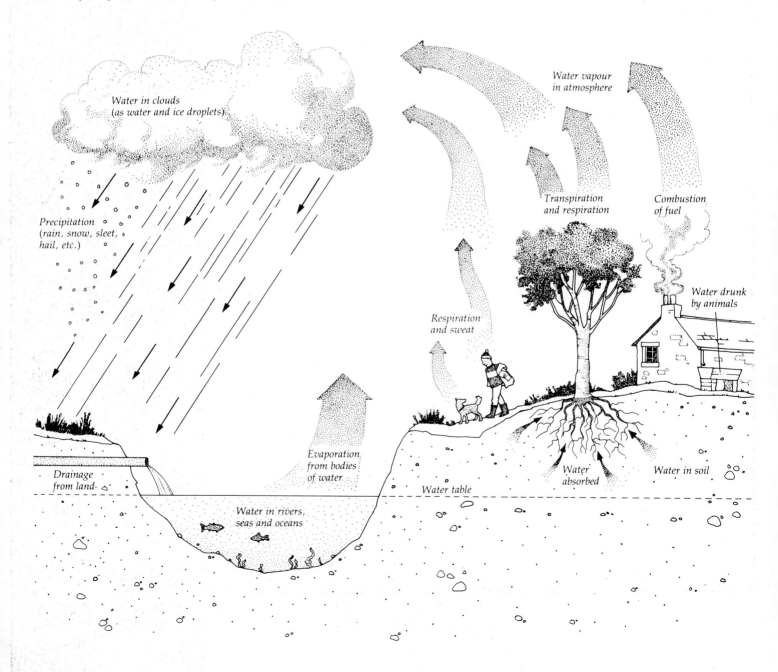

Water in clouds (as water and ice droplets)

Precipitation (rain, snow, sleet, hail, etc.)

Water vapour in atmosphere

Transpiration and respiration

Combustion of fuel

Water drunk by animals

Respiration and sweat

Drainage from land

Evaporation from bodies of water

Water table

Water in rivers, seas and oceans

Water absorbed

Water in soil

SECTION 13

Transport

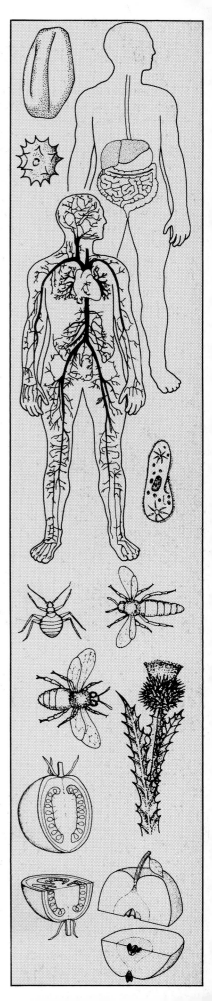

Transport systems

Every cell in an organism must be supplied with oxygen, food, and other necessary substances. Carbon dioxide and other waste, along with any products made by the cell, must be carried away from it. The ways in which an organism moves such things around make up its **transport system**.

The type of transport system used by an organism depends on how big the organism is. A large organism will need a more complicated transport system than a small one. Some examples of transport systems are shown below.

TRANSPORT BY DIFFUSION

Diffusion (see pages 116–7) takes place when a dissolved substance is in higher concentration in one part of a solution than in another. The natural movement of the dissolved particles gradually spreads them out until their concentration is the same all over. We say that the substance has diffused down a **concentration gradient**. For small organisms, or for short distances in larger organisms, transport by diffusion may be all that is needed.

PLANARIAN: A FLATWORM

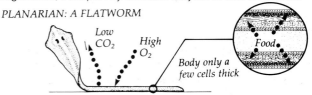

AMOEBA: A PROTOZOAN

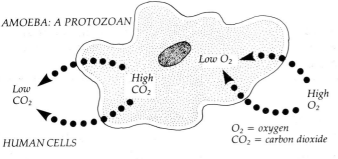

O_2 = oxygen
CO_2 = carbon dioxide

HUMAN CELLS

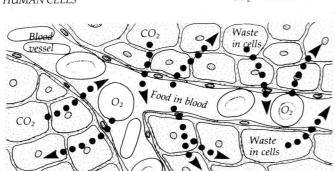

Osmosis (see pages 116–7) is a special case of diffusion. The semi-permeable membrane of cells will let water diffuse through them but may hold back other substances. This can cause a water concentration gradient which results in water diffusing across the membrane. Plant cells use osmosis to absorb water and to transport it short distances.

PLANT ROOT HAIR

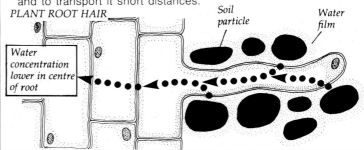

ACTIVE TRANSPORT

This occurs when a substance is moved against a concentration gradient. This means that it is moved from an area where its concentration is low to one where its concentration is high. Unlike diffusion, the cell must use up energy to carry out active transport.

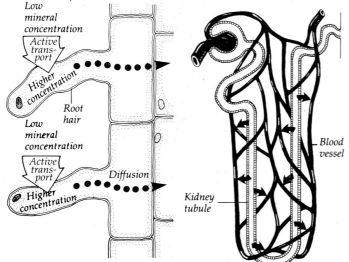

Active transport is used by plant root hairs to absorb minerals from the soil. Kidney tubules also use active transport to move substances like glucose back into the blood.

CYTOPLASMIC STREAMING

Inside cells, materials can diffuse throughout the cytoplasm. In some cells, however, the cytoplasm itself is seen to be moving. This is called cytoplasmic streaming, or **cyclosis**. Cytoplasmic streaming speeds up the distribution of substances around the cell.

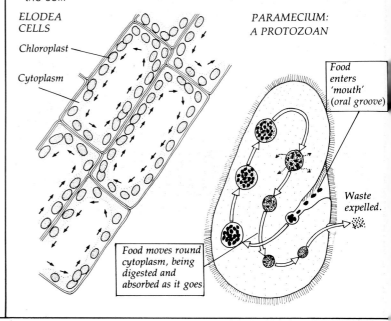

As a method of transport, **diffusion** is suitable only over short distances. When we look at larger organisms, we find that their transport systems do not rely on diffusion alone. While small, simple plants, such as algae and liverworts, can depend on diffusion for transport, the larger, more advanced plants, such as the angiosperms, need something more. They have special **transport tissues** to cover the greater distances involved. These tissues form the **veins** which we can see running through a leaf and, indeed, throughout the whole plant. More details of the transport systems of higher plants are given on pages 134 and 135.

O₂ — Diffusion — CO₂ — Common liverwort — No veins — Thallus

Veins carry food out of leaves and water into them.

Blood systems

Larger animals, like larger plants, cannot rely on diffusion alone for transport. Instead, they have a special transport fluid called blood to carry things around the body. The blood is circulated around the body by a pump called the heart. There are two basic kinds of blood systems – **open blood systems** and **closed blood systems**.

OPEN BLOOD SYSTEMS are used by the arthropods, the phylum which includes the insects and the crustaceans. In an open blood system the blood is not kept inside tubes. Instead, it fills the whole of the body space, where it swirls round the various organs. The heart sucks the blood in at one end and squirts it out of the other, so keeping it circulating around.

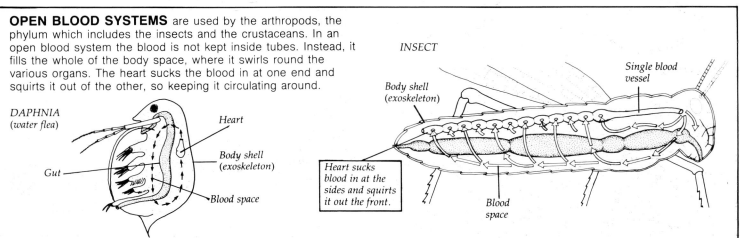

DAPHNIA (water flea) — Heart — Body shell (exoskeleton) — Blood space — Gut

INSECT — Single blood vessel — Body shell (exoskeleton) — Heart sucks blood in at the sides and squirts it out the front. — Blood space

CLOSED BLOOD SYSTEMS are found in most animals, including the vertebrates like ourselves. In a closed blood system, the blood is kept sealed inside tubes called blood vessels. The blood vessels are spread throughout the body so that no cell is ever very far away from one. The heart pumps the blood round and round the system and materials diffuse in and out of the blood vessels to serve the surrounding cells as the blood passes by.

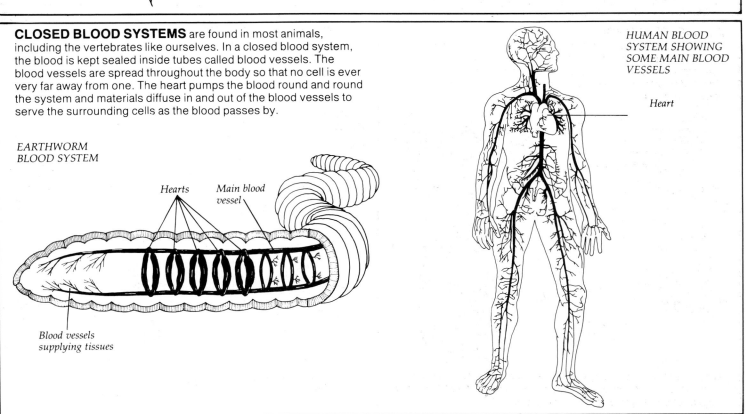

EARTHWORM BLOOD SYSTEM — Hearts — Main blood vessel — Blood vessels supplying tissues

HUMAN BLOOD SYSTEM SHOWING SOME MAIN BLOOD VESSELS — Heart

The human circulation

Like all mammals, human beings have a **closed blood system**. Since the blood in the system goes round and round, we talk of the blood circulation or the **circulatory system**. It is the heart which drives the circulation. Blood leaving the heart travels through vessels called **arteries**. Blood returning to the heart goes through vessels called **veins**. Very tiny blood vessels called **capillaries** connect the arteries to the veins. It is the capillaries which actually supply the body's cells with everything they need.

In fact, the blood travels round not one circuit, but two. When it first leaves the heart, it goes to the lungs to pick up oxygen. The **oxygenated** (oxygen-rich) blood then goes back to the heart which pumps it out to the rest of the body. The cells remove oxygen, etc., and the **deoxygenated** (oxygen-poor) blood returns to the heart to be sent out once more to the lungs. This is called a **double circulation**.

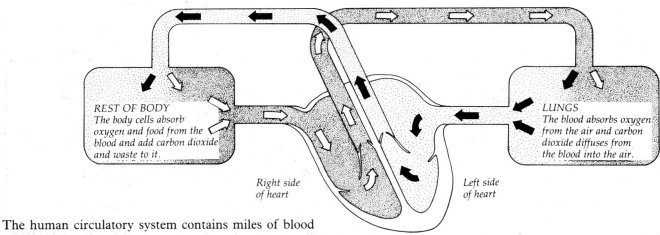

REST OF BODY
The body cells absorb oxygen and food from the blood and add carbon dioxide and waste to it.

Right side of heart

Left side of heart

LUNGS
The blood absorbs oxygen from the air and carbon dioxide diffuses from the blood into the air.

The human circulatory system contains miles of blood vessels which branch again and again, spreading to all parts of the body so that every cell can be taken care of. The diagram below shows a few of the main blood vessels with the organs they serve.

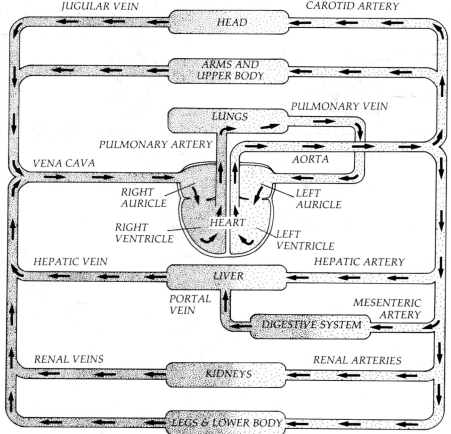

JUGULAR VEIN

CAROTID ARTERY

HEAD

ARMS AND UPPER BODY

PULMONARY VEIN

LUNGS

PULMONARY ARTERY

VENA CAVA

AORTA

RIGHT AURICLE

LEFT AURICLE

RIGHT VENTRICLE

HEART

LEFT VENTRICLE

HEPATIC VEIN

HEPATIC ARTERY

LIVER

PORTAL VEIN

MESENTERIC ARTERY

DIGESTIVE SYSTEM

RENAL VEINS

RENAL ARTERIES

KIDNEYS

Oxygenated blood

Deoxygenated blood

LEGS & LOWER BODY

Blood vessels

The tubes which carry the blood in a closed blood circulation are called blood vessels. There are three main types of blood vessel. These are called **arteries**, **capillaries** and **veins**.

ARTERIES carry blood away from the heart. They have thick walls made mainly of elastic fibres and muscle. When the heart beats and sends a wave of blood along an artery, the elastic fibre allows it to stretch. It is this bulging of the artery which we can feel when we take our pulse.

The smallest arteries, called **arterioles**, have less elastic fibre and more muscle in their walls. This can contract to narrow the vessel and reduce blood flow. This helps the body to control heat loss or to reduce blood loss in injury.

The blood in arteries is under very high pressure. This

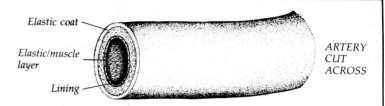

pressure forces the blood through the many branches so that it can reach all the tissues of the body.

CAPILLARIES are the tiniest blood vessels, visible only through a microscope. Their walls are very thin – just one cell thick. As blood flows through a capillary, liquid leaks through the walls to bathe the surrounding cells. The cells take what they need from this liquid, called **tissue fluid**, and put their waste into it. Part of the fluid then drains back into the capillary to be returned to the heart.

Capillaries are so narrow that blood cells can barely squeeze along them. This slows down the blood and helps the exchange of materials between it and the tissues. It also reduces the blood pressure. Blood leaving a capillary has much less energy than blood entering one.

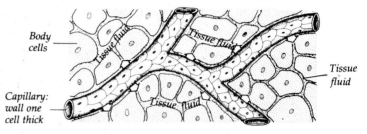

Unlike other blood cells, white blood cells can squeeze out of capillaries. They do this to find and kill germs.

VEINS carry blood back to the heart. Blood from the capillaries drains into small veins called **venules**, which empty it into larger veins. The pressure of this blood is very low – about 10% of what it was. So, to make it easier for the blood to get through, veins are bigger than arteries and have thinner walls and a larger bore. They also have valves. If the blood tries to flow backwards, the valves stop it. The return of the blood to the heart is helped by movements of the body muscles. These squeeze it along the veins, while the valves make sure that it gets squeezed in the right direction.

VALVES IN A VEIN

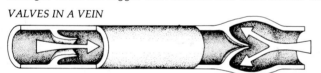

Blood flowing in right direction
Valve open

Blood flowing backwards
Valve closed

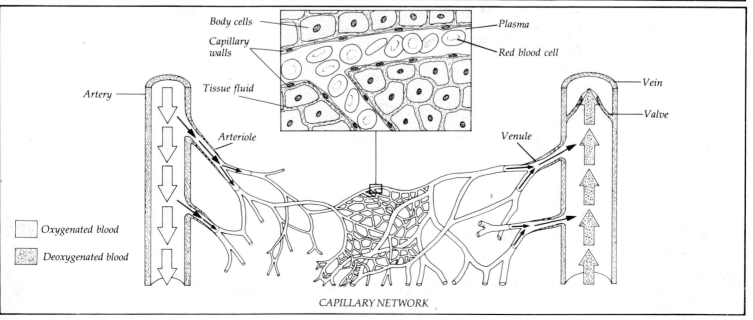

CAPILLARY NETWORK

The heart

The heart's job is to pump blood round the body. It is a hollow organ with walls made of a special kind of muscle called **cardiac muscle** (*cardiac*: heart). Unlike other muscles, cardiac muscle can contract many times each day

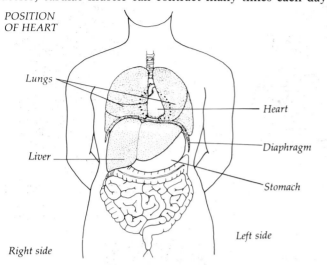

POSITION OF HEART

Lungs

Heart

Diaphragm

Liver

Stomach

Right side

Left side

throughout our lives without getting tired. The heart, along with the lungs, is found inside the **thorax** (chest) just above the **diaphragm**, with its tip pointing to the left-hand side.

Since the human blood system is a **double circulation**, the heart is really two pumps joined together. The right side of the heart collects the **deoxygenated** (oxygen-poor) blood from the **veins** and pumps it to the lungs for oxygen. By the time the blood has forced its way through the **capillaries** in the lungs (see page 109), it has lost most of its

energy. The now **oxygenated** (oxygen-rich) blood is returned to the left side of the heart which pumps it round the rest of the body.

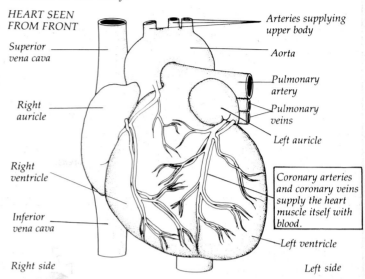

HEART SEEN FROM FRONT

Superior vena cava

Arteries supplying upper body

Aorta

Right auricle

Pulmonary artery

Pulmonary veins

Left auricle

Right ventricle

Inferior vena cava

Coronary arteries and coronary veins supply the heart muscle itself with blood.

Left ventricle

Right side

Left side

Each side of the heart is divided into two chambers. The upper chambers, called **auricles**, collect blood into the heart and send it into the lower chambers, called **ventricles**. The ventricles then send it out of the heart. The different compartments of the heart are separated from each other by **valves**. The valves make sure that the blood flows in the right direction. A diagram of a heart cut open is shown below.

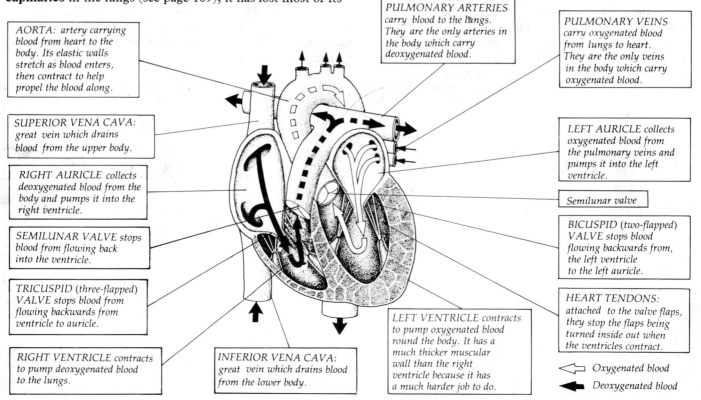

AORTA: artery carrying blood from heart to the body. Its elastic walls stretch as blood enters, then contract to help propel the blood along.

SUPERIOR VENA CAVA: great vein which drains blood from the upper body.

RIGHT AURICLE collects deoxygenated blood from the body and pumps it into the right ventricle.

SEMILUNAR VALVE stops blood from flowing back into the ventricle.

TRICUSPID (three-flapped) VALVE stops blood from flowing backwards from ventricle to auricle.

RIGHT VENTRICLE contracts to pump deoxygenated blood to the lungs.

INFERIOR VENA CAVA: great vein which drains blood from the lower body.

PULMONARY ARTERIES carry blood to the lungs. They are the only arteries in the body which carry deoxygenated blood.

PULMONARY VEINS carry oxygenated blood from lungs to heart. They are the only veins in the body which carry oxygenated blood.

LEFT AURICLE collects oxygenated blood from the pulmonary veins and pumps it into the left ventricle.

Semilunar valve

BICUSPID (two-flapped) VALVE stops blood flowing backwards from, the left ventricle to the left auricle.

HEART TENDONS: attached to the valve flaps, they stop the flaps being turned inside out when the ventricles contract.

LEFT VENTRICLE contracts to pump oxygenated blood round the body. It has a much thicker muscular wall than the right ventricle because it has a much harder job to do.

⇦ Oxygenated blood

⬅ Deoxygenated blood

The cardiac muscle of which the heart is made contracts then relaxes, on average, about 75 times per minute. Each contraction is called a heartbeat. When the ventricles contract, the heart gets smaller and blood is forced out.

When they relax, the heart gets bigger and more blood is drawn in. The diagrams below show the path taken by one batch of blood as it makes its way through the heart.

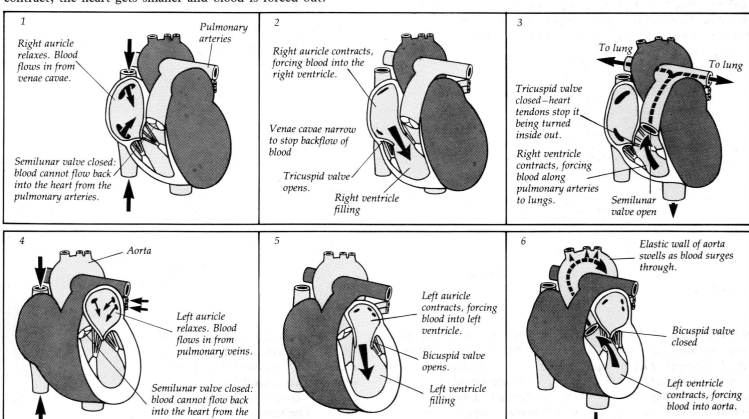

1
Right auricle relaxes. Blood flows in from venae cavae.

Pulmonary arteries

Semilunar valve closed: blood cannot flow back into the heart from the pulmonary arteries.

2
Right auricle contracts, forcing blood into the right ventricle.

Venae cavae narrow to stop backflow of blood

Tricuspid valve opens.

Right ventricle filling

3
Tricuspid valve closed – heart tendons stop it being turned inside out.

Right ventricle contracts, forcing blood along pulmonary arteries to lungs.

To lung

To lung

Semilunar valve open

4
Aorta

Left auricle relaxes. Blood flows in from pulmonary veins.

Semilunar valve closed: blood cannot flow back into the heart from the aorta.

5
Left auricle contracts, forcing blood into left ventricle.

Bicuspid valve opens.

Left ventricle filling

6
Elastic wall of aorta swells as blood surges through.

Bicuspid valve closed

Left ventricle contracts, forcing blood into aorta.

Each batch of blood is actually pumped twice by the heart. The right side pumps it to the lungs and the left side pumps it round the rest of the body. Thus, the right and left sides of the heart are two separate pumps. The wall between them makes sure that the deoxygenated blood in the right side does not get mixed with the oxygenated blood in the left side. Fortunately, however, both sides work in harmony. The two auricles contract at the same time, the two ventricles contract at the same time and the various valves operate together. Thus, the heart works smoothly as a single unit.

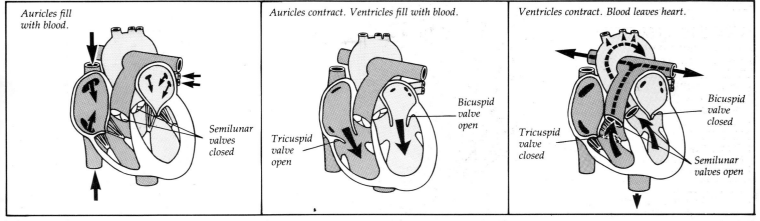

Auricles fill with blood.

Semilunar valves closed

Auricles contract. Ventricles fill with blood.

Tricuspid valve open

Bicuspid valve open

Ventricles contract. Blood leaves heart.

Tricuspid valve closed

Bicuspid valve closed

Semilunar valves open

A number of things can affect the rate at which the heart beats. Exercise, for example, can speed up the heart to 150 or more beats per minute. This is necessary to supply more blood, and the oxygen it carries, to the working muscles.

Physical fitness is also important. A person who is physically fit will have a slower heart rate and exercise will affect it less. After exercise, the heart will return to normal much more quickly than it would in an unfit person.

Excitement, pain and high body temperature are some of the other things which increase the heart rate. During sleep the heart rate slows down.

Blood and lymph

Blood

Blood is the **transport fluid** used by **multicellular** (many-celled) animals. Its job is to carry food and oxygen to all the cells of the body, to carry waste and carbon dioxide away from them, and to take useful substances from one cell to another.

The make-up of blood varies from species to species. In humans, blood consists mainly of a liquid called **plasma**. Floating around in this plasma are various cells. These are called **red blood cells, white blood cells** and **platelets**.

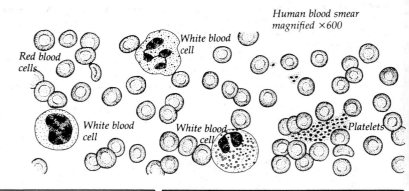

Human blood smear magnified ×600

Red blood cells

White blood cell

White blood cell

White blood cell

Platelets

PLASMA makes up about 55% of the blood. It is a strawcoloured liquid consisting mainly of water. The rest of the plasma is made up of:

Proteins
These include the plasma proteins which are made by the liver. Plasma proteins help thicken the blood. They carry things like fats and hormones around and help produce antibodies to fight disease. One, called **fibrinogen**, is essential for clotting the blood in injury. Other proteins found in blood include chemical messengers called **hormones** (see pages 196–7), **antibodies** and various **enzymes**.

Food, waste and minerals
Among the nutrients dissolved in the plasma are glucose and amino acids. Waste products from the body cells include **urea** (see pages 118–9). The minerals include sodium, calcium and iodine.

Gases
Oxygen does dissolve a little in the plasma, but most is actually carried by the red blood cells as **oxyhaemoglobin**. Carbon dioxide, though, dissolves easily in the plasma to form bicarbonate.

Platelets
These are tiny packets of **cytoplasm** about three microns across. Their job is to reduce bleeding when we are injured. They do this in two ways. Firstly, they gather round any break in a blood vessel and help plug the leak. Secondly, along with other factors like vitamin K and calcium, they are important for normal blood-clotting. In this process, the plasma protein, fibrinogen, is changed into threads of **fibrin** which bind blood cells together to form a clot, so sealing off the wound. Platelets are made in the bone marrow.

Red blood cells or corpuscles, also called **erythrocytes**, make up 45% of the blood. Each drop of blood contains about 300 million red blood cells. Their job is to pick up oxygen in the lungs and take it to all the cells of the body. To do this, they contain a special protein called haemoglobin which attracts oxygen. As the red blood cells go through the lungs, oxygen joins with haemoglobin to make oxyhaemoglobin. Later, as the cells squeeze through the capillaries, the oxygen separates from the haemoglobin and diffuses out to supply the surrounding cells. Haemoglobin allows the blood to carry ten times as much oxygen as it could otherwise. To make haemoglobin, the body must have iron. A lack of iron in the diet can lead to a shortage of red blood cells – an illness called **anaemia**.

Since the job of the red blood cells is to carry oxygen, people who live at high altitudes where the air is thin have more red cells than usual in their blood. Anyone who moves to such a place soon shows an increase in their number of red cells.

Red blood cells, which have no nucleus, are made in the bone marrow.

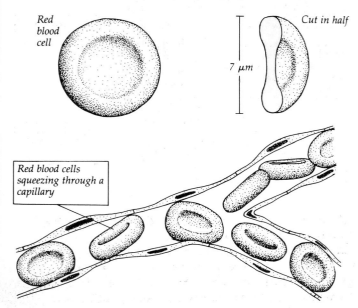

Red blood cell

Cut in half

7 μm

Red blood cells squeezing through a capillary

If a pint of blood is allowed to stand, the cells gradually settle to the bottom, leaving the clear plasma at the top.

Plasma almost clear

Cells, mainly red blood cells. Their colour is due to the haemoglobin they contain.

White blood cells (or corpuscles) are also called **leucocytes**. A drop of blood contains several million of them. Since their job is to fight bacteria, their number increases in sickness and injury. White blood cells have large nuclei and come in various forms. Most of them, called **polymorphs**, have grainy cytoplasm and a nucleus divided into lobes. They kill germs by **phagocytosis** (see below). They can even squeeze their way out of a blood capillary to attack the germs in a cut. The white pus in boils, etc, is a mixture of these cells and the germs they have killed. Other white blood cells, called **lymphocytes**, make antibodies. Antibodies cause germs to clump together and burst.

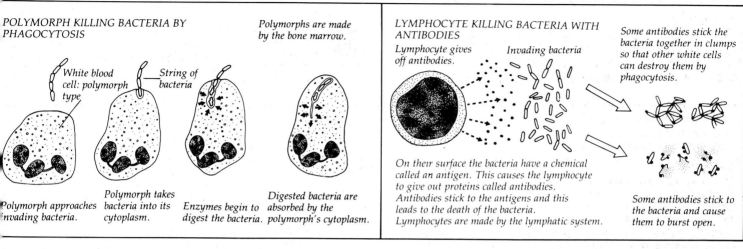

POLYMORPH KILLING BACTERIA BY PHAGOCYTOSIS

Polymorphs are made by the bone marrow.

White blood cell: polymorph type

String of bacteria

Polymorph approaches invading bacteria.

Polymorph takes bacteria into its cytoplasm.

Enzymes begin to digest the bacteria.

Digested bacteria are absorbed by the polymorph's cytoplasm.

LYMPHOCYTE KILLING BACTERIA WITH ANTIBODIES

Lymphocyte gives off antibodies.

Invading bacteria

Some antibodies stick the bacteria together in clumps so that other white cells can destroy them by phagocytosis.

On their surface the bacteria have a chemical called an antigen. This causes the lymphocyte to give out proteins called antibodies. Antibodies stick to the antigens and this leads to the death of the bacteria. Lymphocytes are made by the lymphatic system.

Some antibodies stick to the bacteria and cause them to burst open.

Lymph

Most of our cells do not come into contact with the blood. Instead, they are bathed by a liquid called **tissue fluid** which has leaked out of the capillaries. Tissue fluid is like blood without the cells and larger proteins. It forms a link between the cells and the blood. The cells take food and oxygen from the tissue fluid and put waste and carbon dioxide into it.

Some tissue fluid gets back into the blood, but most of it does not. Instead, it drains into thin-walled tubes called **lymph vessels**. It is then known as **lymph**. Most lymph is clear like tissue fluid. Lymph from the **lacteals** of the small intestine, however, is milky due to the fat it contains (see page 79).

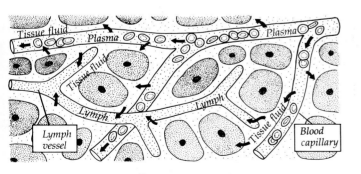

Tissue fluid · Plasma · Plasma · Tissue fluid · Lymph · Lymph · Tissue fluid

Lymph vessel

Blood capillary

lymph gets pushed in the right direction, the vessels have a large number of valves, similar to those in veins.

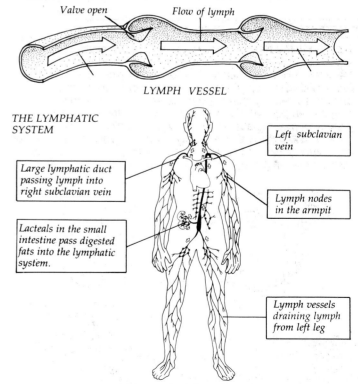

Valve open · Flow of lymph

LYMPH VESSEL

THE LYMPHATIC SYSTEM

Left subclavian vein

Large lymphatic duct passing lymph into right subclavian vein

Lymph nodes in the armpit

Lacteals in the small intestine pass digested fats into the lymphatic system.

Lymph vessels draining lymph from left leg

The small lymph vessels connect up with a whole network of larger vessels which drains tissue fluid from the entire body. This is called the **lymphatic system**. The system eventually ends in two large **lymphatic ducts** which empty the lymph into the two **subclavian veins** (*sub*: under; *clav*: collar bone) near the heart. As we move, the thin-walled lymph vessels are squeezed by surrounding muscles and the lymph is pushed towards these veins. To make sure the

All along the lymph vessels are swellings called **lymph glands** or **lymph nodes**. These are part of the body's defence system. As lymph flows through them, harmful substances or bacteria are 'eaten' by **phagocytes**. Lymph glands also make the white blood cells called **lymphocytes**. Lymphocytes combat disease by making **antibodies**. If we have an infection, lymph glands, for example in the throat, can become quite swollen and painful.

Transport in plants

The roots of a plant absorb water and minerals from the soil. These must then be carried upwards to all parts of the plant. This water-carrying is done by a tissue called **xylem** (see page 136). Food, mainly sugar, is made by **photosynthesis** in the leaves. This must then be transported out of the leaves to supply other parts of the plant. This carrying of sugars from one part of the plant to another – a process called **translocation** – is done by a tissue called **phloem** (see page 136). Xylem and phloem are found together in the **vascular bundles**, or veins, which run throughout the plant. No cell in a plant is very far away from its nearest xylem and phloem. The arrangement of the vascular tissue in the root, leaf, and stem of a **dicotyledon plant** (see page 7) is shown below.

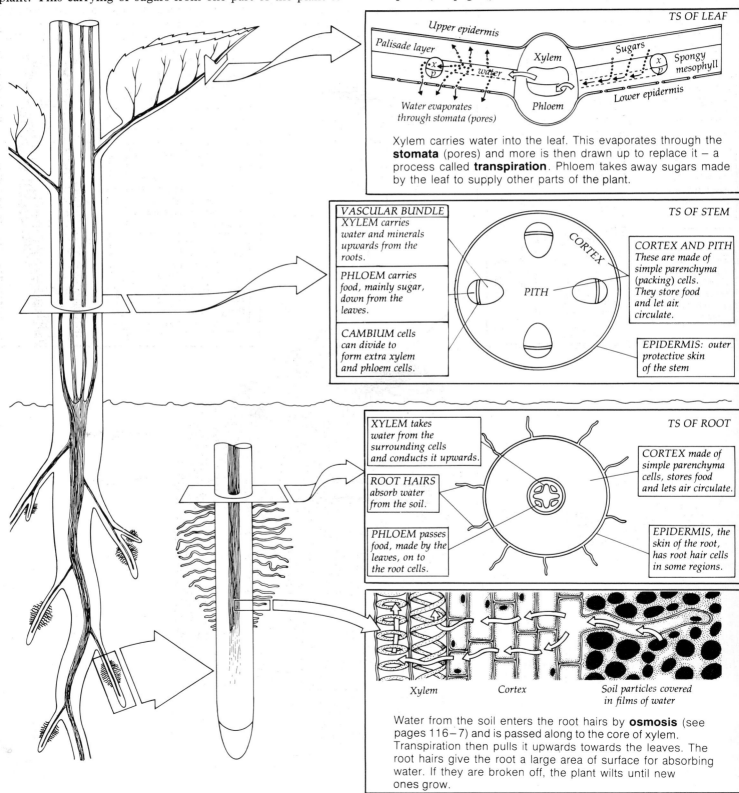

TS OF LEAF

Upper epidermis

Palisade layer

Xylem

Sugars

Spongy mesophyll

water

Water evaporates through stomata (pores)

Phloem

Lower epidermis

Xylem carries water into the leaf. This evaporates through the **stomata** (pores) and more is then drawn up to replace it – a process called **transpiration**. Phloem takes away sugars made by the leaf to supply other parts of the plant.

TS OF STEM

VASCULAR BUNDLE
XYLEM carries water and minerals upwards from the roots.

PHLOEM carries food, mainly sugar, down from the leaves.

CAMBIUM cells can divide to form extra xylem and phloem cells.

CORTEX

PITH

CORTEX AND PITH These are made of simple parenchyma (packing) cells. They store food and let air circulate.

EPIDERMIS: outer protective skin of the stem

TS OF ROOT

XYLEM takes water from the surrounding cells and conducts it upwards.

ROOT HAIRS absorb water from the soil.

PHLOEM passes food, made by the leaves, on to the root cells.

CORTEX made of simple parenchyma cells, stores food and lets air circulate.

EPIDERMIS, the skin of the root, has root hair cells in some regions.

Xylem   Cortex   *Soil particles covered in films of water*

Water from the soil enters the root hairs by **osmosis** (see pages 116–7) and is passed along to the core of xylem. Transpiration then pulls it upwards towards the leaves. The root hairs give the root a large area of surface for absorbing water. If they are broken off, the plant wilts until new ones grow.

If we look at the end of a cut stem, we can easily see the position of the vascular bundles. For a proper look at the cells which make them up, however, we must use a microscope. Even then, the appearance of the cells will depend on how we section (slice) the stem for viewing. We could cut a thin slice across the stem to get a **transverse** section (TS), or we could get quite a different picture by slicing the stem along its length – a **longitudinal section** (LS). The diagrams below illustrate, in TS and LS, the structure of the cells in a vascular bundle and some of the tissues around it.

XYLEM VESSELS are the water-carrying 'pipes' of the plant. They are formed from the empty remains of dead cells. The walls of these cells are coated with a woody substance called **lignin**. This helps to support the stem.

Cell contents die, leaving an empty tube.

The end walls of the cells wither away so that water can pass from one cell to another.

The cell walls are toughened with lignin which is laid down in various patterns.

CAMBIUM consists of cells which can divide to produce more cells. In plants, such tissues are called **meristems**. Cambium forms extra xylem and phloem cells, making the stem both thicker and stronger.

PHLOEM, unlike xylem, is made up of living cells. These are called **sieve tubes** and **companion cells**. It is the sieve tubes which actually transport the sugars, though they seem to need the help of the companion cells.

SIEVE PLATE: the end wall of the sieve tube, so called because it has holes in it to let sugars pass from one cell to the next.

SIEVE TUBE: made of a long line of cells joined end to end. Sieve tubes carry the sugar. The living cells which form them have thin cytoplasm and no nuclei.

COMPANION CELLS have thick cytoplasm and large nuclei. They do not carry sugar, but are thought to help the sieve tubes to do so.

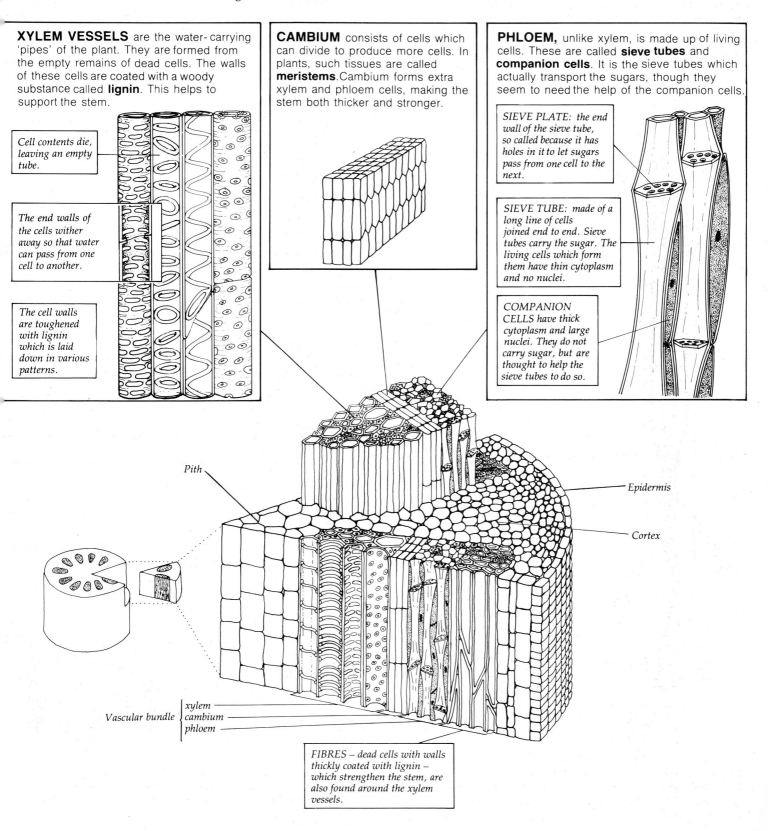

Pith

Epidermis

Cortex

Vascular bundle { xylem — cambium — phloem

FIBRES – dead cells with walls thickly coated with lignin – which strengthen the stem, are also found around the xylem vessels.

Woody stems

When it first begins to grow, the stem of a woody plant is not unlike that of a **herbaceous** (non-woody) plant. Its development goes much further, however, and in time it becomes quite different, as these diagrams show.

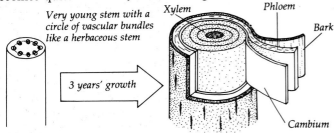

The cylinder of **xylem** in the centre of the stem makes it very strong. It is this which enables woody plants, such as trees, to grow, often to great heights. Xylem, in fact, is wood. It consists mainly of **xylem vessels** and fibres. While these cells are maturing, their walls become coated with a hard substance called **lignin**. We say that these cells become **lignified**. Finally, the cells die, leaving behind their thick, lignified walls. Wood is made of millions of these dead, lignified cells.

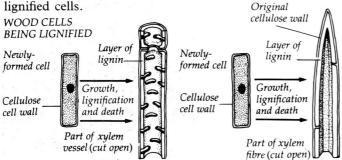

As a tree grows taller and heavier, more wood is needed to support it. It is the job of the **cambium** to provide this new wood. Each spring it starts dividing to form more cells. Most of these are used to form another ring of wood (xylem), wrapped around the previous year's. Since one ring of wood is added each year, these rings are known as **annual rings**. By counting the annual rings in a log, we can tell its age. Also, in a good summer, a thicker ring is formed. So, by the width of an annual ring, we can guess what the weather was like when the ring was formed, perhaps hundreds of years before.

During the growing season, the cambium also produces new **phloem**, though in much smaller amounts. The phloem becomes confined to a narrow band towards the outside of the stem. Thus, the woody stem comes to consist of a dead core of xylem (wood) which transports water upwards from the roots, and around this a living layer of phloem cells which carry food downwards from the leaves. Perhaps we could represent it like this:

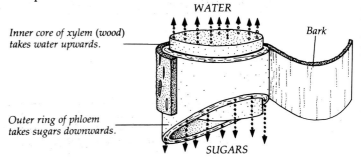

Another feature of woody plants is the tough, protective bark which quickly replaces the original epidermis. Air can enter the stem only through tiny breaks in the bark called **lenticels**. Each year, as the stem (or trunk) gets thicker, its coat of bark becomes too small for it. This causes the bark to split and crack. To prevent damage or disease, new bark is made, underneath the old, by a layer of tissue called **cork cambium**. When bark is stripped from a woody stem, phloem is usually removed along with it. To see the effect this can have on a plant, we can cut a complete ring of bark from a woody stem, leaving just the core of xylem in the middle.

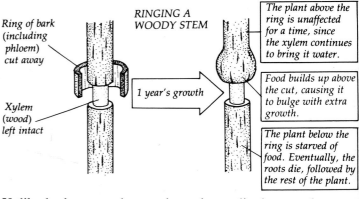

Unlike herbaceous plants, whose shoots die down each year, the woody plants can continue growing for many years. The diagram below shows how the trunk of a tree will develop after a number of years of growth.

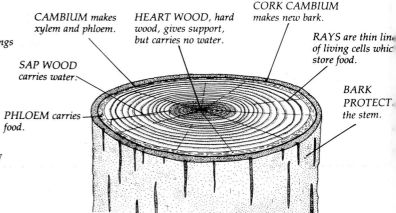

SECTION 14

Size, Support and Movement

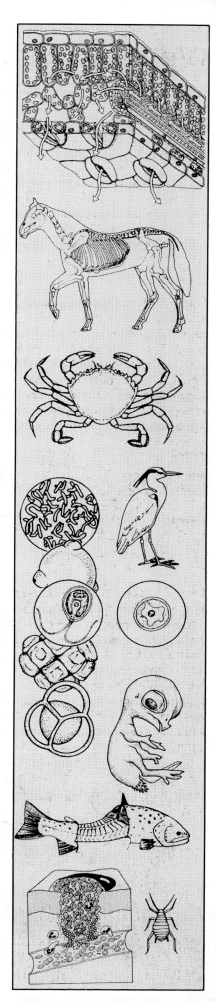

Support in vertebrates

One characteristic which is very typical of animals is movement (see page 142). An animal must be able to move in order to survive. Movement allows an animal to find food and to escape from danger. However, before movement is possible, the animal must be able to support and carry the weight of its body. In vertebrates, the structures most involved in support and movement are the bones of the limbs. Their size and shape, and the use to which they are put will determine how large and heavy the animal can grow and how well it can move.

WHALES

Whales are fully aquatic animals, that is, they spend all of their lives in water. Any object, including an animal, which is immersed in water receives some lift from the water. This is called **buoyancy**. Thus, aquatic animals find it much easier to carry their weight around than land animals do. Therefore, they can grow much larger. In fact, whales are the largest animals on Earth. Since the whale's skeleton and limbs are not needed to support its body, they are very small for its size. Its front limbs are used, not as supports, but as paddles for swimming, while its rear limbs have disappeared completely.

Although a whale's great bulk is no problem to it when underwater, things are different on land. A beached whale, if it is stranded long enough, may be crushed to death by the weight of its own body.

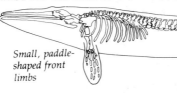

Fairly weak, undeveloped skeleton

Small, paddle-shaped front limbs

Remains of pelvic girdle with no rear limbs attached

SEALS

A seal's limbs are at their best when moving through water. With the rear limbs for a tail and using the front ones as paddles, a seal can swim as fast as 10 km/h. However, seals are not totally aquatic. They must come on land to breed. Then, the front limbs, normally kept to the sides for swimming, are brought under the body to lift it off the ground. The tail can also be used. The body, though, is not well-supported and the seal's movements on land are slow and awkward compared to its easy movement in water.

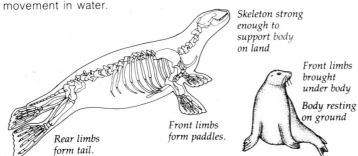

Skeleton strong enough to support body on land

Front limbs brought under body

Body resting on ground

Rear limbs form tail.

Front limbs form paddles.

REPTILES

Most reptiles' legs stick out from the sides of the body. To support the body clear of the ground, the legs must be kept bent at the knee. This position, similar to doing 'push-ups', is very tiring and it requires strong leg muscles. Nonetheless, using these muscles, some lizards can move quite fast, but only over short distances. Larger, heavier reptiles such as the crocodile sometimes walk like this, but, usually, they find it easier to rest the body on the ground and crawl about.

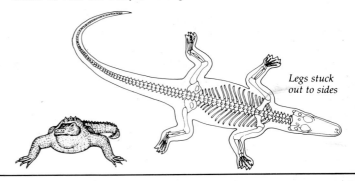

Legs stuck out to sides

FOUR-LEGGED MAMMALS

The most mobile land animals of all are the mammals. In most four-legged mammals, the leg bones are held directly underneath the body. In this position, they act as props or struts and they, rather than the leg muscles, take most of the strain of the body's weight. For this reason, the animal is able to support the body clear of the ground for long periods of time without tiring. This allows such animals to move about easily and, in many cases, very rapidly. To ease the strain on the leg muscles even more, the limbs are rotated to let the feet point to the front.

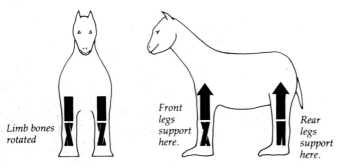

Limb bones rotated

Front legs support here.

Rear legs support here.

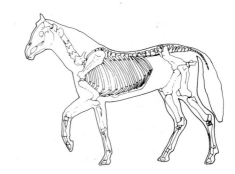

The skeleton

The bodies of all vertebrates are built on a rigid framework called a skeleton. This skeleton gives them their shape, protects vital organs, and along with muscles allows them to move. In land vertebrates the skeleton supports the body off the ground. Without it, vertebrates could not grow to any great size.

Vertebrate bones and skeletons come in all shapes and sizes, but they all have the same basic pattern as the human skeleton.

In most vertebrates, the skeleton is made of bone and cartilage (gristle). There are some, however, like sharks and dogfish, whose skeleton is made entirely of cartilage. There are basically three types of bones in the skeleton:

flat bones – these help to protect vital organs, for example skull bones shield the brain;

long bones – often act as levers, for example long bones like the **femur** (thigh bone) and the **humerus** (arm bone) are concerned mainly with movement;

short bones, sometimes called **irregular bones** – give strength, for example the **carpals** in the wrist.

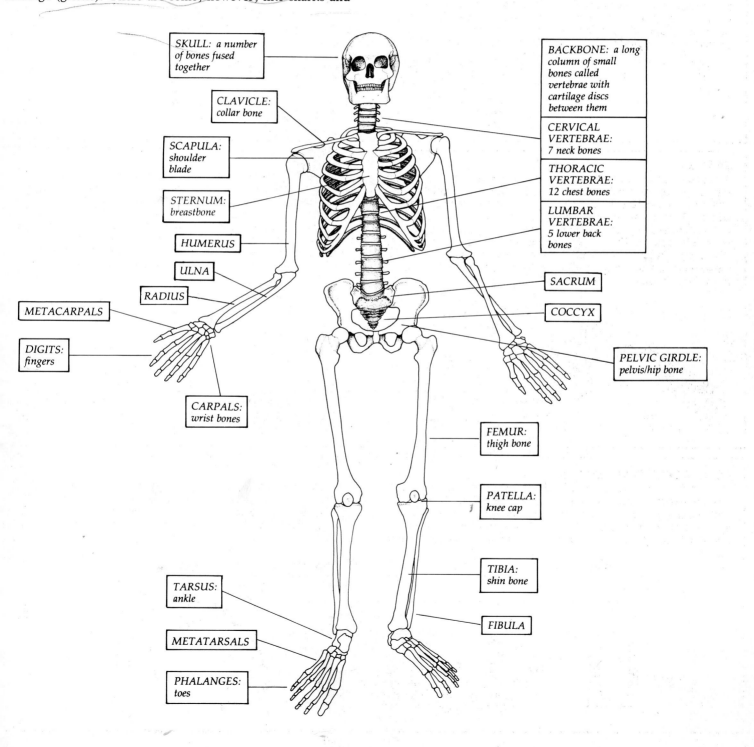

SKULL: a number of bones fused together

CLAVICLE: collar bone

SCAPULA: shoulder blade

STERNUM: breastbone

HUMERUS

ULNA

RADIUS

METACARPALS

DIGITS: fingers

CARPALS: wrist bones

BACKBONE: a long column of small bones called vertebrae with cartilage discs between them

CERVICAL VERTEBRAE: 7 neck bones

THORACIC VERTEBRAE: 12 chest bones

LUMBAR VERTEBRAE: 5 lower back bones

SACRUM

COCCYX

PELVIC GIRDLE: pelvis/hip bone

FEMUR: thigh bone

PATELLA: knee cap

TIBIA: shin bone

FIBULA

TARSUS: ankle

METATARSALS

PHALANGES: toes

Bone

Although bone is a very hard material, it is a living tissue consisting of **bone cells** and **protein fibres** buried in a hard, inorganic substance called **calcium phosphate**. This combination makes bone hard, but also slightly flexible. Bone tissue is arranged in layers called **lamellae** (sing: *lamella*). Each lamella is formed from a single sheet of calcium phosphate with cavities in it called **lacunae** (sing: *lacuna*). The bone cells are found inside these lacunae. They are connected to each other by strands of **cytoplasm** which run through tiny channels called **canaliculi**. Bone tissue is found in two forms – **compact bone** and **spongy bone**.

COMPACT BONE is found in those parts of a bone which are under the most strain. The bone lamellae (layers) are tightly packed round tubes called **Haversian canals**. Through these canals run blood vessels which feed the bone.

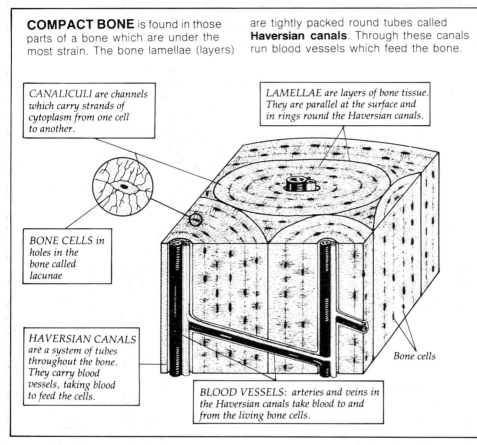

CANALICULI *are channels which carry strands of cytoplasm from one cell to another.*

LAMELLAE *are layers of bone tissue. They are parallel at the surface and in rings round the Haversian canals.*

BONE CELLS *in holes in the bone called lacunae*

HAVERSIAN CANALS *are a system of tubes throughout the bone. They carry blood vessels, taking blood to feed the cells.*

BLOOD VESSELS: *arteries and veins in the Haversian canals take blood to and from the living bone cells.*

Bone cells

SPONGY BONE tissue is similar to compact. However, the lamellae of bone are not tightly packed. Instead, they are formed into a network of plates and spars with **bone marrow** in between. The spars act like girders, able to support the bone yet weighing very little.

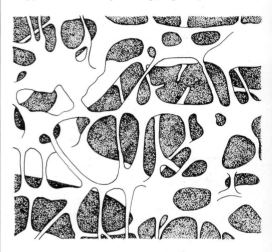

The bone marrow carries the blood supply for the bone. In the flat and long bones it also makes new blood cells, especially red blood cells.

All bones are made partly from compact bone and partly from spongy bone. Compact bone is very strong and is used where the bone is under most stress, but it is also very heavy and so could not be used for the whole bone. These parts of a bone which take less strain are made of spongy bone. Thus the bone can have enough strength, without too much weight. Long bones are hollow for the same reason, since they take a lot of strain round the outside, but very little in the middle.

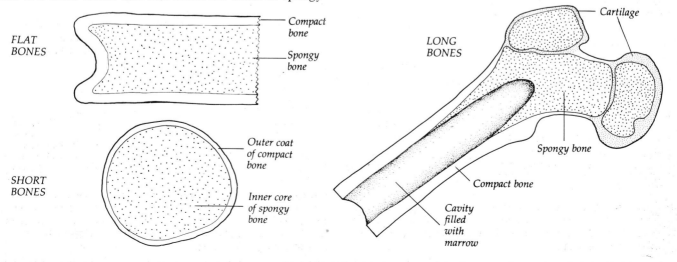

FLAT BONES

Compact bone

Spongy bone

SHORT BONES

Outer coat of compact bone

Inner core of spongy bone

LONG BONES

Cartilage

Spongy bone

Compact bone

Cavity filled with marrow

Joints

The place where two bones meet is called a joint. Some joints are fixed and unable to move, some are slightly movable and some are the freely movable **synovial joints**.

FIXED JOINTS

FIXED JOINTS allow little or no movement of the bones. The zig-zig ends of the skull bones, for example, fit very closely together. This kind of very tight join is called a **suture**.

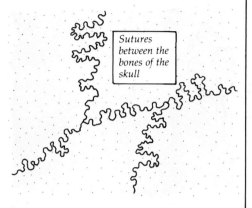

Sutures between the bones of the skull

SLIGHTLY MOVABLE JOINTS

SLIGHTLY MOVABLE JOINTS allow the bones a small degree of movement. In a slightly movable joint, the bones are separated by a pad of **cartilage** (gristle). Cartilage is a smooth tissue which is very firm and tough, yet flexible enough to allow some movement. The vertebrae with their 'discs' are examples of slightly movable joints. The bones of these joints are held together by a 'sleeve' of **ligaments**. These are strands of fibrous (stringy) tissue.

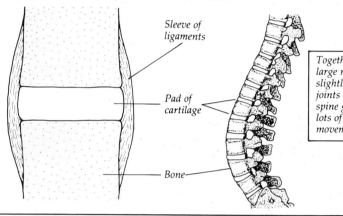

Sleeve of ligaments

Pad of cartilage

Bone

Together, the large number of slightly movable joints in the spine give it lots of movement.

SYNOVIAL JOINTS

SYNOVIAL JOINTS are designed to lubricate and cushion the bones of the joint so that they can move freely. The different types of synovial joint give different types of movement. There are ball and socket joints, hinge joints, double hinge joints, gliding joints and pivot joints.

A SYNOVIAL JOINT

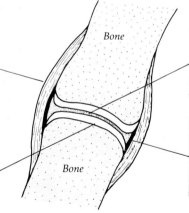

CAPSULE: a sheath of ligaments which tie the bones together. Ligaments are often thickened into bands to strengthen the joint and prevent it being dislocated.

CARTILAGE (gristle): smooth tissue which covers the ends of bones. It cushions the bones from each other as they move.

Bone

Bone

SYNOVIAL CAVITY, or joint cavity: space filled with synovial fluid, a clear, thick fluid which keeps the joint lubricated

SYNOVIAL MEMBRANE: thin layer round the synovial cavity. It makes the synovial fluid which it secretes into the cavity.

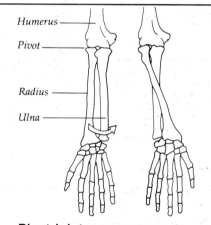

Humerus

Pivot

Radius

Ulna

Pivot joints allow one bone to rotate over another. The **radius** turns on the **humerus** and this allows the hand to turn. Also, the **atlas vertebra** which carries the skull pivots on the **axis** below and lets the head turn.

THE HIP JOINT

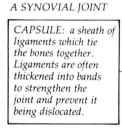

Socket on hip

Ball on femur

LIGAMENTS hold hip and femur together.

Ball and socket joints allow movement in many directions. The end of one bone is shaped like a ball which fits into a socket in the other bone. The hip and shoulder joints are ball and socket joints.

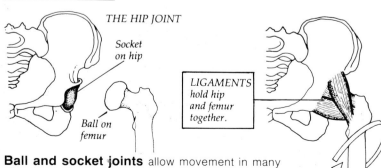

Double hinges between the knuckles

Gliding joints between carpals

Hinge joints in the fingers

Hinge joints, like the finger, knee and elbow joints, allow movement in one direction only. Double hinge joints, as in the knuckles, give movement in two planes. Gliding joints let one bone slide a little over another as in the **carpus** (wrist) and **tarsus** (ankle) bones.

Moving the joints

The joints in the skeleton are moved by muscles. Each muscle is attached to the two bones of a movable joint by means of tendons, cords of inelastic (unstretchable) tissue at each end of the muscle. To move a joint, a muscle will get shorter, or contract, and its tendons will pull on the bones.

This causes one of the two bones in the joint to move. The place where a tendon is attached to the non-moving bone is called the **origin** of the muscle. The place where a tendon is attached to the moving bone of a joint is called the **insertion** of the muscle.

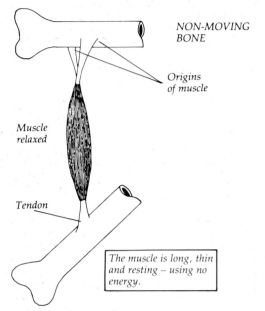

NON-MOVING BONE

Origins of muscle

Muscle relaxed

Tendon

The muscle is long, thin and resting – using no energy.

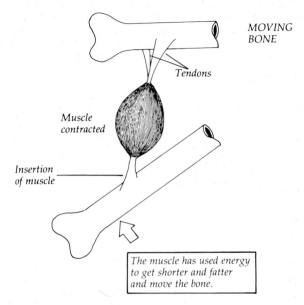

MOVING BONE

Tendons

Muscle contracted

Insertion of muscle

The muscle has used energy to get shorter and fatter and move the bone.

Muscles work by contracting (getting shorter). They can only move a bone by pulling on it as they contract. When a muscle relaxes and gets longer, it *cannot* push a bone back to its original position. This means that for every movement a joint makes, *two* muscles are needed. One muscle will contract to pull the bone one way and the other will contract to pull it back again. Muscles which work against each other like this are said to be **antagonistic**. In a hinge joint, for example, one muscle, known as the **flexor**, bends the joint, while another, the **extensor**, straightens it. The elbow is a hinge joint worked by a pair of antagonistic muscles. The **biceps** muscle at the front is the flexor and bends the elbow, while the **triceps** muscle at the back is the extensor and straightens the elbow.

Origin of triceps

TRICEPS: when relaxed, it is stretched by the action of the biceps.

BICEPS MUSCLE (the flexor) contracts to bend the arm.

Insertion of triceps

LEVER ACTION: a small shortening of the muscle pulling here can cause a large movement of the arm.

Many of the joints in the body, including the elbow joint, are arranged to work as levers. In a lever, a small movement at one end can cause a much larger movement at the other. In this way, a small shortening of a muscle can cause a much larger movement of the bone on which it is pulling. Other joints, for example ball and socket joints, can make a number of different movements – twisting, bending, rotating, etc. However, for every type of movement which a joint can make, a pair of separate, antagonistic muscles are required.

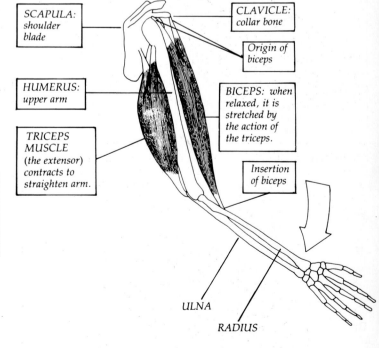

SCAPULA: shoulder blade

CLAVICLE: collar bone

Origin of biceps

HUMERUS: upper arm

BICEPS: when relaxed, it is stretched by the action of the triceps.

TRICEPS MUSCLE (the extensor) contracts to straighten arm.

Insertion of biceps

ULNA

RADIUS

Muscle

Muscle is the special tissue responsible for movement in animals. It consists of long cells which are able to contract (shorten), then relax and return to their original length. These contractions and relaxations cause either the body itself, or things inside the body to move. There are three kinds of muscle tissue. These are **voluntary muscle**, **involuntary muscle** and **cardiac muscle**.

VOLUNTARY MUSCLE, also called skeletal or **striated** (striped) **muscle**, is muscle which an animal can control. It can decide whether to contract a particular voluntary muscle or not. Most muscle is voluntary. It is what we call the 'flesh' or meat of an animal. Voluntary muscle has this kind of structure:

TENDON attaches muscle to bone.

Muscle cell

Bundle of muscle cells

Outer sheath

MUSCLE FIBRILS: tiny striped threads packed inside the cell

MUSCLE CELL (or fibre): long and striped with many nuclei

Nuclei

The contractions of voluntary muscle can be very strong, though it does tire easily. Voluntary muscle contracts only when it receives a signal from the **central nervous system** (see page 154). These signals, or commands, travel along **motor nerves** to the muscle. The end branches of the nerves connect with the individual muscle fibres like this:

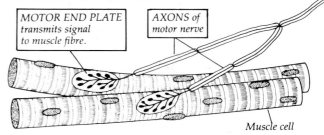

MOTOR END PLATE transmits signal to muscle fibre.

AXONS of motor nerve

Muscle cell

Although we can control our voluntary muscles, we don't always have to. There are so many muscles involved in walking, say, or even in just standing upright, that it would be exhausting if we had to think what each one was doing all the time. Instead, special sensors, called **proprioceptors**, buried in the muscles, tendons and joints, relay information about their activities to the central nervous system. This then makes adjustments, if necessary, without our having to bother about them.

INVOLUNTARY MUSCLE, also called smooth muscle, is not under voluntary control. It contracts and relaxes by itself, although the involuntary nervous system can govern its activities. Layers of smooth muscle form the walls of organs like the gut, bladder and uterus. Under the microscope, its cells look like this:

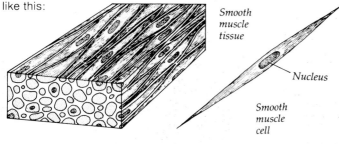

Smooth muscle tissue

Nucleus

Smooth muscle cell

Smooth muscle contracts more slowly and less strongly than voluntary muscle, but it does not tire so quickly.

Two opposing layers of smooth muscle in the gut wall squeeze food along as they contract and relax. This action is known as **peristalsis**.

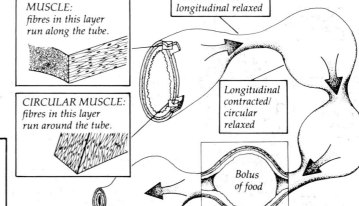

LONGITUDINAL MUSCLE: fibres in this layer run along the tube.

CIRCULAR MUSCLE: fibres in this layer run around the tube.

Circular contracted/ longitudinal relaxed

Longitudinal contracted/ circular relaxed

Bolus of food

CARDIAC MUSCLE makes up the walls of the heart. On its own, it contracts, usually about 70 times per minute, to pump the blood. The nervous system, however, can adjust its speed. It never gets tired. Although not under voluntary control, it is striated like voluntary muscle.

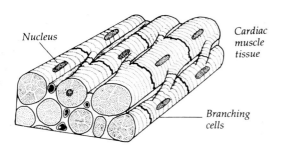

Nucleus

Cardiac muscle tissue

Branching cells

The eyes also have smooth muscle. It is the smooth muscle of the iris which narrows and dilates (widens) the pupils and so regulates the amount of light which can enter the eye.

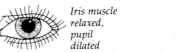

Iris muscle relaxed, pupil dilated

Iris muscle contracted, pupil narrowed

Finally, smooth muscle in the walls of arteries and arterioles can widen or narrow these vessels, when necessary, to control the flow of blood through them (see page 129).

Posture and stability

The way in which an animal holds its body is called its posture. If the animal moves around, its posture will change. If the animal adopts a posture which will make it lose its balance and fall, it is said to be unstable. If there is no danger of the animal falling over, it is said to have a stable posture.

The weight of all objects, including animals, behaves as if it were all concentrated in one spot. This point is the object's **centre of gravity**. As long as an object's centre of gravity is acting inside its base, it will not fall over. If, on the other hand, the centre of gravity comes to lie outside the base, the object will be unstable and liable to topple over, for example:

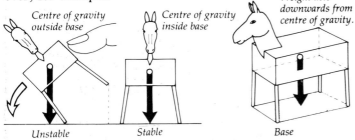

Centre of gravity outside base | Centre of gravity inside base | Weight acts downwards from centre of gravity.

Unstable   Stable   Base

The size of its base makes a big difference to an object's stability. Wide bases give more stability than narrow ones. The way in which the weight is distributed is also important. If the centre of gravity is close to the ground, the object will not be easily pushed over. Here are a few illustrations:

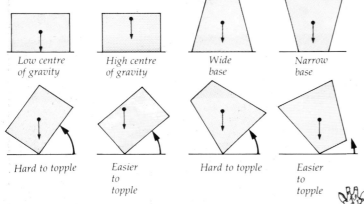

Low centre of gravity | High centre of gravity | Wide base | Narrow base

Hard to topple | Easier to topple | Hard to topple | Easier to topple

These rules apply as much to living animals as to the little models shown in these diagrams. The base of a four-legged animal is the rectangle made where its feet touch the ground. Compare the wide base and low centre of gravity of the crocodile with the narrow base and high centre of gravity of the giraffe. The crocodile is much more stable. Obviously, when the crocodile crawls along with its belly on the ground, as it often does, its stability is even greater.

Low centre of gravity wide base (including large tail) – stable

High centre of gravity, narrow base –unstable

A giraffe might look unstable, but it can run as fast as a racehorse without falling over. To achieve this, it must continually change its posture to keep its centre of gravity safely inside its changing base. The dog in the diagram below shows a simple example of this.

Centre of gravity inside the base made by the four legs: a very stable spread of weight | Animal leans to one side to bring its centre of gravity inside a new base made by just three legs. | The fourth leg can now be raised for walking with no risk of toppling over.

When running or walking, it is impossible for the body's position to be kept stable all the time. However, each unstable posture is held for just a split second, so the animal does not fall.

Humans adopt an upright, or erect, posture. To hold this position, even while standing still, involves the efforts of a whole series of muscles, a few of which are shown below. The degree of stretch of all these muscles must be constantly adjusted, otherwise the body would just flop over.

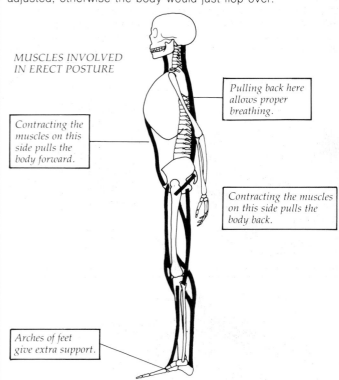

MUSCLES INVOLVED IN ERECT POSTURE

Pulling back here allows proper breathing.

Contracting the muscles on this side pulls the body forward.

Contracting the muscles on this side pulls the body back.

Arches of feet give extra support.

Attached to muscles and tendons are special sense organs called **proprioceptors**. The proprioceptors detect changes in the length of muscles and tendons and inform the brain and spinal cord. Without our being aware of them, adjustments are then made automatically to correct the posture. Other information is supplied by the skin, the eyes and the semi-circular canals of the ears.

More support in vertebrates

The very largest vertebrates, the whales, live in water. This is because the support, or uplift which they get from the water means that they do not need a very large or even a very strong skeleton to support their great weight (see page 138). On land, however, the largest vertebrates need extra thick, reinforced leg bones to bear their weight. Also, since short bones are stronger than long ones, the legs of these vertebrates tend to be short for extra strength. Short, thick legs, however, are not suitable for speedy movement.

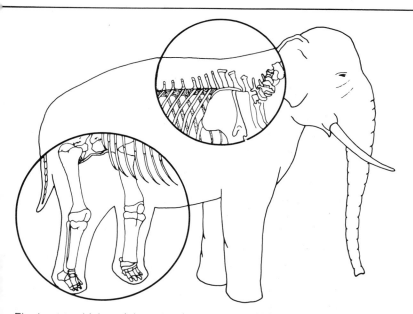

Elephants, which weigh up to six tonnes, and hippopotami, which weigh up to three tonnes, need their short, thick leg bones to carry their weight. Such legs are not suited to speed. However, their large size and thick hides give these animals ample protection from enemies. Hippos also spend most of their time in water so their weight is less of a problem to them.

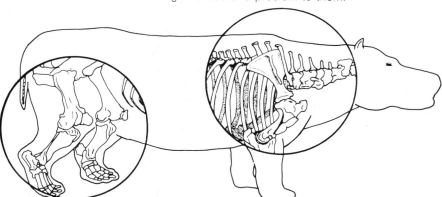

Heavy leg bones can support a very large animal. However, they will also slow down its movement, so, to reduce the bones' weight, they are made hollow. Since most of the strain they have to take acts along the outside, being hollow weakens them very little.

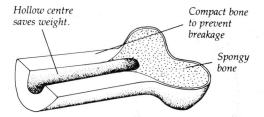

Hollow centre saves weight.

Compact bone to prevent breakage

Spongy bone

Leg bones are most likely to get broken in the middle, so, this region is thickened with **compact bone** (see page 140) for extra strength.

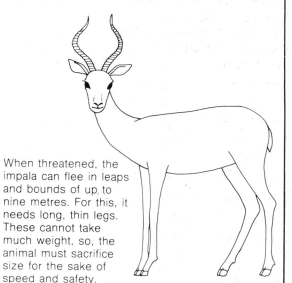

When threatened, the impala can flee in leaps and bounds of up to nine metres. For this, it needs long, thin legs. These cannot take much weight, so, the animal must sacrifice size for the sake of speed and safety.

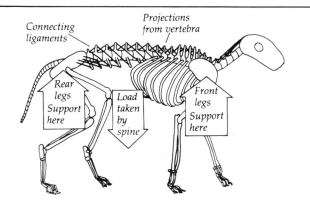

Connecting ligaments

Projections from vertebra

Rear legs Support here

Load taken by spine

Front legs Support here

In the land mammals, the legs act as pillars which transfer the body weight to the ground. However, the weight is not all directly on top of these pillars. Much of it is suspended from the backbone. Since the backbone is not a solid girder, but rather a number of small **vertebrae** (see page 139) jointed together, this weight should cause it to sag in the middle. To prevent this, each vertebra has projections or spines sticking out at the sides and top. These are tied to each other by tough **ligaments**. This makes the many joints of the **vertebral column** strong enough to support the weight, but flexible enough to allow movement of the spine. The spine is also formed into an arch, since an arched structure, as in certain bridges, can carry more weight than a straight structure.

Support and movement in invertebrates

Vertebrates can rely for support and movement on the tough skeleton buried inside their bodies. This is called an **endoskeleton** (*endo*: inside). Invertebrates, of course, have no endoskeleton to support them. Many invertebrates have completely soft bodies. Soft-bodied invertebrates living in water are supported by the water. They have various ways of getting around, for example the jet propulsion of this jellyfish.

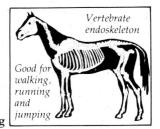

Vertebrate endoskeleton

Good for walking, running and jumping

Bell fills with water.

Water forced out back.

Some soft-bodied invertebrates, like the earthworm, can live on land. Its body is supported by the pressure of the fluids inside it against its outer muscular wall. This is called a **hydrostatic skeleton**. The effect is similar to the air inside a balloon.

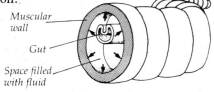

Muscular wall

Gut

Space filled with fluid

The earthworm can drag its body along the ground, but its movement is slow and inefficient (see page 35).

Not all invertebrates are soft-bodied. Many have some kind of hard skeleton on the outside of their bodies. This is called an **exoskeleton** (*exo*: outside). Many molluscs, for example, have one or two hard shells. These shells are more useful for protection than support. As far as

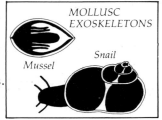

MOLLUSC EXOSKELETONS

Mussel

Snail

movement is concerned, the shells are usually a nuisance, especially on land.

The most successful group of invertebrates is the arthropods. They have an exoskeleton which gives good protection and support, but also allows easy movement. It is made of a light but tough material called **chitin**. A series of hard plates and tubes of chitin are fitted together like a suit of armour. Between the hard regions are thinner, flexible areas which allow movement.

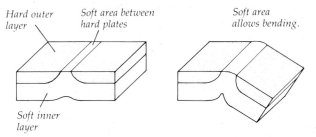

Hard outer layer

Soft area between hard plates

Soft area allows bending.

Soft inner layer

The most mobile arthropods are the insects. Their exoskeleton, made mainly of chitin, is usually called a **cuticle**. Strong enough to support the body clear of the ground, it is also light enough to allow them to fly – the only invertebrates which can do so.

The best protected arthropods are the crustaceans such as the lobster. Their exoskeleton is hardened with calcium salts, like bone, to make them extra hard. However, they are also extra heavy, and, out of water, the exoskeleton can hinder their movement.

Arthropod exoskeletons and growth

The arthropod exoskeleton has one big drawback. It cannot stretch to allow growth. The only way an arthropod can grow is by moulting its exoskeleton. As each old skin is shed, it reveals a new, larger one beneath it. This is soft at first and the animal is able to grow in size before it becomes hard. During this time, while the new exoskeleton is still soft, the arthropod is very vulnerable to attack.

MOVING AN ARTHROPOD JOINT

Each arthropod joint, like those of the vertebrates, is moved by a pair of **antagonistic muscles**. One muscle, called the **flexor**, bends the joint, while the other muscle, called the **extensor**, straightens it. However, the muscles are inside the skeleton, not outside. Also, vertebrate muscles are attached to the bones by means of tendons. Arthropod muscles are attached directly to outgrowths of the exoskeleton. The action of the muscles in moving a typical arthropod joint is shown in the diagram (left) below.

The kind of joint shown is called a **peg and socket joint**. It moves like a hinge in one plane only. Most arthropod joints are like this. However, by having several of these joints arranged to act in different planes, a limb or claw, as a whole, is able to make a complete range of movements. Take, for example, the joints in this lobster's claw:

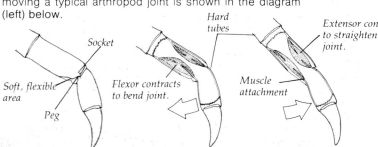

Socket

Hard tubes

Extensor contracts to straighten joint.

Soft, flexible area

Flexor contracts to bend joint.

Muscle attachment

Peg

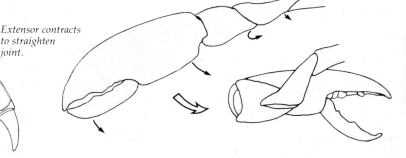

The problem of surface

The parts of an organism which are in contact with its surroundings make up its surface. The outer surface is, of course, the skin. The skin provides a protective barrier to keep out infection, and also provides a means for things to escape from an organism. This can be of value. Some organisms can excrete waste and carbon dioxide through the skin. It can also be a hazard to the organism, if too much heat or water is able to escape from it.

The amount of surface which an organism presents to the outside, called its **surface area**, is affected by its size. We can illustrate this quite simply by means of model animals such as those below.

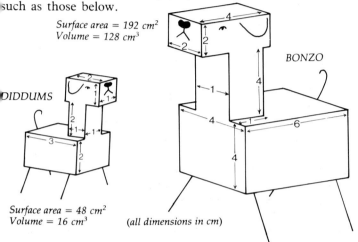

Surface area = 192 cm²
Volume = 128 cm³

BONZO

DIDDUMS

Surface area = 48 cm²
Volume = 16 cm³

(all dimensions in cm)

The larger dog has four times as much surface area as the smaller. Since heat is lost through the skin, does this mean that, in winter, the large dog will be worse off? The answer is no! It would, in fact, be better off. It does have four times the skin, but its body actually has *eight* times the volume of the smaller dog. Quite simply, while the larger dog loses more heat, it can afford to do so more than the smaller animal can.

To properly compare one organism with another, we must consider both its surface area and its bulk. We can best do this by dividing its surface area by its volume. This gives us one handy figure called the **surface area to volume ratio**, for example:

DIDDUMS	BONZO
Surface area = 48 cm² Volume = 16 cm³	Surface area = 192 cm² Volume = 128 cm³
$\dfrac{Surface\ area}{Volume} = \dfrac{48}{16} = 3$	$\dfrac{Surface\ area}{Volume} = \dfrac{192}{128} = 1.5$
i.e. Surface area to volume ratio = 3	*i.e.* Surface area to volume ratio = 1.5

Large organisms have a smaller surface area to volume ratio (written as SA/V) than smaller organisms. In other words, *for their size*, they have less surface area. This means that, on average, each cell in a large organism is less exposed to the outside. To illustrate this, in the models below, we can take a 1 cm cube to represent a single cell.

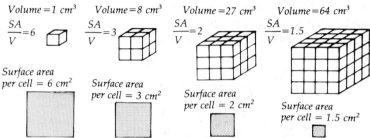

Volume = 1 cm³
$\dfrac{SA}{V} = 6$
Surface area per cell = 6 cm²

Volume = 8 cm³
$\dfrac{SA}{V} = 3$
Surface area per cell = 3 cm²

Volume = 27 cm³
$\dfrac{SA}{V} = 2$
Surface area per cell = 2 cm²

Volume = 64 cm³
$\dfrac{SA}{V} = 1.5$
Surface area per cell = 1.5 cm²

Sometimes a high SA/V is a good thing and sometimes not. Small animals (high SA/V), for example, can breathe through their skins. Large animals (low SA/V) just do not have enough oxygen-absorbing surface to supply their needs. Other examples are given in the diagram below. In these, **surface area to mass ratios** (SA/M) are used. Mass (weight) is a better guide to an organism's bulk than volume.

SURFACE AREA AND HEAT LOSS

Large animals (low SA/M) lose heat less quickly than small animals, so, animals that live in cold regions tend to be bigger than similar species from hot areas. The largest mammals are whales from Antarctica.

Large tropical animals like the elephant spend a lot of time trying to cool off. Its large, floppy ears act as a cooling device, since they lose heat easily. Birds and mammals from cold regions have thicker feathers or fur. Even then, the smallest warm-blooded animals seldom live in cold places. In fact, to replace their escaping body heat, they have to have a very high **metabolic rate** (see page 60), much higher than larger animals.

Emperor Penguin from Antarctica
1.35 m
45 kg

Fairy Penguin from Australia
0.4 m
0.75 kg

SURFACE AREA AND WATER LOSS

Small animals (high SA/M) lose water through their skins more rapidly than large animals. Most animals reduce this by some form of waterproofing. The insect cuticle, for instance, has a thin layer of wax over it. Waterproofing is not always possible. For example, many small animals like the earthworm have such a high SA/M ratio that they can breathe through the skin. To do this, they need a thin, moist skin. Exposed to the air, an earthworm quickly dries up.

Because of their leaves, most plants tend to have a very high SA/M ratio. Many parts are well waterproofed, but water is always lost from the leaves in **transpiration** (see pages 122–3). This must be replaced or the plant wilts. In the desert, where it can't be replaced, plant leaves are often just little spines to reduce surface area. The plants' rounded shapes further reduce the SA/M ratio. Other features are very thick skins and few **stomata** (see pages 122–3).

Normal plant: high SA/M, needs watering.

Desert plant: leaves reduced to spines, low SA/M.

Earthworm: high SA/M allows it to breathe through skin, but water is easily lost.

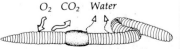

O₂ CO₂ Water

Support in plants

Depending on where and how they grow and on what kind of strain is put upon them, plants and parts of plants need different kinds of support.

AQUATIC PLANTS are plants which live in water. They can rely on uplift from the water to hold them off the bottom. To increase this, the cells of the stem are very loosely packed with many air spaces between them. These plants, therefore, can have a much longer, thinner shape than their land cousins. However, their stems must be able to bend easily as water flows past, or else the force would break them. Since the bending forces of the water are greatest round the outside of the stem, the strongest cells of the stem are kept in the middle. These are the cells of the central vein.

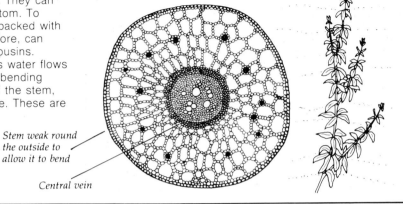

Stem weak round the outside to allow it to bend

Central vein

HERBACEOUS PLANTS are plants which do not contain wood. Much of their support comes from water inside the **vacuoles** of their cells. This pushes the cell contents tightly against the cell wall, making the cell **turgid** (stiff), in the same way as air pushing against the inner tube makes a tyre hard. If the plant is short of water, the cells become **flaccid** (soft) and the plant wilts, unable to support itself. Another problem for non-woody plants is the wind, whose bending effect could snap their stems. To resist this, the stems are packed with cells. The strongest cells are found in the **vascular bundles** (veins). These are **xylem vessels** and **sclerenchyma fibres**, the walls of which are thickened for extra strength with a tough material called **lignin**. The bending force of the wind is greatest round the outside of the stem. In **dicotyledon** stems (see page 7), the veins are arranged in a ring round the outside to counter this. Other parts of the plant are supported with **collenchyma cells** which have extra cellulose in their walls to strengthen them.

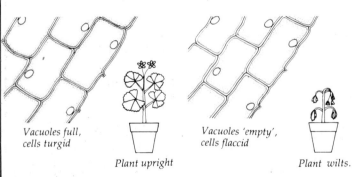

Vacuoles full, cells turgid

Plant upright

Vacuoles 'empty', cells flaccid

Plant wilts.

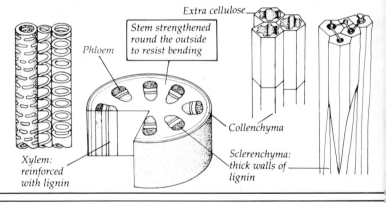

Extra cellulose

Stem strengthened round the outside to resist bending

Phloem

Collenchyma

Xylem: reinforced with lignin

Sclerenchyma: thick walls of lignin

WOODY PLANTS like the trees can grow very tall. To do this, their stems have to be strong enough to resist being broken by the wind, especially near the bottom. So, each year as they get taller, they add another layer of woody tissue to their core, making the stem thicker and stronger. Wood is made up mainly of xylem, with walls thickened with tough lignin. The wood is made by a tissue called **cambium** (see page 136). Cambium cells divide to make new phloem and xylem. In non-woody plants it does not develop much. However, in woody plants it quickly forms a complete ring. Each year, this ring of cambium makes another ring of xylem (wood) outside the last, so making the stem thicker and stronger. As the stem gets thicker, it needs more bark to cover it. This is made by a tissue called **cork cambium**.

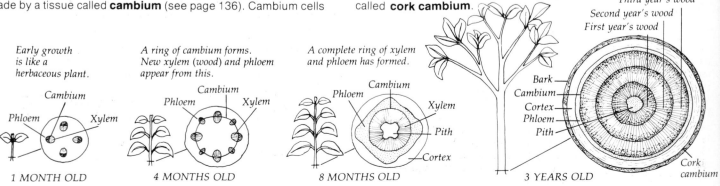

Early growth is like a herbaceous plant.

Cambium

Phloem   Xylem

1 MONTH OLD

A ring of cambium forms. New xylem (wood) and phloem appear from this.

Cambium

Phloem   Xylem

4 MONTHS OLD

A complete ring of xylem and phloem has formed.

Phloem   Cambium

Xylem

Pith

Cortex

8 MONTHS OLD

Third year's wood
Second year's wood
First year's wood

Bark
Cambium
Cortex
Phloem
Pith

Cork cambium

3 YEARS OLD

Movements made by plants

Plants do not move as much as or as quickly as animals. However, it is possible for them to make three different kinds of movements. The thing which causes them to move is called the **stimulus**. If a plant moves towards the stimulus, it is said to have made a **positive** movement. If it moves away from the stimulus, it is said to have made a **negative** movement. The three different types of movement seen in plants are **tropisms, taxes** and **nastic movements.**

TAXES (sing: *taxis*) occur when the *whole* plant moves in response to the stimulus. Taxes are common in animals, but can only be made by simple one-celled 'plants' which have tails called **flagella** (sing: *flagellum*) for swimming. They can use them to swim towards light – a movement called **positive phototaxis** (*photo*: light) – or away from poisons – **negative chemotaxis**, for example:

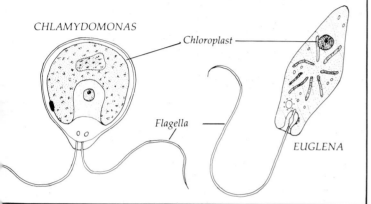

CHLAMYDOMONAS
Chloroplast
Flagella
EUGLENA

NASTIES (or nastic movements) occur when the movement caused by the stimulus is not in any particular direction (neither positive nor negative). If flowers or leaves open with the morning light, this is called **photonasty**. Some plants even respond to touch by folding up their leaves.

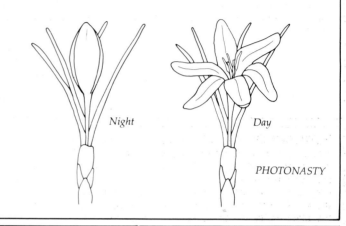

Night
Day
PHOTONASTY

TROPISMS occur when part of a plant, such as a stem or a root, detects the stimulus and either moves towards it (positive tropism) or away from it (negative tropism), for example:

Positive phototropism
Plant stems will bend *towards* the light.

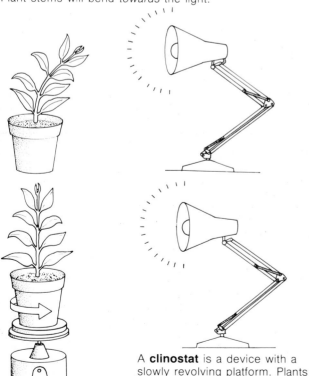

A **clinostat** is a device with a slowly revolving platform. Plants placed on one will receive the stimulus from *all* directions and so will not bend.

Clinostat

Negative geotropism
Plant stems will bend *away* from the ground (*geo*: earth).

Lying horizontally

Fixed horizontally to a revolving clinostat

Stems bend upwards away from the ground.

Horizontal stems grow straight.

Positive geotropism
Plant roots will bend *towards* the ground.

If a seedling is placed horizontally on a stationary clinostat, the root bends downwards towards the ground. On a moving clinostat, it grows straight.

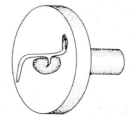
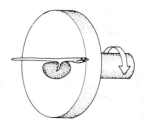

Tropisms

Plant growth, like animal growth, is controlled by **hormones** (see pages 196–7). A hormone is a chemical which is made by one part of an organism, but then travels to another where it has some affect. In this case, it will affect growth. Plant growth hormones are called **auxins**. The main auxin is called **indole acetic acid** (IAA). IAA controls phototropism and geotropism.

IAA is made by the growing tips, or **meristems**, of shoots and roots. It does not have its effect there, though. Instead it diffuses back to the **region of elongation** (see page 193) just behind the tip. This is the area where newly-formed cells are developing their vacuoles and so getting longer. It is, in fact, IAA which causes them to do this. In shoots, high concentrations of IAA increase growth. It is different, however, in roots. Low concentrations of IAA stimulate growth, but high concentrations retard it. Phototropism and geotropism are caused by unequal concentrations of IAA in root and shoot tips.

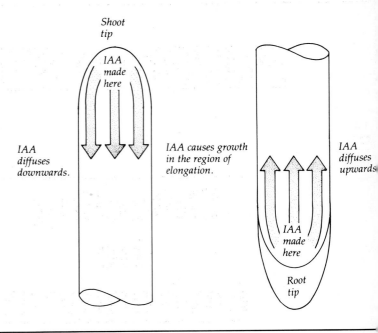

IAA AND PHOTOTROPISM

Only the very tip of the shoot, which makes the IAA, is sensitive to light (the stimulus). If the tip is evenly lit, IAA spreads evenly down from it and the shoot grows straight. If light falls on the tip from one side, however, the IAA seems to drift to the opposite (darker) side. This causes that side to grow faster and so the shoot becomes bent towards the light.

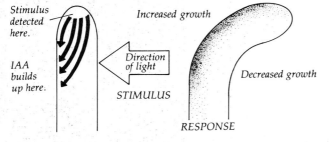

This explanation of phototropism was worked out from the results of many experiments. A few of these are shown in the diagrams opposite.

Since plants need light to make their food by photosynthesis, phototropism is very useful to them. It allows each shoot on a plant to find, and keep to, its best-lit position.

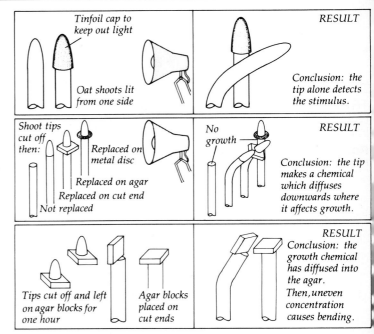

IAA AND GEOTROPISM

When a root or shoot is lying horizontally (on its side), gravity seems to cause IAA to migrate to the lower side. Thus, IAA concentration there becomes high. This increases growth in that part of the shoot, but slows it down in the same part of the root.

As a result, the root bends downwards – **positive geotropism** – while the shoot bends upwards – **negative geotropism**. This response makes sure that, no matter which way a seed falls to the ground, it will always grow the right way up.

Root lying on its side

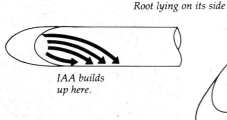

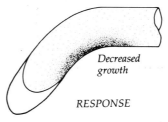

Shoot lying on its side

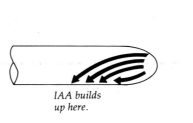

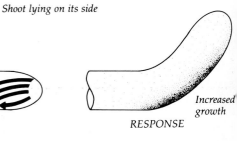

SECTION 15

Detecting the Environment

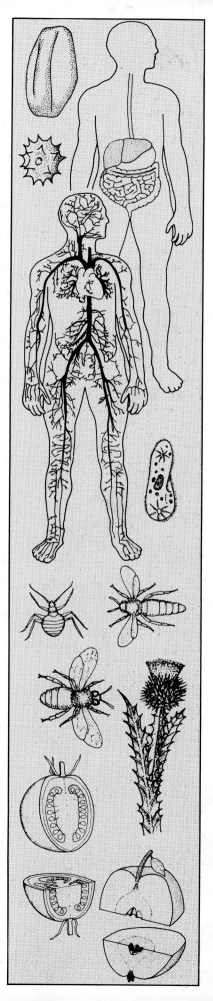

The nervous system

Living organisms are able to detect things going on around them and react to any changes. This ability is called **sensitivity**. Sensitivity is important, since it allows the organism to get food, avoid danger and keep its environment comfortable to live in. In most animals, this is the job of the **nervous system**. Any change which the nervous system can detect in its surroundings is called a **stimulus** (plu: *stimuli*). The stimulus is detected by special cells called **receptors**. In some cases, lots of stimulus receptors are grouped together along with other structures which help them do their job. These are called **sense organs**. The eye, for example, is a sense organ with receptors inside it which can detect light.

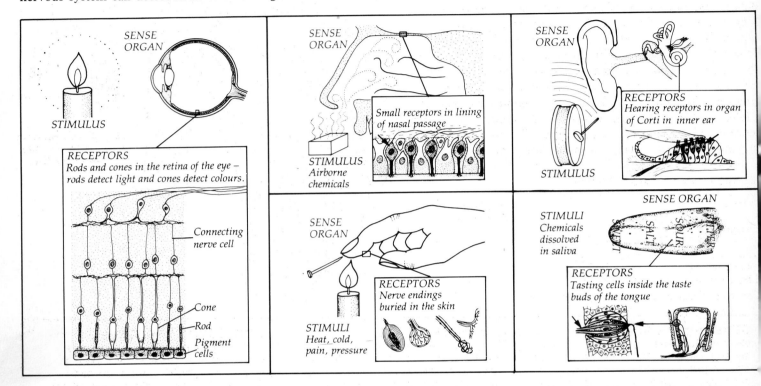

SENSE ORGAN

STIMULUS

RECEPTORS
Rods and cones in the retina of the eye – rods detect light and cones detect colours.

Connecting nerve cell

Cone
Rod
Pigment cells

SENSE ORGAN

STIMULUS
Airborne chemicals

Small receptors in lining of nasal passage

SENSE ORGAN

STIMULUS

RECEPTORS
Hearing receptors in organ of Corti in inner ear

SENSE ORGAN

STIMULI
Heat, cold, pain, pressure

RECEPTORS
Nerve endings buried in the skin

SENSE ORGAN

STIMULI
Chemicals dissolved in saliva

SALT   SOUR   SWEET

RECEPTORS
Tasting cells inside the taste buds of the tongue

When a receptor detects its own particular stimulus, it sends a message to the brain about it. If the brain decides to make a response to the stimulus, it will send a message to an **effector organ**. An effector organ could be a muscle, for example, and the brain might order it to contract and so move the bones of a joint. This movement would be the response to the stimulus. These messages to and from the brain travel along fibres called nerves. Some nerves, for example those in the face, run straight to the brain. These are called **cranial nerves**. Most nerves, however, relay their messages to and from the spinal cord which connects them with the brain. These are called **spinal nerves**. The brain and the spinal cord together make up the **central nervous system**. The cranial nerves and the spinal nerves make up the **peripheral nervous system**.

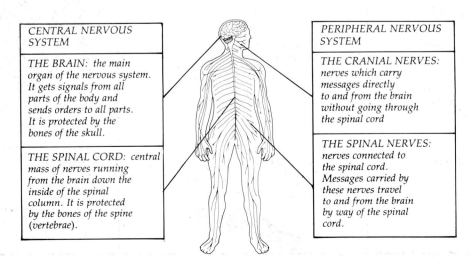

CENTRAL NERVOUS SYSTEM

THE BRAIN: *the main organ of the nervous system. It gets signals from all parts of the body and sends orders to all parts. It is protected by the bones of the skull.*

THE SPINAL CORD: *central mass of nerves running from the brain down the inside of the spinal column. It is protected by the bones of the spine (vertebrae).*

PERIPHERAL NERVOUS SYSTEM

THE CRANIAL NERVES: *nerves which carry messages directly to and from the brain without going through the spinal cord*

THE SPINAL NERVES: *nerves connected to the spinal cord. Messages carried by these nerves travel to and from the brain by way of the spinal cord.*

Nerve cells

The nerves which carry messages to and from the central nervous system look like wires spreading through all the parts of the body. From the main nerves come smaller ones branching off to serve their own area. Inside each nerve are bundles of tiny nerve fibres along which the signals travel. Each of these fibres is part of a single nerve cell or **neurone**. Each neurone has a **nerve cell body** which contains its **nucleus**. Signals go into the nerve cell body along one or more fibres called **dendrites** and leave by another fibre called an **axon**. The signals travelling along these nerve fibres are in the form of tiny pulses of electricity. When a signal reaches an end branch of one neurone, it can be passed on to the dendrites of the next across a gap called a **synapse**. When the pulse reaches the end branch, a chemical is released. This crosses the synapse into the dendrite of the next neurone and starts up a pulse in that one. This system makes sure that the signals can only go in one direction.

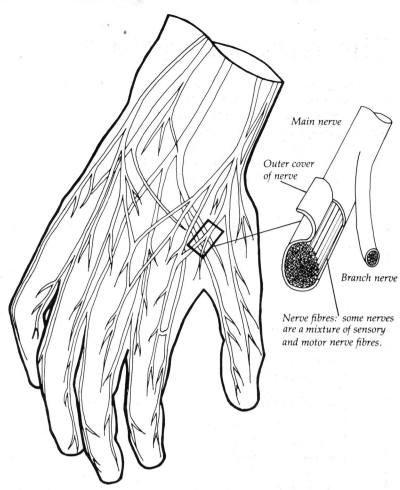

Main nerve

Outer cover of nerve

Branch nerve

Nerve fibres: some nerves are a mixture of sensory and motor nerve fibres.

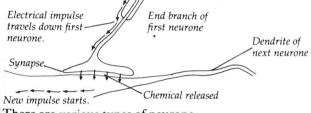

Electrical impulse travels down first neurone.

End branch of first neurone

Dendrite of next neurone

Synapse

New impulse starts.

Chemical released

There are various types of neurone. These are described in the diagrams below.

SENSORY NEURONES

Sensory neurones carry signals from the sense receptors into the central nervous system (brain or spinal cord). Their nerve cell bodies lie alongside the nerve fibre and since all the sensory neurones in a nerve have their cell bodies at the same spot, this forms a lump on the nerve. Such a lump is called a **ganglion** (plu: *ganglia*).

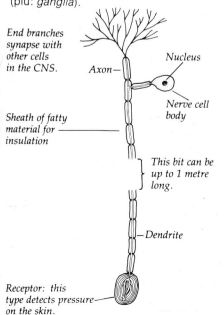

End branches synapse with other cells in the CNS.

Axon

Nucleus

Nerve cell body

Sheath of fatty material for insulation

This bit can be up to 1 metre long.

Dendrite

Receptor: this type detects pressure on the skin.

MOTOR NEURONES

Motor neurones carry signals from the central nervous system to an effector organ (a muscle or gland). The nerve cell body is at one end of the neurone, buried in the brain or spinal cord.

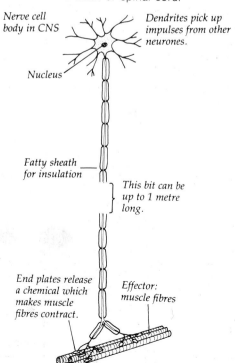

Nerve cell body in CNS

Dendrites pick up impulses from other neurones.

Nucleus

Fatty sheath for insulation

This bit can be up to 1 metre long.

End plates release a chemical which makes muscle fibres contract.

Effector: muscle fibres

CONNECTOR NEURONES

Connector neurones are found in the central nervous system. Their job is to relay messages from one neurone to another. They may make large numbers of connections with other neurones.

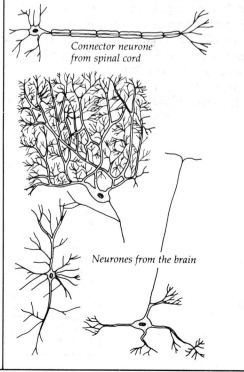

Connector neurone from spinal cord

Neurones from the brain

The central nervous system

The central nervous system consists of the brain and the spinal cord. Its job is to receive information from all over the body, interpret this information and then use it to control all the systems of the body. It contains two kinds of tissue – white matter and grey matter. White matter is made up of the fibres (**axons** or **dendrites**) of nerve cells. It appears white because of the white fatty sheaths which cover these fibres. Grey matter consists mainly of the cell bodies of these nerve cells. These delicate organs are protected from damage in two ways. Firstly, the brain is shielded by the bones of the skull, and the spinal cord is protected by the bones of the spine (the vertebrae). Secondly, they are covered by membranes, between two of which flows a liquid called **cerebro-spinal fluid** (CSF). This fluid protects the nervous tissues below and helps to remove waste from them. The structure of the central nervous system is shown in the diagram below.

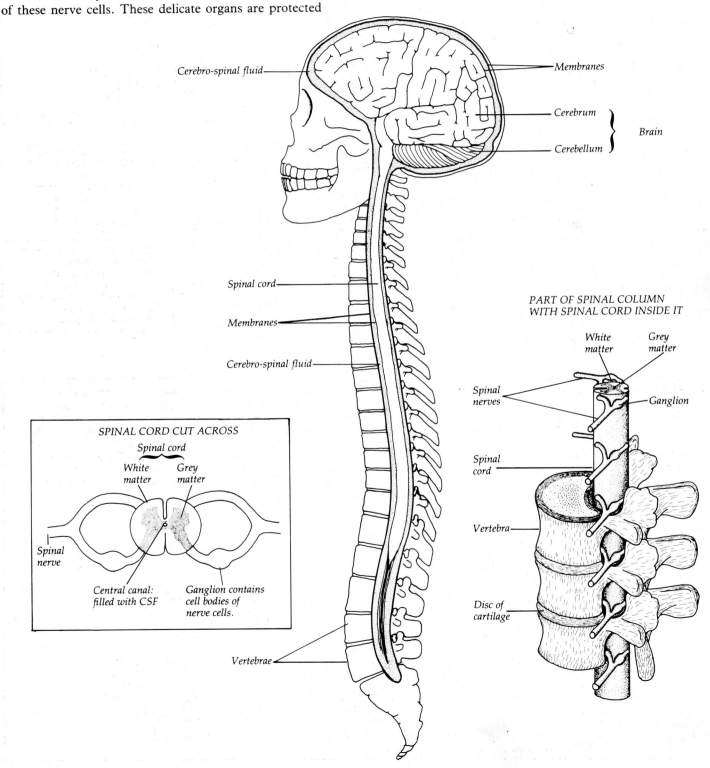

Cerebro-spinal fluid

Membranes

Cerebrum

Cerebellum

} Brain

Spinal cord

Membranes

Cerebro-spinal fluid

Vertebrae

SPINAL CORD CUT ACROSS

Spinal cord

White matter

Grey matter

Spinal nerve

Central canal: filled with CSF

Ganglion contains cell bodies of nerve cells.

PART OF SPINAL COLUMN WITH SPINAL CORD INSIDE IT

White matter

Grey matter

Spinal nerves

Ganglion

Spinal cord

Vertebra

Disc of cartilage

The brain

The brain is the most important organ in the whole body. It is not only the centre of conscious activities like thinking, memory, feeling and making movements, but it also controls vital body functions like heartbeat and breathing, without which life would be impossible. Different areas of the brain are responsible for different parts of its work, though the **neurones** (nerve cells) of the areas are in constant communication with one another. The largest part of the brain is called the **cerebrum**. This is split into two halves called the **cerebral hemispheres**.

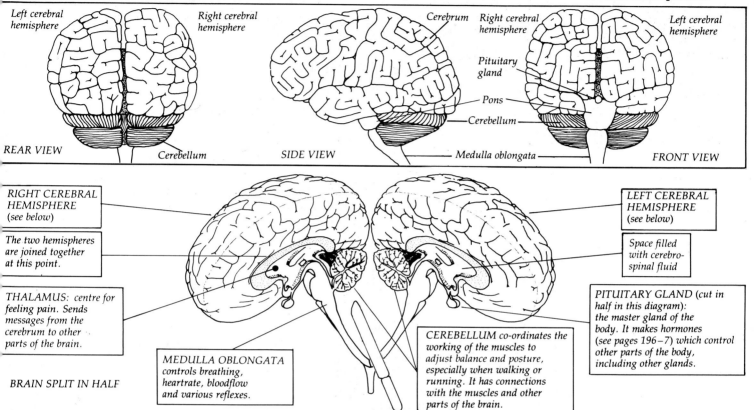

Left cerebral hemisphere

Right cerebral hemisphere

REAR VIEW

Cerebellum

Cerebrum Right cerebral hemisphere

SIDE VIEW

Left cerebral hemisphere

Pituitary gland

Pons

Cerebellum

Medulla oblongata

FRONT VIEW

RIGHT CEREBRAL HEMISPHERE (*see below*)

The two hemispheres are joined together at this point.

THALAMUS: *centre for feeling pain. Sends messages from the cerebrum to other parts of the brain.*

BRAIN SPLIT IN HALF

MEDULLA OBLONGATA *controls breathing, heartrate, bloodflow and various reflexes.*

CEREBELLUM *co-ordinates the working of the muscles to adjust balance and posture, especially when walking or running. It has connections with the muscles and other parts of the brain.*

LEFT CEREBRAL HEMISPHERE (*see below*)

Space filled with cerebro-spinal fluid

PITUITARY GLAND (*cut in half in this diagram*): *the master gland of the body. It makes hormones (see pages 196–7) which control other parts of the body, including other glands.*

THE CEREBRUM is the largest and most important part of the brain. It is the centre of our intelligence. It allows us to think, remember and reason. It allows us to be conscious of our own bodies, of things going on around us, and to make conscious movements. It consists of an outer layer of grey matter over an inner core of white matter. The outer layer, called the **cortex**, has a lot of deep folds in it. This gives it a large amount of surface in which to fit most of the body's nerve cells. Different parts of the cerebrum do different jobs. For instance, the **sensory area** near the middle receives signals from sense receptors all over the body and so enables us to feel these parts. Thus, we actually 'feel' the tips of our toes at the top of our head. Beside the sensory area is the **motor area**. From this region, orders are sent out to muscles all over the body so that we can make movements. The left half of the cerebrum – the left cerebral hemisphere – controls the right side of the body, while the right half – the right cerebral hemisphere controls the left side of the body.

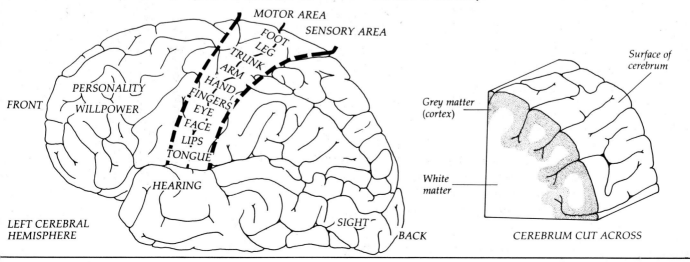

MOTOR AREA

SENSORY AREA

FOOT
LEG
TRUNK
ARM
HAND
FINGERS
EYE
FACE
LIPS
TONGUE

PERSONALITY
WILLPOWER

FRONT

HEARING

SIGHT

LEFT CEREBRAL HEMISPHERE

BACK

Surface of cerebrum

Grey matter (cortex)

White matter

CEREBRUM CUT ACROSS

Reflexes

Many of the responses which we make to outside stimuli are **voluntary**. This means that the brain decides what action to take and that we are aware of what is going on. In a voluntary response, the stimulus is detected by **receptors** which send a message about it along sensory **neurones** to the brain. The brain decides on a response and a command is sent along motor neurones to the appropriate **effector**, for example:

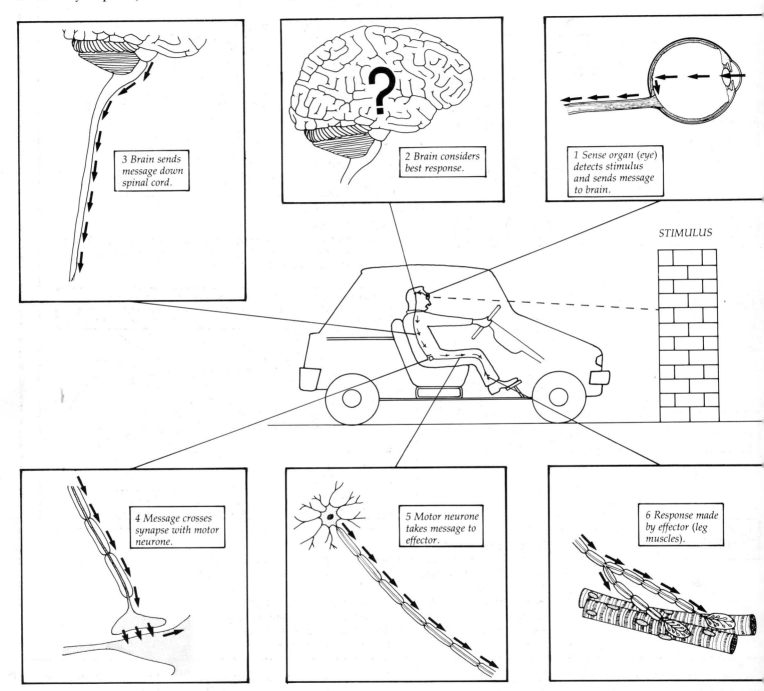

3 Brain sends message down spinal cord.

2 Brain considers best response.

1 Sense organ (eye) detects stimulus and sends message to brain.

STIMULUS

4 Message crosses synapse with motor neurone.

5 Motor neurone takes message to effector.

6 Response made by effector (leg muscles).

With practice, a response like the one above can be very fast. However, it still takes some time for the signals to travel to the brain and back. There is another, faster kind of response which does not need any decision making by the brain. This is called a **reflex**.

In the most common type of reflex, the stimulus is detected by a receptor which then sends a signal along a sensory neurone to the spinal cord. In the spinal cord, a connector neurone passes the message directly along to a motor neurone. It is then passed out of the spinal cord to the effector organ which makes the response. The brain plays no part in the process, although other connections wi eventually tell it what has been going on. This kind of reflex which is very fast helps us avoid injury.

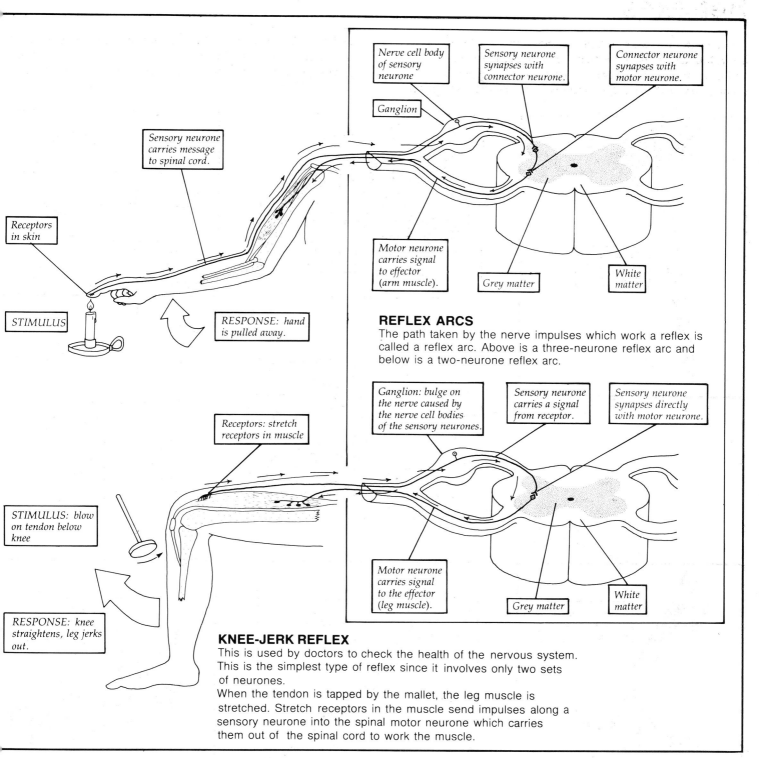

REFLEX ARCS

The path taken by the nerve impulses which work a reflex is called a reflex arc. Above is a three-neurone reflex arc and below is a two-neurone reflex arc.

Nerve cell body of sensory neurone

Sensory neurone synapses with connector neurone.

Connector neurone synapses with motor neurone.

Ganglion

Sensory neurone carries message to spinal cord.

Receptors in skin

STIMULUS

RESPONSE: hand is pulled away.

Motor neurone carries signal to effector (arm muscle).

Grey matter

White matter

Ganglion: bulge on the nerve caused by the nerve cell bodies of the sensory neurones.

Sensory neurone carries a signal from receptor.

Sensory neurone synapses directly with motor neurone.

Receptors: stretch receptors in muscle

STIMULUS: blow on tendon below knee

RESPONSE: knee straightens, leg jerks out.

Motor neurone carries signal to the effector (leg muscle).

Grey matter

White matter

KNEE-JERK REFLEX

This is used by doctors to check the health of the nervous system. This is the simplest type of reflex since it involves only two sets of neurones.

When the tendon is tapped by the mallet, the leg muscle is stretched. Stretch receptors in the muscle send impulses along a sensory neurone into the spinal motor neurone which carries them out of the spinal cord to work the muscle.

reflexes are **involuntary responses**. This means that they appen whether we want them to or not. They can even appen while we are asleep. However, with reflexes like nose shown in the diagram above, we do not become aware f the movements we are making and the stimuli which are ausing them and we can control them only with difficulty. On the other hand, voluntary responses like braking a car n an emergency or rapid movements in sport can, with ractice, become so automatic that we can make them ithout thinking. They become just like reflexes.

There are involuntary responses, however, of which we are never aware and over which we have no control, for example:

1 Bright light causes the pupils of our eyes (see page 158) to constrict (get smaller) and so protect the eyes.
2 **Peristalsis** (see page 75) which is caused by food stretching the gut.
3 Blood vessels get narrower or wider to control the blood flow through them.

The eye

The eyes are the organs of sight. Their job is to collect light rays from round about us, make them into a picture and tell the brain about it.

The left eye sends the brain a slightly different picture from the right eye. The brain takes these two pictures and merges them into one. This gives us three-dimensional vision which allows us to judge the distance and size of the objects we are looking at.

The structure of an eye is shown in the diagrams below.

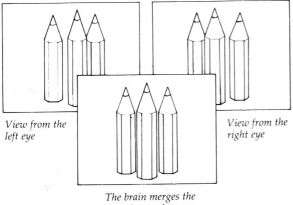

View from the left eye

View from the right eye

The brain merges the two pictures into one.

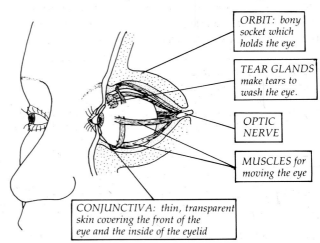

ORBIT: bony socket which holds the eye

TEAR GLANDS make tears to wash the eye.

OPTIC NERVE

MUSCLES for moving the eye

CONJUNCTIVA: thin, transparent skin covering the front of the eye and the inside of the eyelid

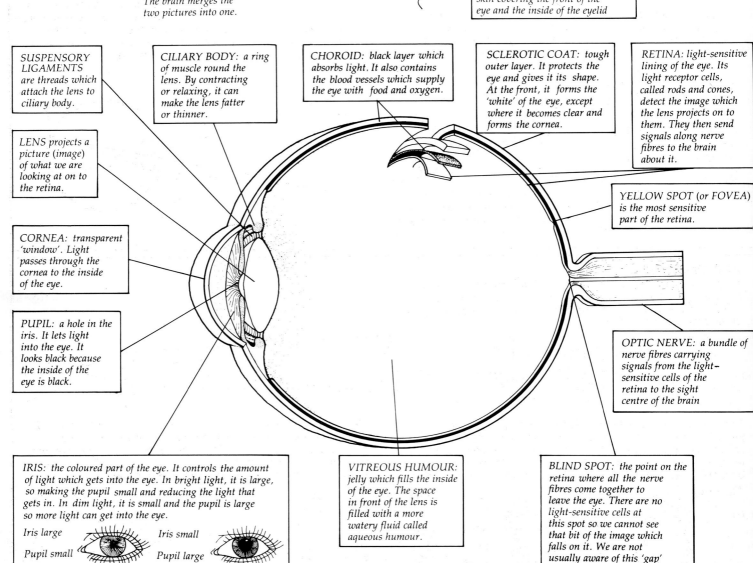

SUSPENSORY LIGAMENTS are threads which attach the lens to ciliary body.

CILIARY BODY: a ring of muscle round the lens. By contracting or relaxing, it can make the lens fatter or thinner.

CHOROID: black layer which absorbs light. It also contains the blood vessels which supply the eye with food and oxygen.

SCLEROTIC COAT: tough outer layer. It protects the eye and gives it its shape. At the front, it forms the 'white' of the eye, except where it becomes clear and forms the cornea.

RETINA: light-sensitive lining of the eye. Its light receptor cells, called rods and cones, detect the image which the lens projects on to them. They then send signals along nerve fibres to the brain about it.

LENS projects a picture (image) of what we are looking at on to the retina.

CORNEA: transparent 'window'. Light passes through the cornea to the inside of the eye.

YELLOW SPOT (or FOVEA) is the most sensitive part of the retina.

PUPIL: a hole in the iris. It lets light into the eye. It looks black because the inside of the eye is black.

OPTIC NERVE: a bundle of nerve fibres carrying signals from the light-sensitive cells of the retina to the sight centre of the brain

IRIS: the coloured part of the eye. It controls the amount of light which gets into the eye. In bright light, it is large, so making the pupil small and reducing the light that gets in. In dim light, it is small and the pupil is large so more light can get into the eye.

Iris large
Pupil small

Iris small
Pupil large

BRIGHT LIGHT

DIM LIGHT

VITREOUS HUMOUR: jelly which fills the inside of the eye. The space in front of the lens is filled with a more watery fluid called aqueous humour.

BLIND SPOT: the point on the retina where all the nerve fibres come together to leave the eye. There are no light-sensitive cells at this spot so we cannot see that bit of the image which falls on it. We are not usually aware of this 'gap' in our vision.

Seeing

The eye is the sense organ we use to detect light. To do this, it has light receptors on its **retina**. However, light rays enter our eyes from all directions. On its own, the retina could tell the brain only that light had entered the eye and how bright it was. To be able to see the things round about us, we need something to organise this jumble of light rays into a picture or **image** of our surroundings. It is the job of the **lens** to make this image and project it on to the retina. Each light receptor can then tell the brain about the tiny part of the image which it has detected and the brain can put together the complete picture. The **ciliary body** with its **suspensory ligaments** helps the lens to form good, clear images.

HOW A LENS WORKS

Lenses are made from a clear, transparent material. The lens in a camera is made from glass, while the lens in the eye is made from a soft, jelly-like substance. There are different kinds of lenses. The lens in the eye is thicker in the middle than round the outside. This type of lens is called a **convex lens**. A convex lens can take light rays which are spreading out and bend them so that they come together again. This is called **focusing** the light.

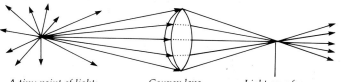

A tiny point of light: light rays leave it in straight lines going in all directions.

Convex lens bends the rays inwards.

Light rays focus at this point before scattering again.

Lens from the eye, cut in two

When we look at something, the lens in the eye (along with the **cornea**) makes an image of that object on the retina at the back of the eye. The image is upside down. However, the brain turns the picture round for us and so we see the object the right way up.

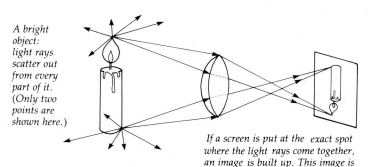

A bright object: light rays scatter out from every part of it. (Only two points are shown here.)

If a screen is put at the exact spot where the light rays come together, an image is built up. This image is upside down.

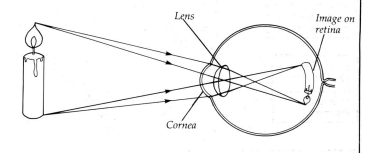

Lens

Image on retina

Cornea

ACCOMMODATION

To give a sharp image of an object, a lens must be just the right thickness. A fat lens will only give a good image of an object which is close to it. A thin lens will only make a good image of an object which is far from it.

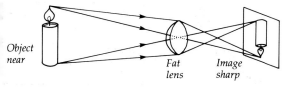

Object near

Fat lens

Image sharp

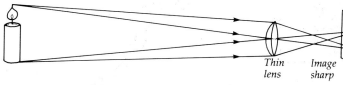

Object far

Thin lens

Image sharp

The lens in the eye is in the middle of a ring of muscle called the ciliary body. It is attached to the ciliary body by threads called suspensory ligaments. If we wish to see a near object (fat lens), the ciliary body contracts (gets smaller), the threads become loose and the lens gets fat. If we wish to see a distant object, the ciliary body relaxes, the threads become tighter and pull on the lens. The lens gets thinner and gives us a clear image of the object. This ability to make the lens in the eye just the right thickness so that we can see objects at different distances is called the **power of accommodation**.

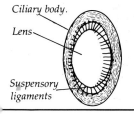

Ciliary body.

Lens

Suspensory ligaments

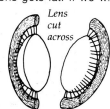

Lens cut across

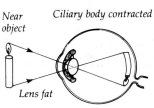

Near object

Ciliary body contracted

Lens fat

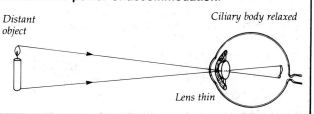

Distant object

Ciliary body relaxed

Lens thin

Long sight and short sight

There are a number of things which can go wrong with our eyes which can make our vision less than perfect. The most common eye defects are long sight and short sight. Both of these can be corrected by wearing the right kind of spectacles.

LONG SIGHT occurs when it is possible to see distant objects clearly, but near objects are blurred and indistinct. It is caused either by the eyeball being too short, or by the lens being unable to get fat enough to focus near objects correctly. Long sight is corrected by wearing glasses with **convex** lenses. These bend the light rays a bit extra to allow them to focus on the retina.

Near object – glasses needed.

Distant object – vision clear.

Eyeball short

Distant object

Near object

Image fuzzy

Correct position for clear focus

Distant object focused clearly

Long sight is corrected by glasses with convex lenses.

Image clear

Convex lens bends light rays before they enter eye.

SHORT SIGHT occurs when it is possible to see near objects clearly, but more distant objects are blurred and indistinct. It is caused either by the eyeball being too long, or by the lens being unable to get thin enough to focus distant objects correctly. Short sight is corrected by wearing glasses with **concave** lenses. A concave lens is one which is thinner in the middle than round the outside. These spread the light rays out a bit before they enter the eye. The lens is then able to focus them correctly.

Distant object – glasses needed.

Near object – vision clear.

Correct position for clear focus

Eyeball long

Near object focused clearly

Distant object

Image fuzzy

Near object

Short sight is corrected by glasses with concave lenses.

Image clear

Distant object

Concave lens spreads out light rays before they enter the eye.

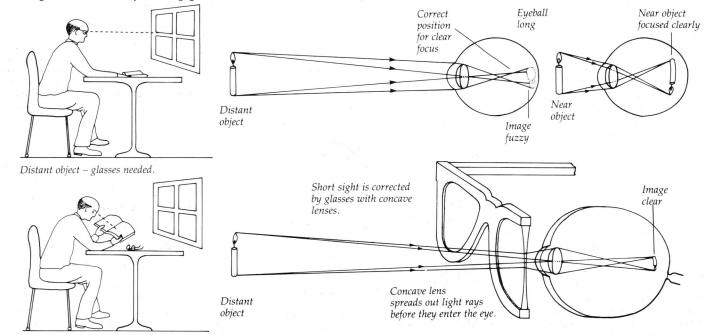

The ear

The ear is a sense organ which does two jobs. Firstly, it detects sound. Secondly, signals from the ear allow us to keep our balance.

Sound is caused by objects vibrating backwards and forwards. When an object vibrates, it makes the molecules of gas in the air vibrate. These vibrations, called **sound waves**, travel through the air from the object to our ears.

The note, or **pitch**, which we hear depends on how fast the object vibrates. A fast, or **high frequency**, vibration makes a high-pitched note, while a slow, or **low frequency**, vibration gives a low note. The human ear can detect sound ranging in frequency from about 20 **cycles** (vibrations) per second up to about 20 000 cycles per second. The structure of the ear is shown below.

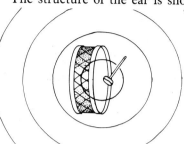

Drumskin vibrates quickly.

HIGH FREQUENCY
SOUND WAVES: *high note*

Drumskin vibrates slowly.

LOW FREQUENCY
SOUND WAVES: *low note*

MIDDLE EAR
The middle ear is a chamber filled with air. Going across it is a chain of three bones – the hammer, anvil, and stirrup. The eardrum vibrates against the hammer which passes the vibrations to the anvil and then to the stirrup. This increases the strength of the vibrations. The stirrup vibrates against the inner ear.

| Hammer | Anvil | Stirrup |

INNER EAR
A fluid-filled organ buried in the bone. The stirrup vibrates against it at a gap in the bone called the **oval window**. This causes vibrations in the fluid. These are detected by the cochlea which sends signals to the brain about them. The brain interprets these as sounds. The front part of the inner ear is concerned with balance.

AUDITORY NERVE carries signals from the cochlea to the hearing centre of the brain.

COCHLEA: coiled tube with receptors to detect vibrations in the fluid which fills it. They send signals to the brain about them (see below).

SEMICIRCULAR CANALS are the organs of balance (see below).

OUTER EAR

PINNA collects sound waves.

AUDITORY CANAL leads sound waves to the eardrum.

EARDRUM: thin membrane. When sound waves hit it, they cause it to vibrate with the same frequency as themselves.

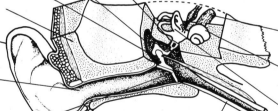

EUSTACHIAN TUBE: tube which connects the middle ear to the back of the throat. It allows air pressure on both sides of the eardrum to be kept the same.

The semicircular canals are tubes filled with liquid. There are three of them, each one in a different plane:

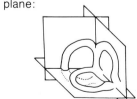

When you move your head, the liquid in the semicircular canals flows back and forth. This moves tiny hairs which then trigger receptor cells. The receptor cells send signals to the brain about these movements and from this information the brain can work out the exact position of the head.

The cochlea is a tube split up into three chambers, each filled with liquid. Vibrations set up in this liquid by the stirrup, travel out along the top chamber and back along the bottom. The middle chamber contains the **organ of Corti**. Receptors in this detect vibrations as they pass through and send signals to the brain about them.

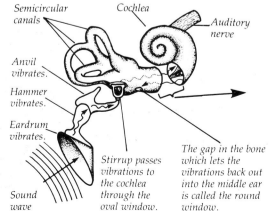

Semicircular canals
Cochlea
Auditory nerve
Anvil vibrates.
Hammer vibrates.
Eardrum vibrates.
Sound wave
Stirrup passes vibrations to the cochlea through the oval window.
The gap in the bone which lets the vibrations back out into the middle ear is called the round window.

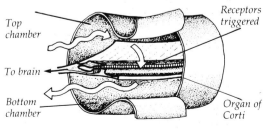

Top chamber
To brain
Bottom chamber
Receptors triggered
Organ of Corti

High-frequency vibrations trigger those receptors near the start of the cochlea and low- frequency trigger those further along. The spent vibrations are got rid of at the round window.

The skin

The skin is not just the outer layer of the body. It is an important organ with a number of vital jobs to do. These jobs include:

1 the protection of the body;
2 acting as a sense organ for the body;
3 helping to control the temperature of the body.

The structure of the skin is shown in the diagram below.

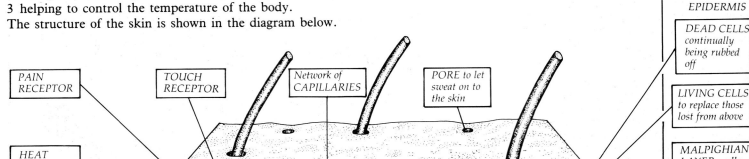

PAIN RECEPTOR

TOUCH RECEPTOR

Network of CAPILLARIES

PORE to let sweat on to the skin

EPIDERMIS

DEAD CELLS continually being rubbed off

LIVING CELLS to replace those lost from above

MALPIGHIAN LAYER: cells which divide to make new cells for the epidermis

HEAT RECEPTOR

DERMIS: elastic layer which lets the skin stretch.

FAT LAYER cushions and insulates the tissue below.

ARTERIOLE takes blood to the skin.

OIL GLAND makes oil to keep the skin waterproof and supple.

ERECTOR MUSCLE contracts to make the hair stand straight.

VENULE takes blood out of the skin.

SWEAT GLAND makes sweat to cool down the skin.

COLD RECEPTOR

PRESSURE RECEPTOR

THE SKIN AS PROTECTION

The top layer of the skin keeps out water and germs. It is made of dead cells tightly packed together. These are continually rubbed off as we move and the living cells underneath are left unharmed. New cells to replace them are made by the **Malpighian layer**. This layer also makes pigment (colour) to protect us from the sun's rays. Oil from the oil glands helps with waterproofing and keeping out germs. The **dermis** is elastic so the skin keeps its shape and the fatty layer gives us protection from knocks and bumps. In some animals the hair may give protection by acting as camouflage. Hair may even be converted into sharp spikes or horns for defence.

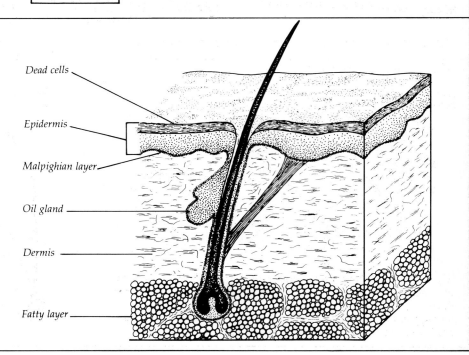

Dead cells

Epidermis

Malpighian layer

Oil gland

Dermis

Fatty layer

THE SKIN AS A SENSE ORGAN

When we speak about our 'sense of touch' we are really talking about a variety of different sensations. The skin has **receptors** which can detect touch, pain, heat, cold and pressure. These receptors are found all over the skin, although there are more in some parts than in others. The fingertips, for example, have a lot of touch receptors to make them extra sensitive. Touch receptors linked to hair can be very effective, e.g. in a cat's whiskers. Pain receptors, which are evenly spread throughout the skin are very important in preventing injury (see pages 156–7). Other sensations which we register with our skin, like sharpness, wetness or softness, are caused by different types of receptor being stimulated at the same time.

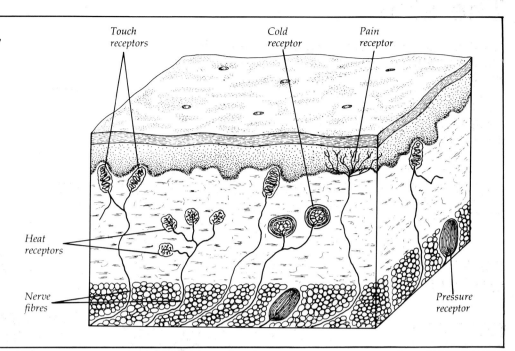

THE SKIN AND TEMPERATURE CONTROL

It is vital that the human body is kept at its correct temperature of around 37°C. However, there are various things which could make it either too high or too low. The air around us, for example, could become warmer or cooler. If we are active, our muscles might generate too much heat, or, if we are inactive, they might not make enough. The body must be able to get rid of heat when it has too much and keep in heat when it has too little. It is the skin's job to adjust the amount of heat lost from the body. It does this in the following ways:

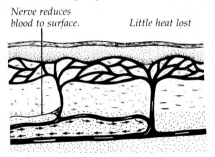 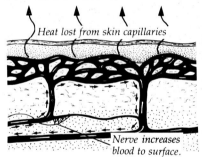 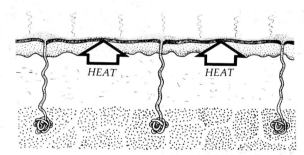

Signals from the brain close down **arterioles** in the skin either to divert blood to the surface to lose heat, or away from the surface so as to keep the heat in the body.

The sweat glands put sweat on to the skin surface. For this to evaporate (dry off) it must take heat out of the skin below.

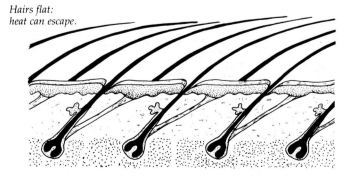 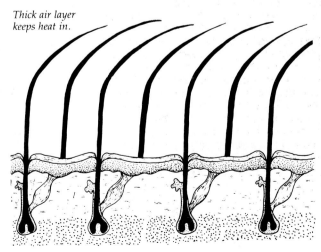

Signals from the brain cause the **erector muscles** of the hairs to contract. The hairs stand up, trapping a thicker layer of air against the skin.

Messages from the heat and cold receptors in the skin tell the brain which of these responses is needed at any one time.

Behaviour

The things which an animal does in order to deal with its environment are called its behaviour. There are two types of behaviour: **instinctive behaviour** and **learned behaviour**.

Instinctive behaviour

This type of behaviour is said to be **innate**. This means that from the moment an animal is born, it knows how to do certain things. Reflexes (see pages 156–7) are also innate, but instincts are much more complicated, as is shown in the diagrams below.

BEHAVIOUR IN BEES

Bees are **social insects** which live together in highly-organised hives or nests. In the hive there are three classes of bee. There is one **queen** whose job is to lay eggs (up to 1500 each day). There are a few hundred **drones** (male), most of which will mate just once with the queen. The rest of the hive, perhaps 100 000, are **workers**, sterile females who do all the work of the hive. They make the wax cells where eggs are laid and food is

do a sort of dance in front of the others. From this, they can tell not only how far away the food is, but also in which direction exactly they must fly to reach it.

In early spring, eggs are laid in the special queen cells. When the larvae hatch, they are given special food called **royal jelly** which makes them develop into new queens. Before they do, the old queen and a lot of the workers leave to start a new hive.

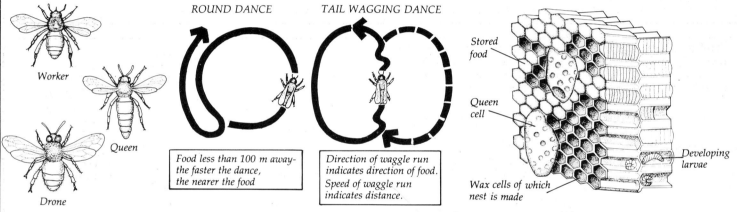

ROUND DANCE   TAIL WAGGING DANCE

Worker

Queen

Drone

Food less than 100 m away- the faster the dance, the nearer the food

Direction of waggle run indicates direction of food. Speed of waggle run indicates distance.

Stored food

Queen cell

Wax cells of which nest is made

Developing larvae

stored, they tend the eggs and they find and gather the food supply for the hive.

To find food, a few workers, called **scout bees**, leave the hive and search for miles around. If successful, they return to the hive and

The first queen to hatch kills the others, mates with some drones and begins the egg-laying process all over again. All the bees' activities, which allow the hive to run so efficiently, are instinctive.

BEHAVIOUR IN BIRDS

Birds are **territorial animals**. They choose a piece of ground as their own and keep other birds out. A large bird like an eagle needs a large area, while a small bird may need only a tree or a bush. The territory is used for breeding and feeding.

Small birds may mark off their territory by song. They fly round, stopping to sing at spots called **song posts**. It is the male who

selects the territory and his song will attract females. Some birds can sing their species' song without ever having heard it, but usually, to get it just right, they must hear it being sung. Nest building is also an instinctive activity of birds. No matter how elaborate the nest, they do not need to be taught how to build it.

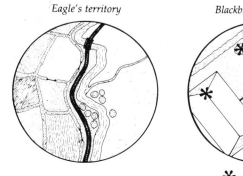

Eagle's territory

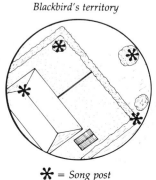

Blackbird's territory

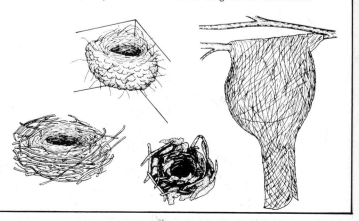

＊ = Song post

Learned behaviour

This is behaviour which has come about because of some experience which an animal has had. Unlike instinctive behaviour, it is not fixed and unchanging, but can be changed again and again as a result of further experiences. There are several types of learning, including **conditioning**, **trial and error learning**, and **insight learning**.

Conditioning is a process by which a response usually caused by one stimulus can be brought about by a different one. Here is an example.

If food is put into a dog's mouth, it produces saliva. This is a simple reflex.

Every time the food is produced, a bell is rung.

After a while, the dog will salivate when the bell is rung, even though the food is not there.

Food: UNCONDITIONED STIMULUS

Saliva: REFLEX RESPONSE

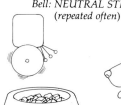

Bell: NEUTRAL STIMULUS (repeated often)

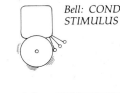
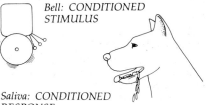

Bell: CONDITIONED STIMULUS

Saliva: CONDITIONED RESPONSE

The saliva is now known as the **conditioned response** and the bell is called the **conditioned stimulus**.

Humans can also be conditioned in some ways. If an alcoholic, for example, is given an unpleasant stimulus such as an electric shock along with the taste of alcohol, it may help him or her to overcome the addiction.

Trial and error learning occurs when an animal is given a reward if it does a certain thing. It associates that behaviour with the reward and so will tend to do it again. It may also be punished if it does the wrong thing, for example:

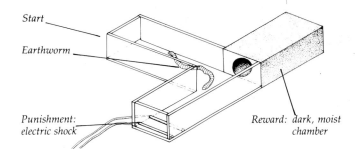

Start

Earthworm

Punishment: electric shock

Reward: dark, moist chamber

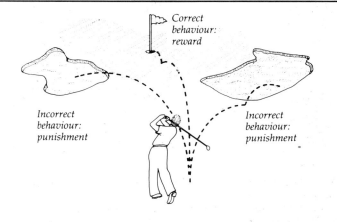

Correct behaviour: reward

Incorrect behaviour: punishment

Incorrect behaviour: punishment

The worm eventually learns to turn to the right if put in this apparatus.

Humans also use trial and error learning. A golfer, for example, might try holding a club in different ways when hitting the ball.

Insight learning, or reasoning, is the highest form of learning. It is the ability to solve a problem directly and not by using trial and error. We think about the problem, recall past experiences which may be useful and so come up with the answer. Reasoning is the basis of intelligence and is very highly developed in humans. The only other animals which seem able to use reasoning are monkeys and chimps as the experiment below indicates.

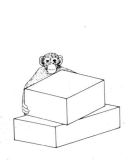

The chimpanzee cannot reach the bananas. He reasons that if he piles the crates one on top of another, he can climb up them and so reach the fruit.

SECTION 16

Reproduction Development and Growth

Reproduction

Organisms do not live for ever. Although some organisms live longer than others, eventually all of them must grow old and die. To prevent their species from becoming extinct, the older organisms produce 'copies' of themselves to carry on after them. Thus, individual members of a species die, but the species itself does not disappear. This is called **reproduction**. There are two kinds of reproduction: **asexual** reproduction and **sexual** reproduction.

ASEXUAL REPRODUCTION occurs when young organisms are produced by just one parent. All the offspring have the same **genes** (see pages 206–7) as each other and as the parent. They are said to be **genetically identical** (like identical twins). Such a group of genetically identical organisms is called a **clone**.

Asexual reproduction is normal among plants and single-celled organisms. It is less common in animals except for simple types such as Hydra (see pages 32–3). Larger, more complex animals have too many specialised cells and organs for asexual reproduction to be successful. Some examples of asexual reproduction are illustrated below.

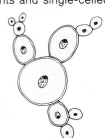

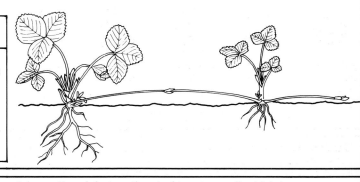

> **ADVANTAGES OF ASEXUAL REPRODUCTION**
>
> *It is fast.*
>
> *Only one parent is involved, but this parent, to which the young are genetically identical, has proved itself able to grow and survive successfully.*
>
> *The parent may supply food, water, etc.*
>
> *Rapid spreading may enable the species to crowd out competitors.*
>
> *No outside agents, e.g. to carry pollen or spread seeds, are required.*

> **DISADVANTAGES OF ASEXUAL REPRODUCTION**
>
> *All the offspring are genetically identical. This reduces the variation in the population as a whole and so makes it less able to survive if conditions change.*
>
> *Offspring may be less vigorous.*
>
> *Overcrowding may occur.*

SEXUAL REPRODUCTION involves not one, but two, parent organisms. The parents produce special cells for reproduction. These reproductive cells are called **gametes** or sex cells. Most species produce two distinct types of gametes – male and female. Gametes are **haploid** cells. This means that their nucleus has only half the number of genes which a normal, or **diploid**, cell contains. For this reason, a gamete cannot develop into a new organism by itself. For a new organism to grow, a male gamete and a female gamete must meet. Their two 'half-nuclei can then join together to form one cell which has a complete nucleus. This process is called **fertilisation**. The new cell which is formed is called a **zygote**. The zygote, with its complete set of genes, can now grow into a new organism. Since half of its genes have come from one parent and half from the other, the young organism will be a bit like both parents, but can never be exactly identical to either one. Some organisms which use sexual reproduction are illustrated below.

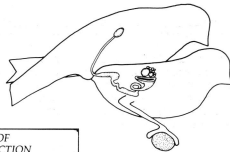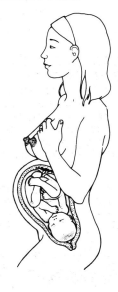

> **ADVANTAGES OF SEXUAL REPRODUCTION**
>
> *Leads to increased variation in the population, so giving the species a better chance of survival in changing conditions.*
>
> *Offspring are often more vigorous.*

> **DISADVANTAGES OF SEXUAL REPRODUCTION**
>
> *Two parent organisms are required.*
>
> *Young may be vulnerable and take some time to develop into adults.*
>
> *Outside agents, e.g. to carry pollen or seeds, may be required.*

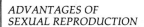

Asexual reproduction

Asexual reproduction is reproduction from just one parent organism. It is common in plants (see pages 170–1) and in various simple forms of life. Larger animals, which are made of large numbers of cells each differentiated to form specialised tissues and organs, are too complex to reproduce in this way.

Under the right conditions, asexual reproduction can be very fast and can result very quickly in the production of large numbers of offspring. All such offspring, coming from a single parent, are **genetically identical** to each other (like identical twins), and, together, all the descendants form a group called a **clone**. Among the common types of asexual reproduction are **binary fission**, **budding** and **spore formation.**

BINARY FISSION means splitting in two. It is a common method of reproduction in single-celled organisms. It happens like this. First, the organism grows to its maximum size. Then the nucleus reproduces to form two complete and identical daughter nuclei, one for each new cell. Finally, the cytoplasm is divided and the parent cell splits into identical daughter cells.

BINARY FISSION IN AMOEBA, a single-celled animal

  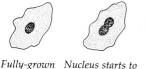

Fully-grown Amoeba | *Nucleus starts to replicate (copy) itself.* | *Daughter nuclei form.* | *Cell constricts.* | *Daughter cells separate.*

BINARY FISSION IN PARAMECIUM, a single-celled animal

Fully-grown Paramecium | *Paramecium's two nuclei divide.* | *Cell begins to constrict.* | *Daughter cells separate.*

BINARY FISSION IN PLEUROCOCCUS, a single-celled alga, which forms a green powder on walls and fences

Fully-grown cell | *Nucleus divides.* | *Chloroplast divides.* | *Cytoplasm divides.* | *New wall forms.*

The cells often fail to separate after division and so are found in groups of 2, 4, 8, etc.

BINARY FISSION IN BACTERIA Bacteria do not have a proper nucleus, just a single thread of nuclear material. During binary fission, however, this is reproduced, as in other organisms, so that each daughter cell gets a copy.

Fully-grown cell | *Nuclear material divides.* | *Cross wall starts to form.* | *Daughter cells separate.*

Under ideal conditions, bacteria can reproduce every 20 minutes to form huge numbers of progeny.

BUDDING occurs in yeast, a fungus which consists of single cells instead of hyphae (see pages 28–9). A bulge called a bud forms on the yeast cell. Its nucleus divides and a daughter nucleus goes into the bud. The bud gets bigger until it eventually separates to form a daughter cell. If growth conditions are good, small buds may form on the larger ones before they have broken off. In this way, chains of yeast cells are formed.

A type of budding also occurs in simple animals such as Hydra. In a multicellular organism such as Hydra, it is **undifferentiated** cells which are able to form into buds.

BUDDING IN YEAST

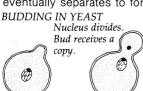 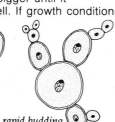

Nucleus divides. Bud receives a copy.

Bud begins to form on parent cell. | *Bud is now a daughter cell.* | *Very rapid budding produces chains of cells.*

BUDDING IN HYDRA

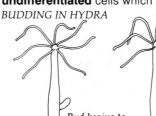 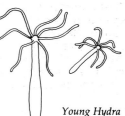

Bud begins to form on parent. | *Bud develops into young Hydra.* | *Young Hydra breaks away.*

SPORE FORMATION is the usual method of reproduction for fungi, including Mucor, the common pin mould. The body, or **mycelium**, of Mucor is made of a tangled mass of fine threads called **hyphae** (sing: *hypha*). The hyphae spread through a suitable food source, digesting and absorbing it. Eventually, some hyphae grow upwards out of the food. Swellings called **sporangia** (sing: *sporangium*) develop at the top of these.

Inside the sporangia are formed the reproductive cells called spores. When the sporangia burst open, these tough little cells are released and are carried off in the air. They can survive very harsh conditions until they chance to land on some moist food. They then germinate quickly, sending hyphae into the food and so forming a new mycelium.

 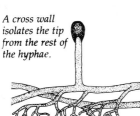 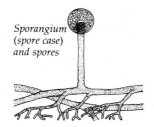 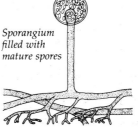 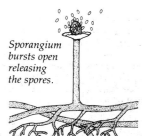

A branch begins to grow upwards away from the feeding hyphae. | *A cross wall isolates the tip from the rest of the hyphae.* | *Sporangium (spore case) and spores* | *Sporangium filled with mature spores* | *Sporangium bursts open releasing the spores.*

Vegetative reproduction in angiosperms

When **angiosperms** (flowering plants) reproduce sexually, seeds are formed. Plants formed from seed are often very vigorous and show a lot of variety. However, asexual reproduction, usually called **vegetative reproduction**, is common among the flowering plants. This kind of reproduction allows plants to spread much more quickly than by seed. Also, while young seedlings are weak and vulnerable, young plants produced vegetatively can often rely on food and water from the parent plant. On the other hand, like all offspring produced asexually, such plants are all **genetically identical** (clones) and this lack of variety can be a source of weakness for the species.

RUNNERS are long, thin stems which grow along the ground from the parent plant. Roots and buds appear at the ends of the runners and new plants develop from these. Eventually, the runner rots, leaving each new plant on its own. Since each parent plant produces a number of runners, a very dense patch of plants can form, crowding out the competition. Strawberries and creeping buttercups spread by means of runners.

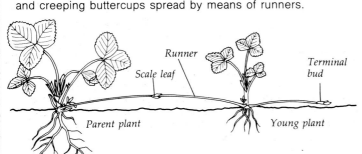

Runner · *Terminal bud* · *Scale leaf* · *Parent plant* · *Young plant*

PLANTLETS are little buds which grow along the edges of Bryophyllum leaves. They fall to the ground and grow into new plants. The little plants can often become very crowded around the parent plant.

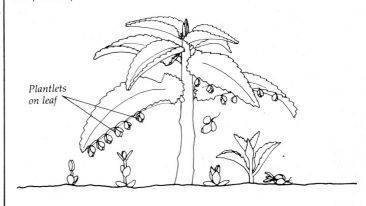

Plantlets on leaf

Perennation

Many herbaceous (non-woody) plants seem to die off at the end of each season, yet they appear again at the start of the next. Plants like these are called **perennials**. They can come back 'from the dead' like this because, during their growing season, they store food under the ground in special food-storage organs. When winter is over, they can use this food to put up new shoots. This is called **perennation**.

It is really a sort of plant hibernation. However, each year perennials produce extra food-storage organs and new plant can grow from any of these. Since in this way one plant can give rise to many new plants, this is a form of vegetative reproduction as well as hibernation. Examples of perennation include the formation of bulbs, corms, tubers and rhizomes.

TUBERS are the food storage organs of plants like the potato. During the summer, tubers form at the ends of underground stems as they swell up with food (mainly starch) made by the leaves. Being stems, tubers have buds on them, commonly called 'eyes'. After the winter, these buds use the food store to produce new shoots. New plants and finally, more tubers grow from these.

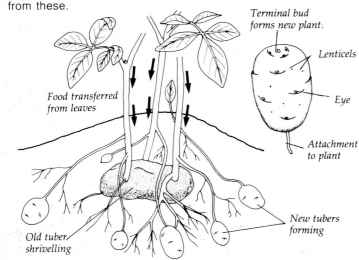

Food transferred from leaves · *Terminal bud forms new plant.* · *Lenticels* · *Eye* · *Attachment to plant* · *New tubers forming* · *Old tuber shrivelling*

RHIZOMES, like tubers, are underground stems swollen with stored food. However, unlike tubers, the food is stored all along the stem. Each spring, a **terminal (end) bud** uses some food to send up new flowers and leaves. Food from these leaves is then sent back for storage. Food stored in **lateral (side) buds** causes the rhizome to branch. Rhizomes last for years, but when the older parts eventually die, this leaves the younger branches as separate plants on their own.

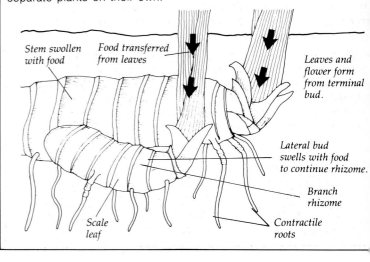

Stem swollen with food · *Food transferred from leaves* · *Leaves and flower form from terminal bud.* · *Lateral bud swells with food to continue rhizome.* · *Branch rhizome* · *Scale leaf* · *Contractile roots*

BULBS consist of a central bud surrounded by thick, fleshy leaves swollen with stored food. In spring, the bud uses the stored food to develop into flowers and green leaves above the ground. These green foliage leaves now make food which they send underground to their bases, causing them to swell. They have thus become the next year's fleshy, food-storing leaves.

The old food-storing leaves shrivel and dry up to form a protective cover on next year's bulb. A new terminal bud grows and the new bulb is ready. Lateral buds may also sprout during the season and, by laying down their own food store, become daughter bulbs. Plants such as onions, daffodils and tulips form bulbs. The diagrams below show the life cycle of a typical bulb.

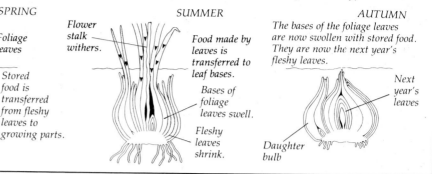

CORMS are short, underground stems swollen with stored food. On top of these food-storing stems is a bud. In spring, the bud uses the food to grow into flowers and green leaves above the ground. The leaves make fresh food which they send back underground. This is stored on top of the old shrivelled corm, forming a new corm. As well as the main bud, lateral buds also sprout during the season and produce daughter corms. Since,

each year, the new corm grows on top of the old one, they gradually tend to get nearer the surface. To prevent this, special roots, called **contractile roots**, grow from the new corm. When these are firmly anchored in the soil, they shorten and pull the corm deeper under the ground. Plants such as the crocus and the gladiolus produce corms.

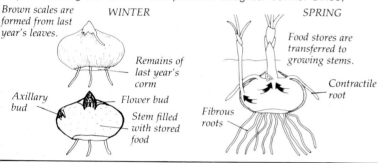
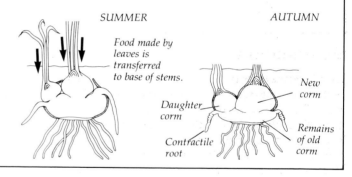

Artificial propagation

Plant growers can make use of vegetative reproduction by plants to **propagate** (spread) a useful variety quickly. For example, by cutting up rhizomes or tubers, and by breaking off and planting separately the daughter bulbs and corms, they can soon multiply the number of corms they have. In this case, the fact that all the offspring come from one parent and are genetically identical is an advantage. It means that the grower knows exactly which variety each corm or bulb will become.

Apart from these methods, growers can also artificially propagate their plants by taking cuttings or by grafting.

Cuttings are usually shoots cut from a desired plant. When planted in moist soil, they grow roots and form a new plant. Geraniums and carnations are often spread by cuttings.

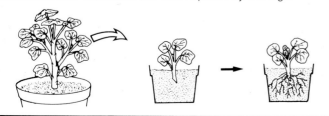

Grafting is used by commercial growers to get the most out of woody plants such as fruit trees or rose bushes. A cutting, called a **scion**, from a valuable variety is closely fitted to the **root stock** of a worthless variety of the same species. Provided the cambium (growing) layers of the two are in contact, the join will heal. The fruit or flowers produced will be those of the scion, while the root system will be that of the stock. Grafting allows new varieties of fruits or flowers to be supplied quickly and abundantly to the market. Also, many commercial varieties of plant are too delicate to survive and grafting provides them with a tough, disease-resistant root system.

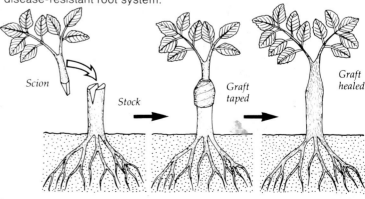

Fertilisation in animals

Apart from some very simple species, all animals use only sexual reproduction to produce offspring. In sexual reproduction there are two parent organisms – a male and a female. The two parents produce special cells for reproduction. These are known as sex cells or **gametes**. The gametes made by male animals are called **sperms** and those made by the female are called **ova** (sing: *ovum*) or, more commonly, eggs. The organs in an animal's body where its gametes are made are known as its **gonads**. Male gonads, which make the sperm, are called **testes** (sing: *testis*). Female gonads, where the ova are made, are called **ovaries**.

SPERMS, the male gametes, are very tiny cells, the smallest cells in a male animal's body. Each sperm consists of a head, which is mainly nucleus, a middle piece and a long tail. By thrashing its tail about, the sperm can swim. Its job is to swim to the female egg cell. Since sperms are so small and 'cheap' to make, they are produced, and wasted, by the hundreds of millions. Some kinds of sperms are shown below.

Human sperm magnified ×1500
Middle piece
Tail
Nucleus *Head*
Chicken sperm magnified ×500
Frog sperm magnified ×500
Rat sperm magnified ×500

EGGS, the female gametes, are very large cells, the largest cells in a female animal's body. Their size is due to the supply of food which they carry to feed the young organisms which will develop from them. The more food an egg must supply, the larger it will be. Mammals' eggs are the smallest, since a young mammal gets its food from its mother's blood. Since their food supply makes them 'expensive' to produce, they are made in smaller numbers than sperm. Some eggs are shown below.

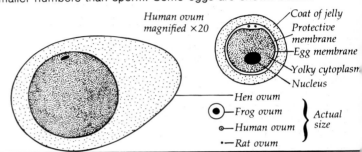

Human ovum magnified ×20
Coat of jelly
Protective membrane
Egg membrane
Yolky cytoplasm
Nucleus
Hen ovum
Frog ovum
Human ovum
Rat ovum
Actual size

The nucleus of a cell contains a number of 'threads' called **chromosomes**. These chromosomes carry the **genes**, or instructions, which the cell needs in order to do its job in the organism. Gametes, however, are different from ordinary cells since they have only half the normal number of chromosomes. We say that gametes carry the **haploid** number of chromosomes, while ordinary cells have the **diploid** number. For example, normal diploid human cells have 46 chromosomes, while human sperm or eggs, which are haploid, have only 23. Because of this, gametes cannot develop into new organisms. They can survive on their own for only a short time before they die. If a new organism is to grow, a sperm must find an egg, penetrate it and join its haploid nucleus with the egg's haploid nucleus. This is called fertilisation. The fertilised egg, or **zygote**, is now a diploid cell with a complete set of chromosomes. During fertilisation, only one sperm is allowed to enter each egg. As soon as one sperm has successfully penetrated an egg, a barrier is set up which keeps out all the other sperms. The diagrams below show how fertilisation takes place in animals.

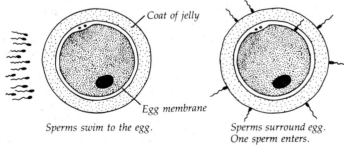

Coat of jelly
Egg membrane
Sperms swim to the egg.
Sperms surround egg. One sperm enters.

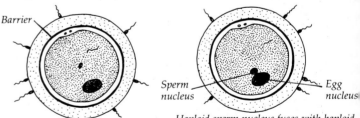

Barrier
Sperm nucleus
Egg nucleus
Barrier forms to keep out other sperms. Successful sperm loses tail.
Haploid sperm nucleus fuses with haploid egg nucleus to form the diploid zygote. The egg has now been fertilised.

Unlike the gametes which formed it, the zygote is able to develop into a new organism. During its period of development the young organism is called an embryo. The first part of the embryo's development consists of the zygote dividing over and over again until it has formed a tight ball of cells. This process is called **cleavage**. After cleavage, the embryo begins to grow in size and gradually change in shape until it starts to resemble the future animal.

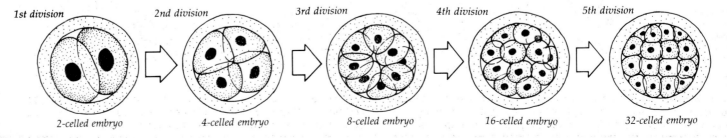

1st division
2nd division
3rd division
4th division
5th division
2-celled embryo
4-celled embryo
8-celled embryo
16-celled embryo
32-celled embryo

External fertilisation

Sexual reproduction by animals is not possible without water. The sperms must have water to swim in to reach the eggs. The eggs, both before and after fertilisation, must be kept moist or they will dry up and die. This is no problem for those animals which live in water or which return to water to breed. They simply release their gametes (eggs or sperms) into the water around them and let fertilisation take place there. This is called external fertilisation. Among the animals which use external fertilisation are pomatoceros, herring, sticklebacks and frogs.

POMATOCEROS is a small bristleworm which lives inside 'cement' tubes on rocks by the seashore. When covered by the tide, male and female worms release their sperms or eggs into the water. There, with luck, sperms will find and fertilise the eggs.

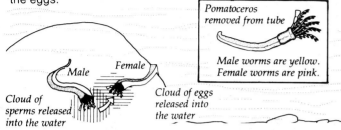

Pomatoceros removed from tube.

Male worms are yellow. Female worms are pink.

Male Female

Cloud of sperms released into the water

Cloud of eggs released into the water

Several things can go wrong. Eggs and sperms may not be released at the same time. They might be swept away by the water or, even if they are successfully fertilised, since they are unprotected, they may be eaten. To get round these problems, Pomatoceros has to produce large numbers of eggs all year round. This is very wasteful.

HERRING leave the open sea at a certain time of year, called the breeding season, to return to the shallow spawning grounds. There males and females spawn (release eggs or sperm) together. The eggs sink to the bottom and stick to seaweed or between stones.

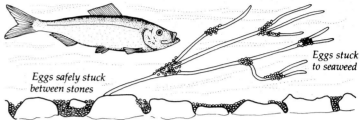

Eggs stuck to seaweed

Eggs safely stuck between stones

Because males and females spawn in the same place and at the same time, most eggs get fertilised. Stuck on the seabed, they are protected to some extent until they hatch a few weeks later. Many do get eaten, however, both before and after hatching. To make up for the losses, females must lay about 30 000 eggs each time.

STICKLEBACKS usually swim in mixed shoals of males and females. In spring, however, when the breeding season starts, each male goes off to find his own territory. There he builds a little nest of weeds and his body takes on its **breeding colours** – a red belly and blue eyes. When a female arrives heavy with eggs, they perform a series of actions called a **courtship ritual**.

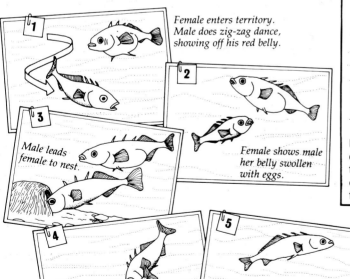

1. Female enters territory. Male does zig-zag dance, showing off his red belly.

2. Female shows male her belly swollen with eggs.

3. Male leads female to nest.

4. Female enters nest. Male quivers against her tail and she lays her eggs.

5. Female leaves nest. Male enters and covers the eggs with sperms.

6. Male fans fertilised eggs to give them oxygen.

7. Male protects young for 10 days after hatching.

FROGS return to a pond each spring to breed. Males go first and their croaking then attracts females who arrive swollen with eggs. The males cling to the females' backs. When the female lays her eggs, the male covers them with a fluid containing his sperms. He must do this immediately because on contact with water a coat of jelly forms on the eggs and the sperms cannot swim through this.

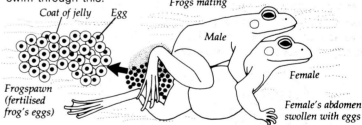

Coat of jelly   Egg

Frogs mating

Male

Female

Frogspawn (fertilised frog's eggs)

Female's abdomen swollen with eggs

By pairing off and spawning together, frogs manage to get most of their eggs fertilised. They then leave them. The jelly holds them together and gives them some protection. Some do get eaten, however, and more are lost after hatching. To make up for the losses, each female must lay about 1000 eggs.

Sticklebacks make sure of successful reproduction in a number of ways. They pair off, but only when both are in breeding condition. Their courtship routine brings eggs and sperms together at the same time. Finally, the male protects both eggs and young. Because of this, sticklebacks need lay only 50–100 eggs and some are almost certain to survive till adulthood.

Internal fertilisation

Terrestrial (land) animals cannot use external fertilisation. If they did, their eggs would dry up and die as soon as they were laid. Also, their sperms, with nothing to swim in, would not be able to reach the eggs to fertilise them. For land animals the only suitable place for the eggs to be fertilised is inside the body of the female. This is called internal fertilisation.

Apart from there being plenty of moisture, internal fertilisation has other advantages. Since the sperms are actually placed inside the female's body, there is a very good chance that they will find and fertilise the eggs. Also, once fertilised, the eggs can be better protected and so are more likely to survive and develop. Among the animals which use internal fertilisation are the insects, birds and mammals.

Before a male can pass his sperms into a female, their bodies must be coupled firmly together. This is known as **copulation** or sexual intercourse. Some examples of copulation are shown in the diagrams below.

INTERNAL FERTILISATION IN LOCUSTS

Locusts live in desert areas. They mate after rain when the sand is warm and damp. The male courts the female by stalking her and making chirping noises with his legs. He then jumps on her back and curves his abdomen down under hers so that the ends meet.

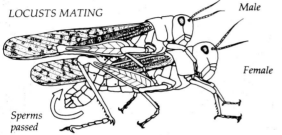

LOCUSTS MATING
Male
Female
Sperms passed

A bag of sperm is passed from his abdomen into hers. The bag bursts and she uses the sperm to fertilise her eggs. Making use of her very stretchy abdomen with its little 'spades' at the end,

she buries the fertilised eggs – 50 to 100 of them – deep under the damp sand.

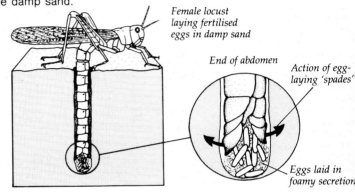

Female locust laying fertilised eggs in damp sand

End of abdomen

Action of egg-laying 'spades'

Eggs laid in foamy secretion

Finally, she covers the eggs in a foamy substance. Later on, this hardens to form a protective 'pod' round the eggs until they hatch.

INTERNAL FERTILISATION IN BIRDS

During the breeding season, each species of bird shows its own special pattern of behaviour.

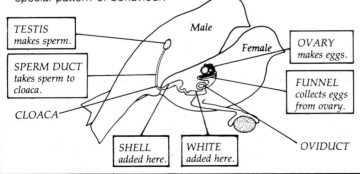

TESTIS makes sperm.
Male
SPERM DUCT takes sperm to cloaca.
Female
OVARY makes eggs.
FUNNEL collects eggs from ovary.
CLOACA
SHELL added here.
WHITE added here.
OVIDUCT

In general, though, the male bird will select a territory and defend it against intruders. He then tries to attract a female, perhaps by singing, by showing off brightly-coloured feathers, or by going through a certain series of movements. When this courtship has been successful, a nest is built. The male and female then **copulate**. The male bird perches on the female's back and the two press their reproductive openings, called **cloaca**, together. The male passes a fluid containing sperms into the female. The sperms travel along a tube called the **oviduct** until they meet the female egg cells which they then fertilise. The fertilised egg cells, which have already had yolk added to them, pass down the oviduct. First the white, then the hard, protective shell is added and the eggs are laid. The female **incubates** the eggs by sitting on them to keep them warm until they hatch.

INTERNAL FERTILISATION IN MAMMALS

Male mammals have a special organ for passing sperms into the female. This is called the **penis**. The penis is made of a spongy kind of material called **erectile tissue**. During sexual intercourse, this tissue fills with blood and the penis becomes stiff and erect. It is now possible for the male to insert it into the female's birth canal or **vagina**. By moving it back and forth inside the vagina, the male can cause a fluid, known as **semen**, to spurt out of the penis into the vagina. This is called **ejaculation**. Semen is a mixture of nourishing liquids and sperms. The sperms start to swim up through the female's reproductive system. Some will reach the tubes called **oviducts**. There they meet and fertilise the eggs. The fertilised eggs are not laid. Instead they travel to the **uterus**, where they are nourished and protected, until, having developed to a fairly advanced stage, the young are ready to be born.

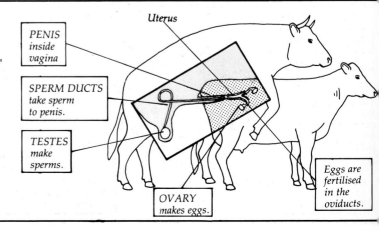

Uterus
PENIS inside vagina
SPERM DUCTS take sperm to penis.
TESTES make sperms.
OVARY makes eggs.
Eggs are fertilised in the oviducts.

The human male reproductive system

The job of the male reproductive system is to make huge numbers of sperms and deliver them inside the body of the female. The sperms are made by two glands called **testes** (sing: *testis*) which are held between the legs in a bag of skin called the **scrotum**. Other glands, called the **prostate gland** and the **seminal vesicles**, make fluids to mix with the sperms. These keep the sperms alive and allow them to swim. This mixture of sperms and fluid is called **semen**.

During sexual intercourse, sperms are forced out of the testes along the two tubes called **sperm ducts**. As they go along, the fluids are added to form the semen. The semen is ejaculated (shot out) from the erect penis into the top of the female's vagina. Apart from later helping to care for the child, the male's part in reproduction is now over. Diagrams of the human male reproductive system are given below.

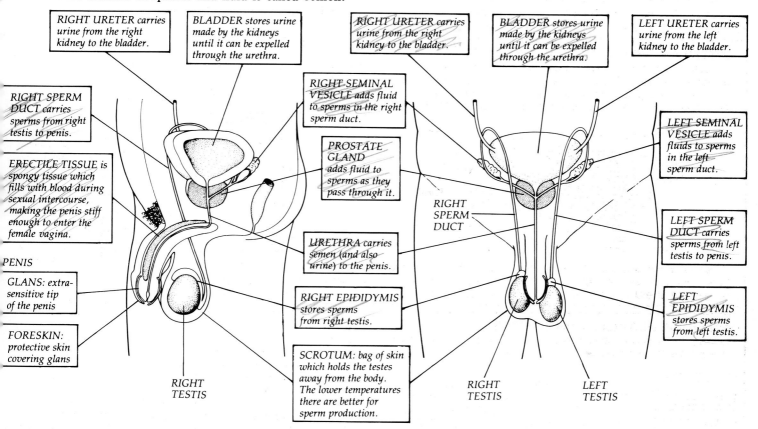

RIGHT URETER carries urine from the right kidney to the bladder.

BLADDER stores urine made by the kidneys until it can be expelled through the urethra.

RIGHT URETER carries urine from the right kidney to the bladder.

BLADDER stores urine made by the kidneys until it can be expelled through the urethra.

LEFT URETER carries urine from the left kidney to the bladder.

RIGHT SPERM DUCT carries sperms from right testis to penis.

RIGHT SEMINAL VESICLE adds fluid to sperms in the right sperm duct.

LEFT SEMINAL VESICLE adds fluids to sperms in the left sperm duct.

ERECTILE TISSUE is spongy tissue which fills with blood during sexual intercourse, making the penis stiff enough to enter the female vagina.

PROSTATE GLAND adds fluid to sperms as they pass through it.

RIGHT SPERM DUCT

LEFT SPERM DUCT carries sperms from left testis to penis.

PENIS

GLANS: extra-sensitive tip of the penis

URETHRA carries semen (and also urine) to the penis.

FORESKIN: protective skin covering glans

RIGHT EPIDIDYMIS stores sperms from right testis.

LEFT EPIDIDYMIS stores sperms from left testis.

RIGHT TESTIS

SCROTUM: bag of skin which holds the testes away from the body. The lower temperatures there are better for sperm production.

RIGHT TESTIS

LEFT TESTIS

TESTES: THE SPERM FACTORIES

The testes make millions of sperms every day. They start production about the age of twelve and go on until about the age of seventy. Each ejaculation contains about 400 million sperms. However, even this makes up only half of one per cent of the total volume of the semen. The fluids make up the rest.

There are a number of compartments inside each testis. These are packed with the **sperm tubules**. It is the cells lining the insides of these tiny tubes which develop to form the sperm.

The sperms are collected from the tubules and stored in the **epididymis** where they mature. They can survive there for about 40 days, but, if unused, they die and are absorbed.

Other cells in the testes, which surround the tubules, make the male sex hormone, **testosterone**. This causes the appearance of the male **secondary sexual characteristics** (see page 180).

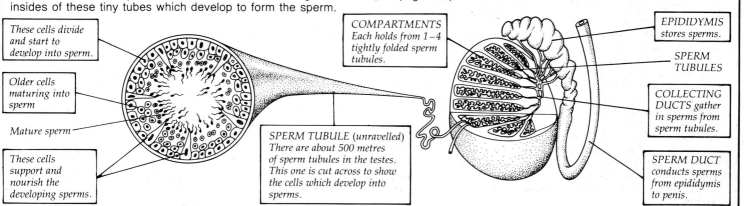

These cells divide and start to develop into sperm.

Older cells maturing into sperm

Mature sperm

These cells support and nourish the developing sperms.

COMPARTMENTS Each holds from 1–4 tightly folded sperm tubules.

SPERM TUBULE (unravelled) There are about 500 metres of sperm tubules in the testes. This one is cut across to show the cells which develop into sperms.

EPIDIDYMIS stores sperms.

SPERM TUBULES

COLLECTING DUCTS gather in sperms from sperm tubules.

SPERM DUCT conducts sperms from epididymis to penis.

The human female reproductive system

While the man's part in human reproduction is simply the production and delivery of **gametes**, the woman's role is much more complex. Her body not only produces the female gametes (called **ova** or eggs), but also receives the sperm, allows fertilisation to take place and then provides protection for the developing baby. After the baby is born, her body, as is the case in all mammals, will produce milk with which to feed it.

The eggs are made by the two **ovaries**. The sperms with which to fertilise them are received from the male's **penis** by the birth canal or **vagina**. The eggs are fertilised inside tubes called **oviducts** which connect the ovaries with an organ called the **uterus** or womb. It is inside the uterus that the fertilised egg will develop and grow into a baby.

Diagrams of the human female reproductive system are drawn below.

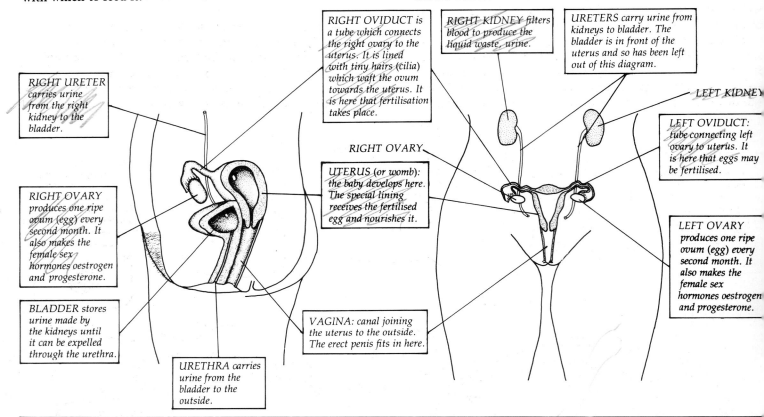

RIGHT OVIDUCT is a tube which connects the right ovary to the uterus. It is lined with tiny hairs (cilia) which waft the ovum towards the uterus. It is here that fertilisation takes place.

RIGHT KIDNEY filters blood to produce the liquid waste, urine.

URETERS carry urine from kidneys to bladder. The bladder is in front of the uterus and so has been left out of this diagram.

LEFT KIDNEY

RIGHT URETER carries urine from the right kidney to the bladder.

LEFT OVIDUCT: tube connecting left ovary to uterus. It is here that eggs may be fertilised.

RIGHT OVARY

RIGHT OVARY produces one ripe ovum (egg) every second month. It also makes the female sex hormones oestrogen and progesterone.

UTERUS (or womb): the baby develops here. The special lining receives the fertilised egg and nourishes it.

LEFT OVARY produces one ripe ovum (egg) every second month. It also makes the female sex hormones oestrogen and progesterone.

BLADDER stores urine made by the kidneys until it can be expelled through the urethra.

VAGINA: canal joining the uterus to the outside. The erect penis fits in here.

URETHRA carries urine from the bladder to the outside.

THE OVARIES

The ovaries produce between them just one ripe egg each month. This egg ripens inside a ball of cells called a **Graafian follicle**. The follicle nourishes the egg and also makes the sex hormone, **oestrogen**. About the 14th day of the **menstrual cycle** (see page 197), the ripe egg bursts from the ovary. This is called **ovulation**. It is then moved along the oviduct where it may be fertilised if sperms are present. If it is not fertilised within 36 hours, it will die. The empty follicle then becomes a **corpus luteum** and starts to make a second hormone, **progesterone**. Oestrogen and progesterone, between them, control the condition of the uterus during the menstrual cycle. The diagrams below show how an ovary develops during a 28-day menstrual cycle.

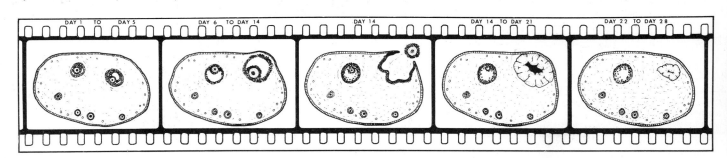

Several follicles start to ripen at once. Follicle cells secrete oestrogen into the bloodstream.

One follicle starts to grow rapidly. The others begin to degenerate.

OVULATION takes place – the egg bursts from the ovary. The funnel-like end of the oviduct curls round the ovary to gather the egg.

The empty follicle develops into a corpus luteum. This secretes progesterone into the bloodstream.

The corpus luteum starts to degenerate and make less hormones. This brings on menstruation.

Fertilisation and implantation

During sexual intercourse a man will ejaculate about 4 ml of semen. On average, this will contain about 400 million sperms. These are deposited at the top of the woman's vagina, around the neck of the womb, called the **cervix**. The sperms begin to swim upwards through the cervix, then through the uterus, then out along the oviducts. Of the hundreds of millions of sperms which start the journey, only a few thousand get this far. A few hundred of these will eventually reach the end of the oviduct. It is at the end of the oviduct that fertilisation takes place.

After ovulation, an egg can survive for up to 36 hours. If sperms reach it within that time, one of them may fertilise it. The fertilised egg, or **zygote**, will then start to divide. As it does so, tiny microscopic hairs called **cilia**, which line the oviduct, push it gently towards the uterus, a journey of about four days. By the time it arrives there, it has developed into a little ball of cells. Meanwhile, the hormones, **oestrogen** and **progesterone**, made by the ovary, have caused the lining of the uterus to become thicker. Food leaks from this lining and is absorbed by the little embryo. Thus, soon after fertilisation, the human ovum has an outside supply of food. For this reason, human ova, and those of other mammals, are small compared to those of birds, etc.

A few days after arriving in the uterus, the embryo attaches itself to the lining and begins to receive food directly from it. It then sinks down into the lining until it is completely buried. This process is called **implantation**. The woman is now pregnant. The diagrams below show the whole sequence of events as it occurs.

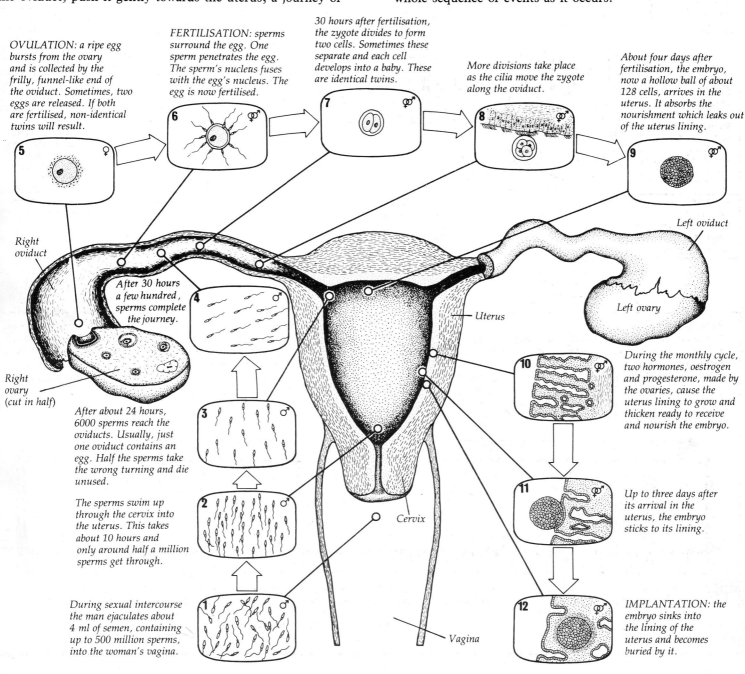

OVULATION: a ripe egg bursts from the ovary and is collected by the frilly, funnel-like end of the oviduct. Sometimes, two eggs are released. If both are fertilised, non-identical twins will result.

FERTILISATION: sperms surround the egg. One sperm penetrates the egg. The sperm's nucleus fuses with the egg's nucleus. The egg is now fertilised.

30 hours after fertilisation, the zygote divides to form two cells. Sometimes these separate and each cell develops into a baby. These are identical twins.

More divisions take place as the cilia move the zygote along the oviduct.

About four days after fertilisation, the embryo, now a hollow ball of about 128 cells, arrives in the uterus. It absorbs the nourishment which leaks out of the uterus lining.

Right oviduct

Left oviduct

After 30 hours a few hundred, sperms complete the journey.

Left ovary

Right ovary (cut in half)

After about 24 hours, 6000 sperms reach the oviducts. Usually, just one oviduct contains an egg. Half the sperms take the wrong turning and die unused.

The sperms swim up through the cervix into the uterus. This takes about 10 hours and only around half a million sperms get through.

Uterus

During the monthly cycle, two hormones, oestrogen and progesterone, made by the ovaries, cause the uterus lining to grow and thicken ready to receive and nourish the embryo.

Up to three days after its arrival in the uterus, the embryo sticks to its lining.

Cervix

During sexual intercourse the man ejaculates about 4 ml of semen, containing up to 500 million sperms, into the woman's vagina.

Vagina

IMPLANTATION: the embryo sinks into the lining of the uterus and becomes buried by it.

Pregnancy and birth

Once the embryo has implanted itself in the lining of the uterus, it grows quickly. Rapid divisions lead to the formation of more and more cells. Some of these cells go on to become the baby. Others form a link between it and its mother. This link starts with 'fingers' called **villi** growing out of the embryo into the spongy uterus lining. From the lining's rich blood supply they absorb all the food and oxygen needed by the embryo and into it they dump the embryo's waste. This system gradually develops into an organ called the **placenta** joined to the baby by the **umbilical cord**.

The following diagrams outline some of the developments which take place during pregnancy.

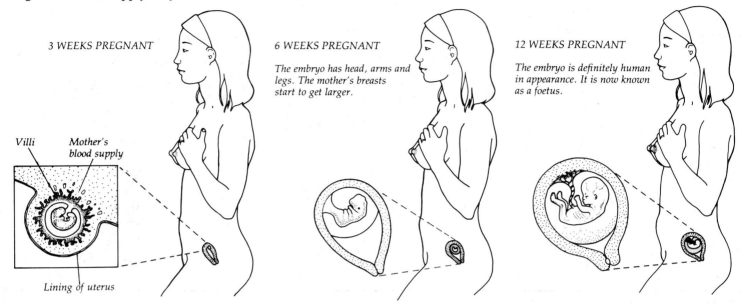

3 WEEKS PREGNANT

6 WEEKS PREGNANT

The embryo has head, arms and legs. The mother's breasts start to get larger.

12 WEEKS PREGNANT

The embryo is definitely human in appearance. It is now known as a foetus.

Villi
Mother's blood supply
Lining of uterus

THE PLACENTA

The placenta is a plate-shaped organ formed partly of the mother's tissues and partly from the baby's. Inside the placenta there are large blood spaces through which the mother's blood flows. Bathed in this blood are the **villi**, which now contain the thin-walled capillaries carrying the foetus' blood. Food and oxygen can pass easily from the mother's blood into the foetus, while waste (such as urea) and carbon dioxide pass in the other direction into the mother's blood for disposal. This exchange of materials between the two blood systems is very fast and efficient, but, as the diagrams show, the blood of mother and foetus are not allowed to mix. This is because the mother's blood will contain substances – hormones, drugs, germs, etc. – which would harm the growing baby. Unfortunately, this system is not foolproof. Many poisons and diseases can cross the placenta and harm the foetus.

The foetal blood is carried to and from the placenta in the blood vessels of the umbilical cord. The placenta also makes the hormones, oestrogen and progesterone, which keep the uterus in the right condition during pregnancy.

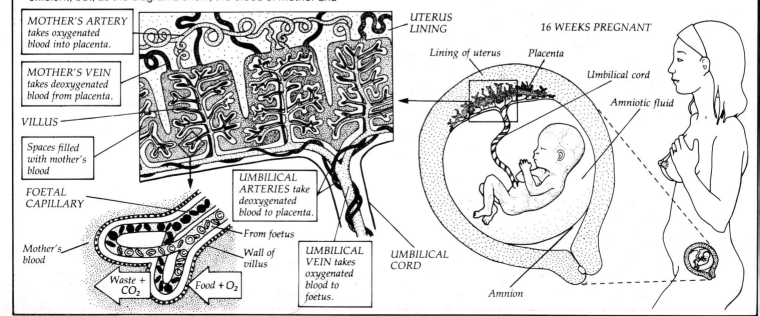

MOTHER'S ARTERY takes oxygenated blood into placenta.

MOTHER'S VEIN takes deoxygenated blood from placenta.

VILLUS

Spaces filled with mother's blood

FOETAL CAPILLARY

Mother's blood

Waste + CO_2

Food + O_2

From foetus

Wall of villus

UMBILICAL ARTERIES take deoxygenated blood to placenta.

UMBILICAL VEIN takes oxygenated blood to foetus.

UTERUS LINING

UMBILICAL CORD

16 WEEKS PREGNANT

Lining of uterus
Placenta
Umbilical cord
Amniotic fluid

Amnion

As the baby grows inside the uterus, a watery liquid called **amniotic fluid** forms around it. The fluid is held inside a thin-walled water sac or **amnion**. The foetus floats in the amniotic fluid. This helps to keep its temperature steady and cushions it against knocks and bumps as its mother moves around. Although it is surrounded by liquid, the foetus is in no danger of drowning. It gets all the oxygen it needs from its mother's blood through the placenta and umbilical cord. It does not need to use its developing lungs.

The time taken for the baby to develop, from fertilisation to birth, is called the **gestation period**. For humans the gestation period is about 40 weeks (9 months). If a baby is born before its full term is up, it is said to be **premature**. Premature babies need special care if they are to survive. The gestation periods of other mammals depend on how big they must grow before they are born. A mouse's gestation period, for example, is only 2½ weeks, while an elephant has a gestation period of 18 months.

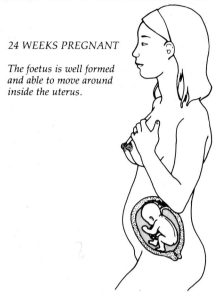

24 WEEKS PREGNANT

The foetus is well formed and able to move around inside the uterus.

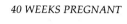

28 WEEKS PREGNANT

The baby moves into a head-down position. Most babies are born head first, though occasionally, a feet first, or breech birth, occurs.

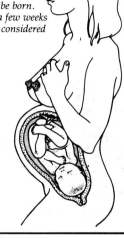

40 WEEKS PREGNANT

The baby is ready to be born. A few weeks less or a few weeks more than 40 is still considered to be normal.

BIRTH

Birth is sparked off by changes in the amounts of hormones in the mother's blood. This causes the wall of the uterus, which has become more muscular during pregnancy, to start contracting every so often. The beginning of these contractions is called 'going into labour'.

Further contractions push the baby's head down into the vagina which stretches open to allow this. At this stage in its life, the baby's skull bones are not fused together. This lets the shape of the skull be changed slightly to help ease its passage through the vagina.

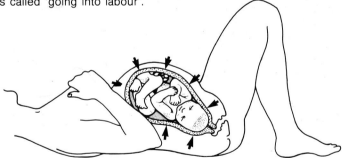

The contractions come more strongly and more often. The amnion bursts, releasing the amniotic fluid. This is known as 'the breaking of the waters'. The cervix is stretched open as the baby's head moves downwards.

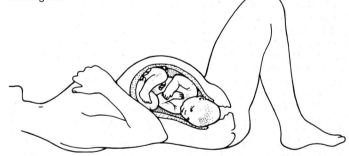

The baby's head emerges, followed shortly by the rest of its body and it takes its first breath of air. The midwife cuts and ties the umbilical cord. Its shrivelled remains will later become the navel. Shortly after the birth, the placenta and other membranes are pushed out of the vagina. For this reason, the placenta is commonly called the afterbirth.

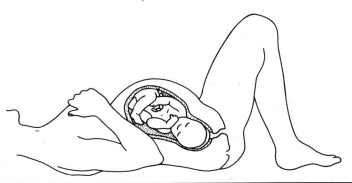

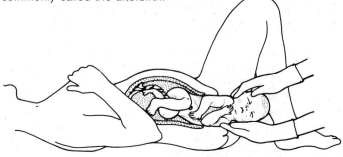

Human growth

Like other new-born mammals, babies cannot cope with solid food. So, during pregnancy, the thousands of tiny **mammary glands** inside the mother's breasts begin to develop until they are ready to produce milk for the baby when it is born. Milk production by these glands is triggered off by the baby suckling at the mother's breasts. It can go on for several months until the baby is able to eat solid food. Mother's milk is the perfect food for a baby. It contains just the right balance of nutrients, it is germ-free, and it is delivered at just the right temperature. Cow's milk, on the other hand, is ideal for a calf, but not so good for a baby. However, for a variety of reasons, many babies are fed from a bottle on cow's milk and they come to no harm.

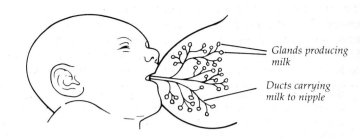

Glands producing milk

Ducts carrying milk to nipple

During the first year, growth is very rapid. It then proceeds more slowly until puberty. As the following diagrams show, during childhood, the proportions of the body, as well as its height, gradually change.

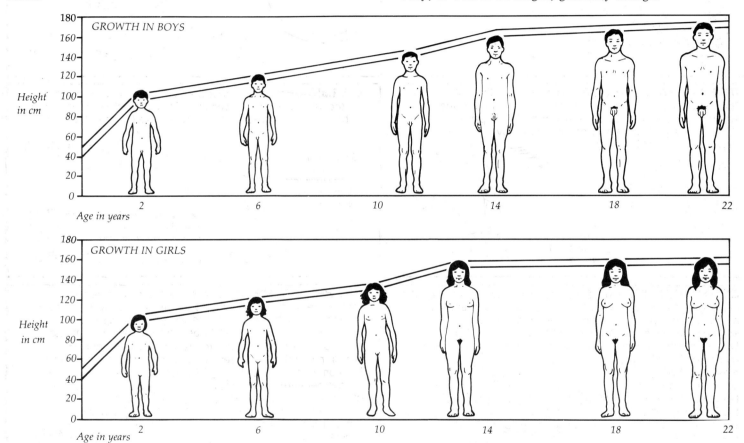

There comes a time in a child's life when its **gonads** (sex organs) start to develop. A girl's **ovaries** start to produce eggs and a boy's **testes** start to make sperm. This stage is called **puberty**. The onset of puberty is caused by hormones made by the **pituitary gland** (see pages 196–7) reaching the gonads in the bloodstream.

With girls, puberty usually begins between the ages of 10 and 14 with the start of **menstruation** (the periods). Periods are irregular at first, but eventually settle down to around one each month. Another feature of puberty is the development of **secondary sexual characteristics**. In girls, these include the growth of breasts, the growth of hair under the arms and between the legs, and the body taking on a more feminine shape.

Puberty begins later in boys, usually between 12 and 16. They begin to produce **semen**, sometimes while sleeping. The male secondary sexual characteristics appear. These include the deepening ('breaking') of the voice, the growth of the penis, the growth of hair on the face, under the arms, between the legs and elsewhere, and the body suddenly becoming more muscular. Puberty in both boys and girls also brings on a sudden growth spurt.

Growing up, however, involves more than physical changes. It also requires changes in outlook and behaviour. These mental changes start at puberty, but usually go on beyond it. This whole period of mental development is called **adolescence**. The adolescent boy or girl is gradually changing into an adult.

Contraception

The fertilisation of an egg is often referred to as **conception**. We say that a child has been conceived. As we have seen, conception results from sexual intercourse. However, there may be many occasions when a couple wish to have sexual intercourse without conception taking place.

To achieve this, they must use some method of **contraception** (*contra*: against). Contraception is also known as birth control or family planning. Some of the most commonly used contraceptive methods are shown in the diagrams below.

SHEATHS or **condoms** are thin rubber sleeves which are rolled on to the erect penis before intercourse. They keep the sperm out of the vagina after ejaculation. They are a simple and effective method of birth control.

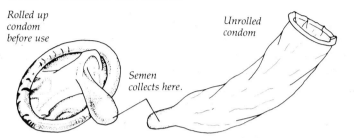

Rolled up condom before use

Unrolled condom

Semen collects here.

THE CAP or **diaphragm** is a dome of soft rubber which the woman fits over the mouth of her womb before intercourse and removes about six hours after. Used together with a spermicidal cream, the cap is very effective at keeping sperms out of the uterus. The correct size of cap is decided by a doctor.

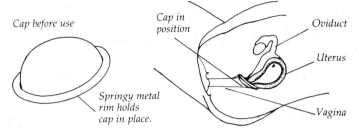

Cap before use

Cap in position

Oviduct

Uterus

Springy metal rim holds cap in place.

Vagina

INTRA-UTERINE DEVICE called the **IUD**, the **coil**, or the **loop** is a small piece of plastic. An IUD is placed in the woman's uterus by a doctor and can be left in place for years. IUDs are very effective and seem to work by preventing the implantation of fertilised eggs.

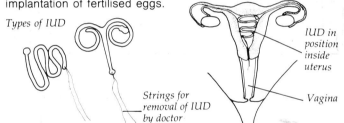

Types of IUD

IUD in position inside uterus

Strings for removal of IUD by doctor

Vagina

SPERMICIDES are chemicals which kill sperms. They are put into the vagina before intercourse. They are not very reliable and are best used as an extra precaution along with some other method.

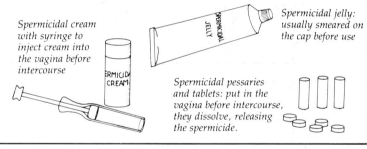

Spermicidal cream with syringe to inject cream into the vagina before intercourse

Spermicidal jelly: usually smeared on the cap before use

Spermicidal pessaries and tablets: put in the vagina before intercourse, they dissolve, releasing the spermicide.

CONTRACEPTIVE PILLS contain hormones which stop the monthly eggs being released from the woman's ovaries and so make pregnancy impossible. The woman takes a pill each day for 21 days. She then takes none for 7 days. During this time normal menstruation occurs. Pill-taking is then resumed. The pill is the most effective contraceptive of all. However, the woman must always remember to take the pill and there can be unpleasant side-effects.

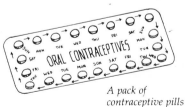

A pack of contraceptive pills

THE RHYTHM METHOD involves the couple having no intercourse on those few days each month around the time of ovulation when the woman is most likely to get pregnant. However, since it is difficult to be sure exactly when this is, intercourse must be avoided for 12 days each month. This makes the method inconvenient and unreliable. To improve it, the woman can chart her temperature each day. A sudden change in temperature is a sign that ovulation is likely to occur and that pregnancy is possible.

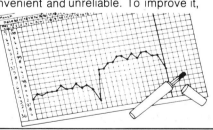

MALE STERILISATION involves a simple operation called a **vasectomy**. The surgeon cuts and ties the sperm ducts which take sperms from the testes to the penis. Since sperms make up only a very small part of a man's semen, a vasectomy does not affect his ability to have intercourse. Six months later the man's semen is tested to make sure it contains no sperms. If it does not, the man is **sterile**, i.e. unable to have any more children.

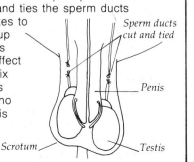

Sperm ducts cut and tied

Penis

Scrotum

Testis

FEMALE STERILISATION involves a slightly more complex operation. The surgeon cuts and ties the oviducts which take the eggs from the ovaries to the uterus. Sperms can no longer reach the eggs and so the woman can have no more children. Male and female sterilisations are very difficult to reverse and so should be considered very seriously before one decides to have them done.

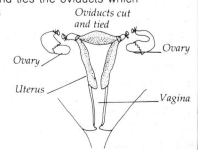

Oviducts cut and tied

Ovary

Ovary

Uterus

Vagina

Insect development

An insect's skin, or **cuticle**, is made of a hard substance called **chitin**. Chitin cannot stretch much. This means that, as a young insect with its huge appetite puts on weight, its cuticle soon becomes too small for its body. It must then moult to get rid of its old cuticle. During a moult, the old skin splits open and is cast off. Underneath is a new, larger skin. This is soft at first and for a short time, until it hardens, the young insect grows rapidly. Little growth then occurs until the next moult. The period between moults is called an **instar**. The number of moults a young insect goes through varies according to the species, but ranges from 2–50.

As well as growth, development for most insects also involves a change in form or type of body, the young form of most insects being quite different from the adult, or **imago** form. Such a change in body form during development is called a **metamorphosis** (*meta*: change; *morph*: form). Some insects go through a gradual or incomplete metamorphosis. Others undergo a complete metamorphosis.

INCOMPLETE METAMORPHOSIS

This is the gradual change in body form during development which is seen in such insects as the locust or the cockroach. When the fertilised eggs hatch, the young insects, although much smaller, are not unlike the adults. However, their colouring may be different, they have no wings and their sex organs are undeveloped. These young insects are called **nymphs**. In order to grow, the nymph must go through a number of moults to get rid of its old, hard skin. As it sheds each old skin, the new cuticle underneath is not only larger, but also more adult in form than the previous one. The biggest change occurs at the last moult from which the nymph emerges as a sexually mature, winged adult insect.

The diagrams below show one such insect – the locust – undergoing an incomplete metamorphosis.

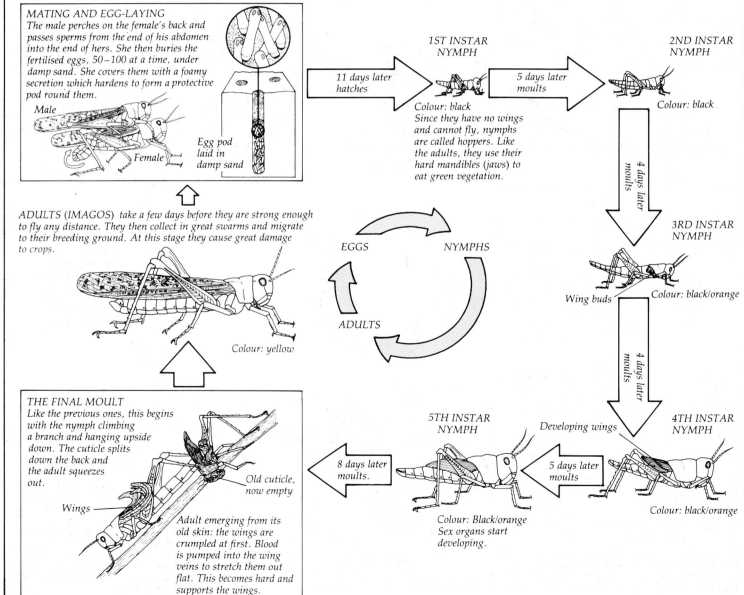

MATING AND EGG-LAYING
The male perches on the female's back and passes sperms from the end of his abdomen into the end of hers. She then buries the fertilised eggs, 50–100 at a time, under damp sand. She covers them with a foamy secretion which hardens to form a protective pod round them.
Male
Female
Egg pod laid in damp sand

11 days later hatches

1ST INSTAR NYMPH
Colour: black
Since they have no wings and cannot fly, nymphs are called hoppers. Like the adults, they use their hard mandibles (jaws) to eat green vegetation.

5 days later moults

2ND INSTAR NYMPH
Colour: black

4 days later moults

3RD INSTAR NYMPH
Wing buds   *Colour: black/orange*

4 days later moults

4TH INSTAR NYMPH
Developing wings
Colour: black/orange

5 days later moults

5TH INSTAR NYMPH
Colour: Black/orange
Sex organs start developing.

8 days later moults.

EGGS   NYMPHS
ADULTS

ADULTS (IMAGOS) *take a few days before they are strong enough to fly any distance. They then collect in great swarms and migrate to their breeding ground. At this stage they cause great damage to crops.*
Colour: yellow

THE FINAL MOULT
Like the previous ones, this begins with the nymph climbing a branch and hanging upside down. The cuticle splits down the back and the adult squeezes out.
Wings
Old cuticle, now empty
Adult emerging from its old skin: the wings are crumpled at first. Blood is pumped into the wing veins to stretch them out flat. This becomes hard and supports the wings.

COMPLETE METAMORPHOSIS

This involves a dramatic change from young to adult insect. It is the type of development seen in butterflies and moths, bees and wasps, beetles and flies. When the eggs of such insects hatch, the young emerge as **larvae** (sing: *larva*). Butterfly larvae are commonly called caterpillars, beetle larvae are grubs and fly larvae are maggots. Larvae are completely different in appearance from adults. In fact, from its appearance alone, it is impossible to tell what kind of insect a larva will develop into. There are also other important differences between the stages. Larvae and adults have different habitats and feed on different kinds of food. This is handy since it means that they will not be in competition with each other.

Larvae have huge appetites and spend all their time eating. They grow quickly and, as each old skin gets too small, they moult, revealing a new, bigger skin underneath. Curiously, during this period of growth, their cells are not dividing. They simply swell up as they become bloated with food. Finally, the larvae stop eating, find a suitable spot, and go through their last moult. From this they emerge as **pupae** (sing: *pupa*). The pupae appear to be lifeless or resting. However, inside the case, the larval tissues break down into a kind of soup. This is then rebuilt to form the body of the adult. Sometimes this process takes only a few weeks. Other pupae remain dormant for months in order to survive the rigours of winter. Eventually, the pupa case splits open and the adult emerges. It pumps blood into its wings to expand them. This hardens in the veins and, when the wings are ready, the insect can fly off. Its job is to find a mate. It will eat only enough food to provide energy for this task. Some adult insects eat nothing at all.

After mating, the eggs are laid on a source of food to provide for the larvae when they hatch. The adult life is usually short – many insects spend only a few hours as adults.

The diagrams below show how one such insect – the Cabbage White Butterfly – undergoes a complete metamorphosis.

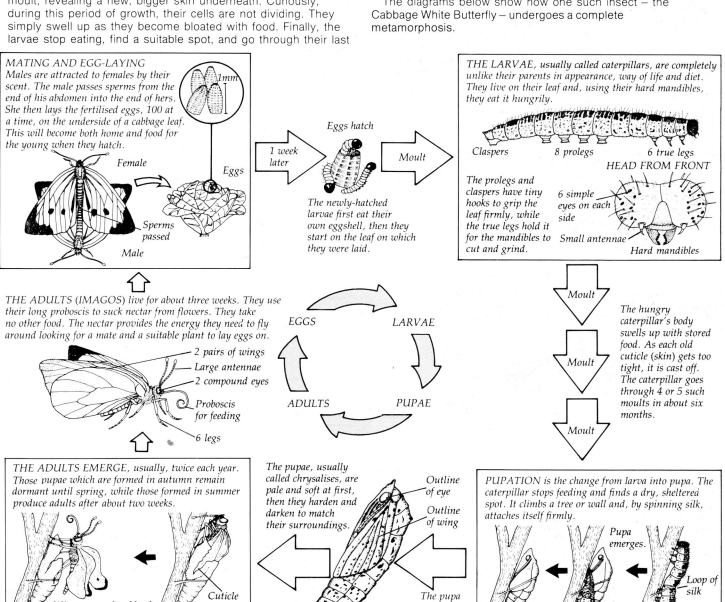

MATING AND EGG-LAYING
Males are attracted to females by their scent. The male passes sperms from the end of his abdomen into the end of hers. She then lays the fertilised eggs, 100 at a time, on the underside of a cabbage leaf. This will become both home and food for the young when they hatch.

1mm

Female

Eggs

Sperms passed

Male

1 week later

Eggs hatch

The newly-hatched larvae first eat their own eggshell, then they start on the leaf on which they were laid.

Moult

THE LARVAE, usually called caterpillars, are completely unlike their parents in appearance, way of life and diet. They live on their leaf and, using their hard mandibles, they eat it hungrily.

Claspers   8 prolegs   6 true legs
                                 HEAD FROM FRONT

The prolegs and claspers have tiny hooks to grip the leaf firmly, while the true legs hold it for the mandibles to cut and grind.

6 simple eyes on each side

Small antennae

Hard mandibles

Moult

THE ADULTS (IMAGOS) live for about three weeks. They use their long proboscis to suck nectar from flowers. They take no other food. The nectar provides the energy they need to fly around looking for a mate and a suitable plant to lay eggs on.

— 2 pairs of wings
— Large antennae
— 2 compound eyes
— Proboscis for feeding
— 6 legs

EGGS   LARVAE

ADULTS   PUPAE

Moult

Moult

The hungry caterpillar's body swells up with stored food. As each old cuticle (skin) gets too tight, it is cast off. The caterpillar goes through 4 or 5 such moults in about six months.

Moult

THE ADULTS EMERGE, usually, twice each year. Those pupae which are formed in autumn remain dormant until spring, while those formed in summer produce adults after about two weeks.

Wings expand as blood is pumped into them.

Cuticle splits.

The cuticle splits open and the adult butterfly pushes itself out. Its wings are small and folded in such a way that hanging upside down, it pumps blood into them. This hardens in the veins and stiffens the wings.

The pupae, usually called chrysalises, are pale and soft at first, then they harden and darken to match their surroundings.

Outline of eye

Outline of wing

The pupa seems to be lifeless or resting. However, inside it, the bloated larval cells are broken down into a sort of soup and the material is used to form the body of the adult.

PUPATION is the change from larva into pupa. The caterpillar stops feeding and finds a dry, sheltered spot. It climbs a tree or wall and, by spinning silk, attaches itself firmly.

Pupa emerges.

Loop of silk

Old cuticle

Cuticle splits open.

Claspers dug into pad of silk

For the next day, it gets shorter and fatter. Its cuticle then splits open and the pupa emerges, gradually pushing the old skin off the end.

Development in fish and amphibians

Fish eggs hatch out before all their **yolk** has been used up. Since the yolk is the food supply for the developing embryo, the newly-hatched fish, known as **larvae** (sing: larva), are still poorly developed at this stage. The larvae carry the unused yolk in a **yolk sac** attached to their bodies. Blood vessels absorb food from the yolk sac and transfer it to the larvae. While the food lasts, the larvae do not eat. They do get eaten, however, in large numbers, fish larvae being an important source of food for many species.

Some fish, for example the stickleback, protect their young during this stage. Others are left to fend for themselves.

Within a few weeks the yolk is all absorbed and the young fish, which are now known as **fry**, emerge. The fry, though very small, are similar in appearance to the adults and are now capable of finding and eating their own food.

The diagrams below show how one fish, the trout, develops.

FERTILISED EGGS are laid in a batch, thousands of them at a time, on the bottom of a river, and covered with gravel.

2 MONTHS LATER, just before hatching, the embryo trout develop. They are kept fresh and healthy by the fast-flowing river water.

NEWLY-HATCHED LARVA is commonly called an alevin. For a few days after hatching, the alevins rest. Then they leave their trench and bury themselves in the gravel.

4 WEEKS AFTER HATCHING, most of the yolk has been absorbed. This is the alevin's only source of food. The gravel protects the alevin from being eaten by predators.

6 WEEKS AFTER HATCHING, all the yolk is finished and the young fry leave the gravel. They now start feeding on small pond animals. In about three years, they will be ready to breed.

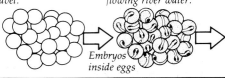

Embryos inside eggs

Yolk sac — Blood vessels absorbing yolk

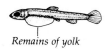

Remains of yolk

Amphibians hatch from their eggs in the form of tadpoles. The tadpole is the **larval** stage of the amphibian. A tadpole's body and way of life are completely different from the adult form. Therefore, to become an adult, the tadpole must go through a drastic **metamorphosis** (change of form). The diagrams below show the life cycle and metamorphosis of one amphibian – the frog.

FROG SPAWN, a mass of jelly, containing thousands of fertilised frog's eggs, is abandoned by the adults as soon as they have produced it. The jelly, however, which is called albumen and is similar to egg white,

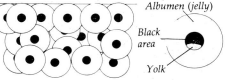

Albumen (jelly)

Black area

Yolk

gives the eggs some protection. The jelly prevents them drying out, being swept away, eaten or damaged. It may also help them resist disease.

10 DAYS LATER, the tadpoles hatch out. Below their mouths there are two sticky mucous glands. They use these to cling on to water weeds. Their mouths cannot open and they cannot feed. Instead, they digest the

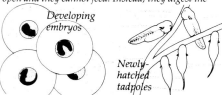

Developing embryos

Newly-hatched tadpoles

remains of their yolk. The gills are not quite ready, so they breathe through their skin.

3 DAYS LATER, the tadpoles can now swim. Their mouths can open and they have developed rough,

Rough lips

External gills

Mucous glands

horny lips with which they can scrape algae from the surface of weeds and stones. They now have external gills for breathing. The branching gill filaments present a large area of surface to the water, from which they absorb dissolved oxygen.

3 YEARS LATER, the frogs are now fully grown and ready to breed. In spring, they make their way, often in large numbers, to the nearest pond. Males cling to

Male

Female

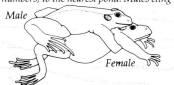

the backs of females and sperms and eggs are released together underwater. Jelly forms round the eggs. These big blobs of jelly, containing thousands of eggs, are called frog spawn.

3 WEEKS LATER, the external gills have withered away. The tadpole now has internal gills like a fish. Water is passed over the gills, then out of the left side

Spiracle

Intestine

Tail muscles similar to fish

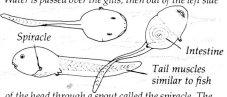

of the head through a spout called the spiracle. The mucous glands have disappeared. The intestine, visible through the thin skin, has become long and coiled to deal with the tadpole's diet of plants.

4 WEEKS LATER, about four months after hatching, metamorphosis is complete. The tadpole has become a tiny frog. It leaves the water to begin life on dry land.

Remains of tail

It has lungs for breathing, though it also absorbs oxygen through its skin. It has legs for hopping and swimming. It feeds on insects and worms.

4 WEEKS LATER, about three months after hatching, the tadpole stops eating and metamorphosis begins. The tail begins to get shorter as it is absorbed and used for food by the rest of the body. The front legs appear.

Bulge made by right limb

The left leg comes through the spiracle and the right breaks through the gill cover. The mouth gets wider and the eyes get bigger.

4 WEEKS LATER, the lungs are now developing and the tadpole frequently comes to the surface to breathe air. The internal gills will soon disappear. The hind legs grow, though they are not yet used for swimming.

Ear

Gill cover

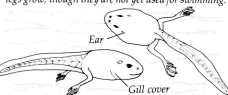

The tadpole loses its scraping lips and develops jaws for eating small pond animals. The intestine becomes shorter, more suitable for a meat diet.

Development in birds

Birds lay their eggs about 12 hours after they have been fertilised. During those 12 hours, the egg white, or **albumen**, and the egg shell are added to the egg. At the same time, a disc of cells has been formed on top of the yolk. Provided the egg is kept warm, the future chick will develop from these cells. It is the mother bird's job to sit on the eggs and warm them with the heat of her body. This is called **incubating** the eggs. From time to time, the mother bird stands up and turns the eggs over. This prevents the embryo inside from becoming stuck to the egg shell.

For most birds, the **incubation period** lasts only a few weeks. The young birds then hatch out. Tree-nesting birds are born blind, naked and helpless. Ground-nesting birds, on the other hand, are much more developed when born and can soon get around on their own. The diagrams below trace the development of one such bird – the hen.

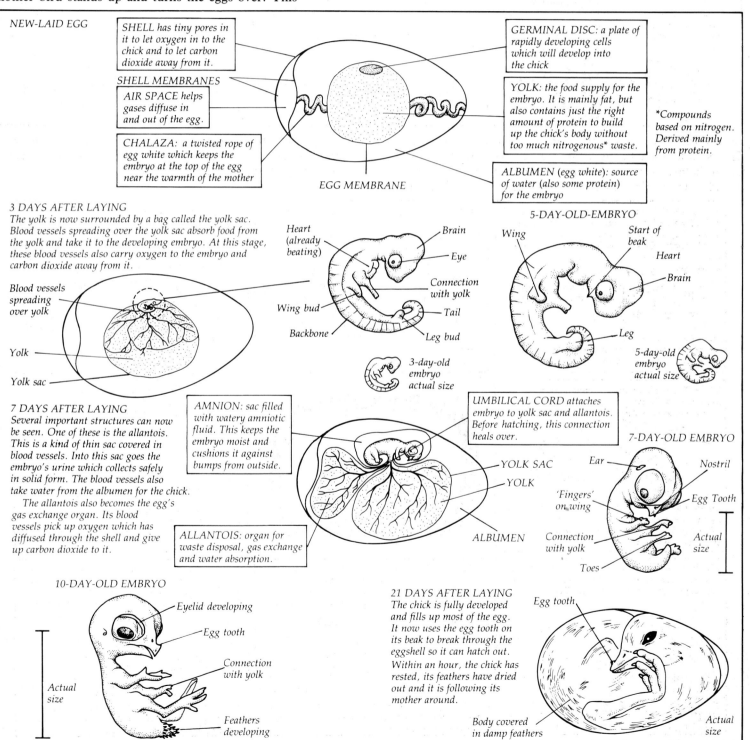

NEW-LAID EGG

SHELL has tiny pores in it to let oxygen in to the chick and to let carbon dioxide away from it.

SHELL MEMBRANES

AIR SPACE helps gases diffuse in and out of the egg.

CHALAZA: a twisted rope of egg white which keeps the embryo at the top of the egg near the warmth of the mother

EGG MEMBRANE

GERMINAL DISC: a plate of rapidly developing cells which will develop into the chick

YOLK: the food supply for the embryo. It is mainly fat, but also contains just the right amount of protein to build up the chick's body without too much nitrogenous* waste.

*Compounds based on nitrogen. Derived mainly from protein.

ALBUMEN (egg white): source of water (also some protein) for the embryo

3 DAYS AFTER LAYING
The yolk is now surrounded by a bag called the yolk sac. Blood vessels spreading over the yolk sac absorb food from the yolk and take it to the developing embryo. At this stage, these blood vessels also carry oxygen to the embryo and carbon dioxide away from it.

Blood vessels spreading over yolk

Yolk

Yolk sac

Heart (already beating)

Brain

Eye

Connection with yolk

Wing bud

Tail

Backbone

Leg bud

3-day-old embryo actual size

5-DAY-OLD-EMBRYO

Wing

Start of beak

Heart

Brain

Leg

5-day-old embryo actual size

7 DAYS AFTER LAYING
Several important structures can now be seen. One of these is the allantois. This is a kind of thin sac covered in blood vessels. Into this sac goes the embryo's urine which collects safely in solid form. The blood vessels also take water from the albumen for the chick.
The allantois also becomes the egg's gas exchange organ. Its blood vessels pick up oxygen which has diffused through the shell and give up carbon dioxide to it.

AMNION: sac filled with watery amniotic fluid. This keeps the embryo moist and cushions it against bumps from outside.

ALLANTOIS: organ for waste disposal, gas exchange and water absorption.

UMBILICAL CORD attaches embryo to yolk sac and allantois. Before hatching, this connection heals over.

YOLK SAC

YOLK

ALBUMEN

7-DAY-OLD EMBRYO

Ear

Nostril

'Fingers' on wing

Egg Tooth

Connection with yolk

Toes

Actual size

10-DAY-OLD EMBRYO

Eyelid developing

Egg tooth

Connection with yolk

Actual size

Feathers developing

21 DAYS AFTER LAYING
The chick is fully developed and fills up most of the egg. It now uses the egg tooth on its beak to break through the eggshell so it can hatch out. Within an hour, the chick has rested, its feathers have dried out and it is following its mother around.

Egg tooth

Body covered in damp feathers

Actual size

Flowers

The flower is the sex organ of the flowering plants. Its job is to produce the male and female gametes (sex cells) and have them brought together so that fertilisation can take place. This results in the production of seeds from which the young plants will grow. Flowers come in a huge variety of shapes, sizes and colours and each kind of flower has its own particular way of bringing about successful reproduction.

The basic parts of a flower are the **sepals**, the **petals**, the **stamens** and the **carpels**. They are not all found in every flower and, like flowers themselves, they come in a variety of forms. The diagram below, therefore, is not of any single species of flower, but is a general guide to the structure of all flowers.

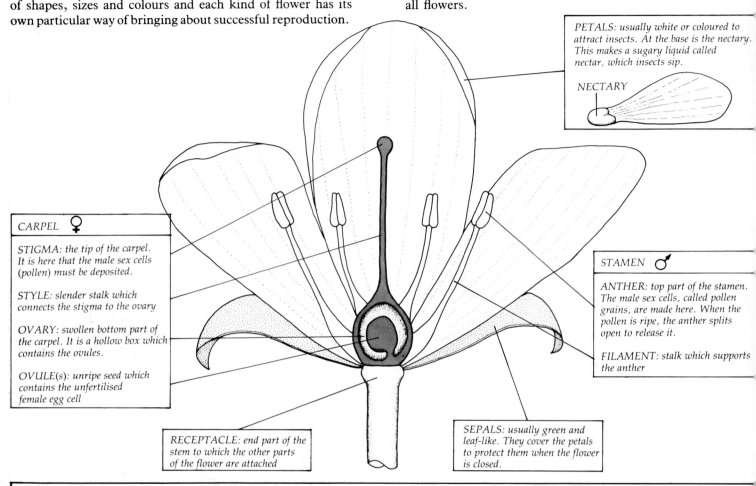

PETALS: usually white or coloured to attract insects. At the base is the nectary. This makes a sugary liquid called nectar, which insects sip.

NECTARY

CARPEL ♀

STIGMA: the tip of the carpel. It is here that the male sex cells (pollen) must be deposited.

STYLE: slender stalk which connects the stigma to the ovary

OVARY: swollen bottom part of the carpel. It is a hollow box which contains the ovules.

OVULE(s): unripe seed which contains the unfertilised female egg cell

STAMEN ♂

ANTHER: top part of the stamen. The male sex cells, called pollen grains, are made here. When the pollen is ripe, the anther splits open to release it.

FILAMENT: stalk which supports the anther

RECEPTACLE: end part of the stem to which the other parts of the flower are attached

SEPALS: usually green and leaf-like. They cover the petals to protect them when the flower is closed.

CARPELS are the female parts of a flower. Each carpel consists of an ovary, a style and a stigma. Inside the ovary are the ovules which contain the female gametes waiting to be fertilised. Here are a few of the ways in which carpels are found to be arranged inside flowers:

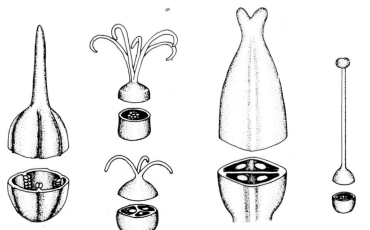

STAMENS are the male parts of a flower. Each stamen consists of a stalk or **filament** with an **anther** at the top. The male gametes, called **pollen grains**, are formed inside the anther. When the pollen is ready, the anther bursts open, as shown below, to release it.

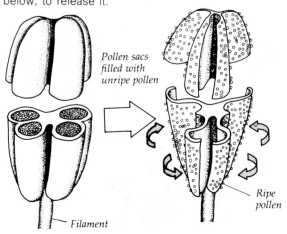

Pollen sacs filled with unripe pollen

Ripe pollen

Filament

The diagram on the previous page shows the basic layout of a flower. However, we do not have to look very far to find a great many variations on the basic design. Here are just a few of these.

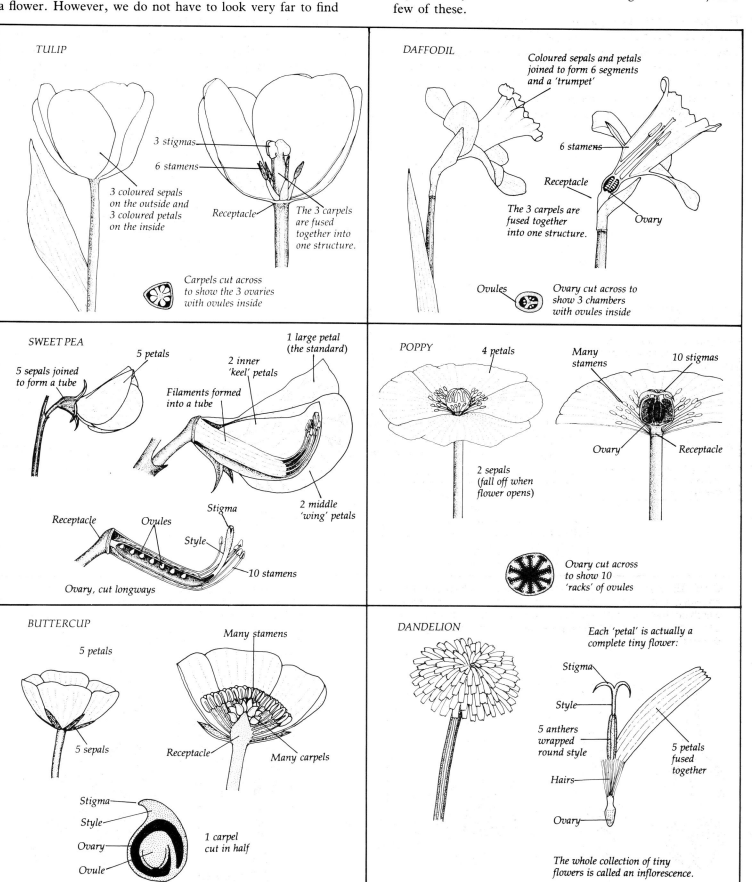

TULIP

3 stigmas

6 stamens

3 coloured sepals on the outside and 3 coloured petals on the inside

Receptacle

The 3 carpels are fused together into one structure.

Carpels cut across to show the 3 ovaries with ovules inside

DAFFODIL

Coloured sepals and petals joined to form 6 segments and a 'trumpet'

6 stamens

Receptacle

The 3 carpels are fused together into one structure.

Ovary

Ovules

Ovary cut across to show 3 chambers with ovules inside

SWEET PEA

5 petals

5 sepals joined to form a tube

1 large petal (the standard)

2 inner 'keel' petals

Filaments formed into a tube

Receptacle

Ovules

Stigma

Style

10 stamens

Ovary, cut longways

2 middle 'wing' petals

POPPY

4 petals

Many stamens

10 stigmas

2 sepals (fall off when flower opens)

Ovary

Receptacle

Ovary cut across to show 10 'racks' of ovules

BUTTERCUP

5 petals

Many stamens

5 sepals

Receptacle

Many carpels

Stigma

Style

Ovary

Ovule

1 carpel cut in half

DANDELION

Each 'petal' is actually a complete tiny flower:

Stigma

Style

5 anthers wrapped round style

Hairs

Ovary

5 petals fused together

The whole collection of tiny flowers is called an inflorescence.

Pollination and fertilisation

The male gametes (sex cells) of a flowering plant are called **pollen grains**. Pollen is made by the **anthers** of a flower. When the anthers burst open to release it, the pollen is visible as a sort of dust. Under the microscope this dust is seen to consist of a large number of single cells. Each single cell, or pollen grain, is the plant's equivalent of a sperm cell. Like sperms, pollen from different species is differently shaped, for example:

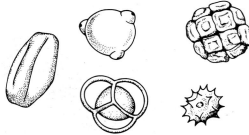

The first stage in the sexual reproduction of a flowering plant is called **pollination**. Pollination is the transfer of pollen from the male anthers to the female **stigmas**. To help them catch the pollen, stigmas may be sticky, feathery, or covered in fine hairs. During pollination the pollen is usually transferred from the anthers of one flower to the stigma of another. This is called **cross pollination**, for example:

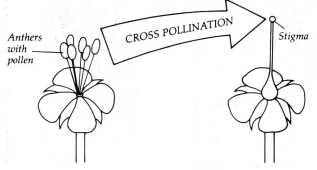

Anthers with pollen

CROSS POLLINATION

Stigma

In this simple example, the flowers were unisex – either male or female. Most flowers, however, are **hermaphrodite**. This means that they contain both male **stamens** and female **carpels**. Obviously, in a hermaphrodite flower, there is always a chance that it will pollinate itself. This is called **self pollination**.

SELF POLLINATION

SELF POLLINATION

For some plants self pollination is quite normal. However, after cross pollination flowers produce more and better seeds. Therefore, most flowers, as in the examples below, try to make sure that they are cross pollinated.

Unlike an animal's sperm, pollen cannot move by itself. It has to be carried. Insects may transfer pollen when they visit flowers to collect nectar or pollen (insect pollination), or it may be done by the wind (wind pollination). There are a number of differences between wind-pollinated and insect-pollinated flowers.

DIFFERENCES BETWEEN WIND AND INSECT-POLLINATED FLOWERS		
STRUCTURE	WIND-POLLINATED FLOWERS	INSECT-POLLINATED FLOWERS
FLOWERS	Small and dull with no petals, scent or nectar. Flower heads often at the top of stiff stems which are rocked by the wind.	Large and gaudy with colourful petals, and scent to attract insects and often nectar for them to collect.
STAMENS	Large anthers hang outside the flower on long, thin filaments to scatter their pollen into the wind.	Anthers are held inside the flower on stiff filaments so that they brush against insects.
POLLEN	Large amount of small, light pollen grains produced.	Small amount of large sticky pollen grains produced
STIGMAS	Long, feathery stigmas hang outside the flower to catch pollen.	Sticky stigmas are kept inside the flower to brush against insects.

INSECT POLLINATION: PRIMROSES

Primroses produce two kinds of flower. Some plants have flowers with a long style and stamens halfway down the flower. In others the stamens are at the top and the style is short. Bees visit the flowers looking for nectar and, as the diagrams show, there is a very good chance that they will transfer pollen from one type of flower to the other.

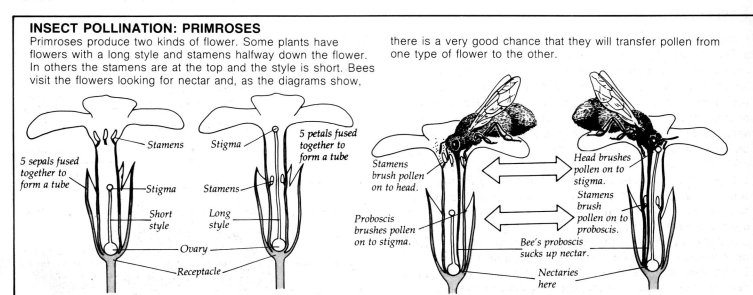

5 sepals fused together to form a tube

Stamens

Stigma

Short style

Stigma

5 petals fused together to form a tube

Stamens

Long style

Ovary

Receptacle

Stamens brush pollen on to head.

Proboscis brushes pollen on to stigma.

Head brushes pollen on to stigma.

Stamens brush pollen on to proboscis.

Bee's proboscis sucks up nectar.

Nectaries here

INSECT POLLINATION: FOXGLOVES

Foxglove flowers have stiff hairs at their entrance which keep out all insects except large bees. The bees come to collect nectar and pollen is brushed on to their backs. Since the pollen is usually all shed before the stigmas are ready, self pollination is unlikely. The bees fly off and the pollen is rubbed off on to the stigmas of an older flower.

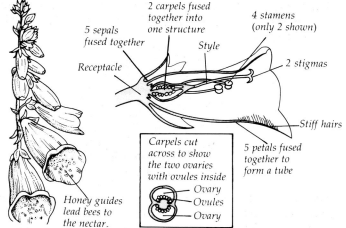

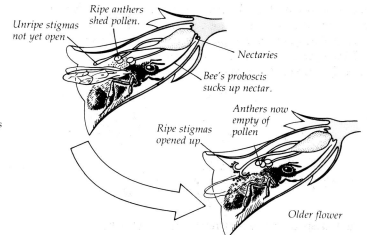

WIND POLLINATION: GRASSES

Grasses, which include the important cereal plants, are typical wind-pollinated plants. The small flowers have no sepals or petals, but are protected by leaf-like covers called **bracts**. The long, feathery stigmas ripen before the anthers are ready to shed their large amounts of very light pollen into the wind. While this helps to ensure cross pollination, self pollination is very common among the grasses. The flowers are unscented and produce no nectar.

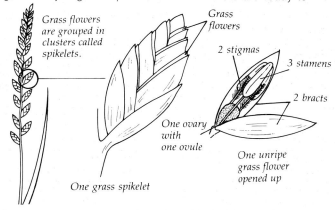

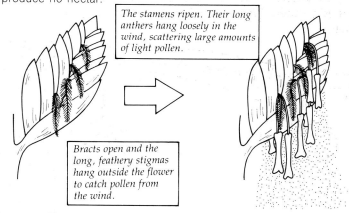

Fertilisation

Fertilisation and pollination are two quite separate events in a flower's life. After pollination, a flower's stigmas may be covered in male gametes (pollen grains). However, the female egg cells are at the other end of the carpel, inside the **ovary**. Ovaries contain the undeveloped seeds called **ovules**. In each ovule there is a little bag called the **embryo sac**. Inside the embryo sac are several cells, including the unfertilised egg cell. For fertilisation to take place, this egg cell and the pollen must somehow get together. To make this possible, the stigma produces chemicals, including sugar, which cause a sort of 'root', called the **pollen tube**, to grow out of the pollen. The pollen tube grows down the **style** into the ovary and enters an ovule through a hole called the **micropyle**. It penetrates the embryo sac and its male nucleus fuses with the egg's female nucleus. Fertilisation has now taken place and the ovule can begin to develop into a seed. The fertilised egg cell, or **zygote**, becomes the embryo plant and the other parts of the ovule develop into the seed's food store and protective coat. The ovary, too, begins to change. It will develop into the fruit which will help to spread the seeds around.

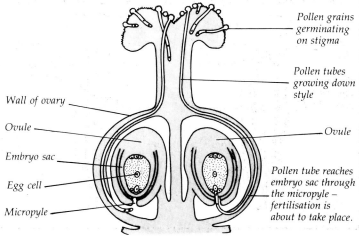

Seeds and fruits

Seeds

Once fertilised, each ovule in a flower begins to grow and develop into a seed. The ovule's outer layers expand and then harden to form the seed's tough, protective coat or **testa**. In the embryo sac, one cell, the zygote (fertilised egg cell) develops into a baby plant (the embryo). Other cells become a tissue called **endosperm**. Endosperm cells are filled with food which the embryo will use later when it

begins to grow into a young plant. Attached to the embryo are the seed leaves or **cotyledons**. If the seed has one cotyledon, the plant is said to be a **monocotyledon**. If it has two, it is a **dicotyledon**. In many seeds it is the cotyledons which carry the embryo's food supply. Such seeds will have little or no endosperm.

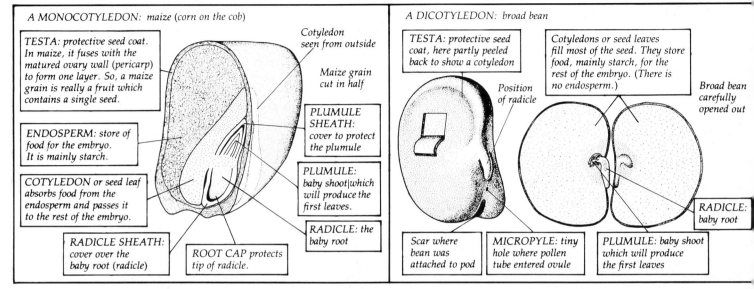

A MONOCOTYLEDON: maize (corn on the cob)

TESTA: protective seed coat. In maize, it fuses with the matured ovary wall (pericarp) to form one layer. So, a maize grain is really a fruit which contains a single seed.

ENDOSPERM: store of food for the embryo. It is mainly starch.

COTYLEDON or seed leaf absorbs food from the endosperm and passes it to the rest of the embryo.

RADICLE SHEATH: cover over the baby root (radicle)

ROOT CAP protects tip of radicle.

Cotyledon seen from outside

Maize grain cut in half

PLUMULE SHEATH: cover to protect the plumule

PLUMULE: baby shoot|which will produce the first leaves.

RADICLE: the baby root

A DICOTYLEDON: broad bean

TESTA: protective seed coat, here partly peeled back to show a cotyledon

Position of radicle

Cotyledons or seed leaves fill most of the seed. They store food, mainly starch, for the rest of the embryo. (There is no endosperm.)

Broad bean carefully opened out

RADICLE: baby root

Scar where bean was attached to pod

MICROPYLE: tiny hole where pollen tube entered ovule

PLUMULE: baby shoot which will produce the first leaves

Fruits

As the seeds begin to grow, the flower withers and most of its parts die and fall off. The ovary, however, like the ovules inside it, now begins to grow and develop. It becomes a structure known as a fruit. The fruit's function is to scatter the ripe seeds over as large an area as possible. This is called **seed dispersal**. Dispersing the seeds gives the young plants room to grow without getting in each other's way. It also gives the plants the chance to spread to new,

and perhaps better, places to grow.

That part of a fruit which has developed from the wall of the ovary is called the **pericarp**. In many species the pericarp will form most of the fruit. In some, however, part of the fruit is formed from other parts of the flower and these other parts, and not the pericarp, may come to make up most of the fruit. When ripe, a fruit may be either fleshy or dry.

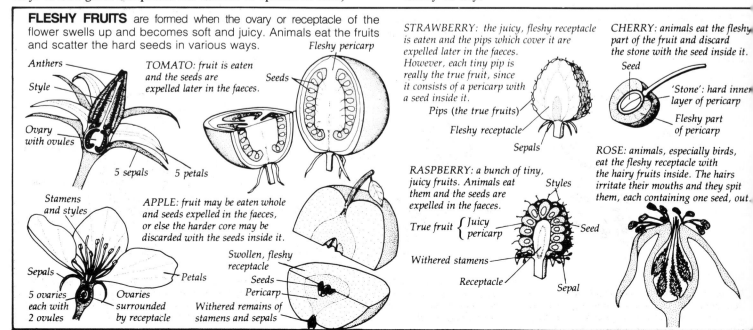

FLESHY FRUITS are formed when the ovary or receptacle of the flower swells up and becomes soft and juicy. Animals eat the fruits and scatter the hard seeds in various ways.

Anthers
Style
Ovary with ovules
5 sepals
5 petals

TOMATO: fruit is eaten and the seeds are expelled later in the faeces.

Fleshy pericarp
Seeds

Stamens and styles

APPLE: fruit may be eaten whole and seeds expelled in the faeces, or else the harder core may be discarded with the seeds inside it.

Sepals
Petals
5 ovaries each with 2 ovules
Ovaries surrounded by receptacle
Swollen, fleshy receptacle
Seeds
Pericarp
Withered remains of stamens and sepals

STRAWBERRY: the juicy, fleshy receptacle is eaten and the pips which cover it are expelled later in the faeces. However, each tiny pip is really the true fruit, since it consists of a pericarp with a seed inside it.

Pips (the true fruits)
Fleshy receptacle
Sepals

RASPBERRY: a bunch of tiny, juicy fruits. Animals eat them and the seeds are expelled in the faeces.

True fruit { Juicy pericarp
Withered stamens
Receptacle
Styles
Seed
Sepal

CHERRY: animals eat the fleshy part of the fruit and discard the stone with the seed inside it.

Seed
'Stone': hard inner layer of pericarp
Fleshy part of pericarp

ROSE: animals, especially birds, eat the fleshy receptacle with the hairy fruits inside. The hairs irritate their mouths and they spit them, each containing one seed, out.

DRY FRUITS are formed when the ovaries and other parts of the flower become hard and dry as they develop into the fruit. They come in a variety of shapes and sizes and their seeds can be dispersed in a number of different ways.

WIND DISPERSAL

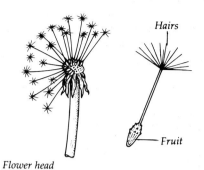

Hairs

Fruit

Flower head
with ripe fruits

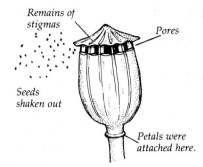

Remains of
stigmas

Pores

Seeds
shaken out

Petals were
attached here.

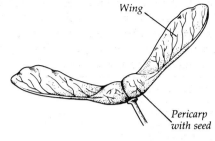

Wing

Pericarp
with seed

Dandelion fruits have a light, feathery 'parachute'. They are blown from the flower head and can be carried long distances by the wind.

Poppy fruits are in the form of a 'pepper pot' at the top of a long stalk. As the wind rocks the stalk back and forth, the small, light seeds are shaken out of the holes in the fruit and carried off.

Sycamore fruits have a wing attached to them. When blown from the tree, the wing makes the fruit spin round and round. This slows down its fall so that the wind can catch it and blow it away.

SELF DISPERSAL

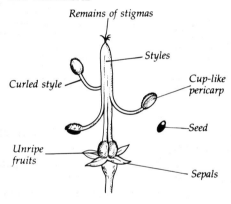

Remains of stigmas

Styles

Curled style

Cup-like
pericarp

Seed

Unripe
fruits

Sepals

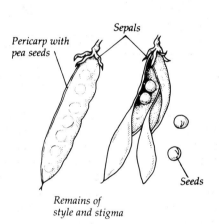

Sepals

Pericarp with
pea seeds

Seeds

Remains of
style and stigma

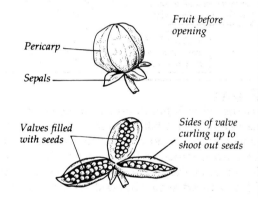

Fruit before
opening

Pericarp

Sepals

Valves filled
with seeds

Sides of valve
curling up to
shoot out seeds

Geranium fruits develop from the ovaries and styles of the flower. When the fruit is ripe, the long style suddenly curls up and throws the seed out like a slingshot.

Pea fruits, and those of lupin, gorse and broom, are called pods. When ripe, the pod splits in half. Each half then curls up, forcing out the seeds.

Pansy fruits open out in three parts called valves, each packed with seeds. The sides of the valves curl up and squeeze on the seeds which get shot out, often to a fair distance.

ANIMAL DISPERSAL

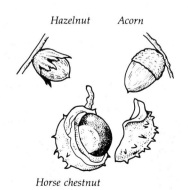

Hazelnut

Acorn

Horse chestnut

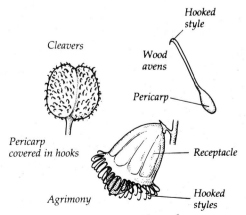

Hooked
style

Cleavers

Wood
avens

Pericarp

Pericarp
covered in hooks

Receptacle

Agrimony

Hooked
styles

WATER DISPERSAL

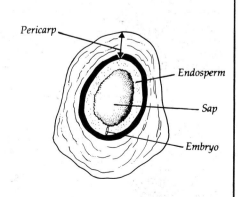

Pericarp

Endosperm

Sap

Embryo

Acorns and nuts are gathered and hidden, perhaps even buried, by squirrels and birds. They may drop some or may not manage to collect them all later.

Hooked fruits, such as those above, catch on to the fur of animals and are carried off. Later on, perhaps some distance away, they either fall off or are scratched off.

Coconuts grow beside water and the fruits may fall in and be carried great distances by currents.
Some seeds can travel thousands of miles in this way and still grow when they reach land.

Seed germination

Inside every seed there is a little embryo with its own supply of stored food. Under certain conditions, the embryo starts to consume the food and grow into a new plant. This is called **germination**. Before a seed can germinate, it must have:

1 a supply of water – most seeds are very dry (about 10% water), so they must absorb a lot of water if they are to grow.
2 a supply of oxygen – without oxygen, the embryo cannot obtain the energy it needs to live and grow.
3 a suitable temperature – very high (50°C) or very low (0°C) temperatures prevent seeds from germinating.

Some seeds are also affected by the presence or absence of light.

Even if a seed does not get the right conditions to allow it to germinate, it will not die. Most seeds can survive for many months or even years, sometimes through the very harshest of weather, and still be able to grow when things improve. This resting state is called **dormancy**. A dormant seed can stay alive through weather conditions which would kill a growing plant. In fact, most seeds are unable to germinate at the time they are produced, no matter how good the weather. They must go through a dormant period first. Without this, the plant may not survive. Many seeds, produced at the height of summer, for example, cannot be germinated unless they are kept at low temperatures for some months. This ensures that young plants will not be formed until the seeds have survived the frosts and cold of winter.

When conditions are suitable, seeds show two basic ways of germinating. These are called **hypogeal** and **epigeal germination.**

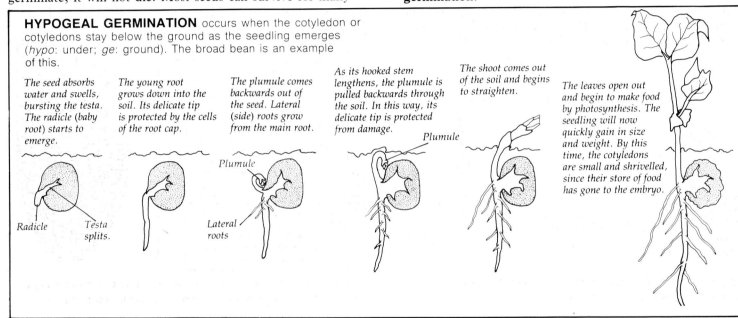

HYPOGEAL GERMINATION occurs when the cotyledon or cotyledons stay below the ground as the seedling emerges (*hypo*: under; *ge*: ground). The broad bean is an example of this.

The seed absorbs water and swells, bursting the testa. The radicle (baby root) starts to emerge.

The young root grows down into the soil. Its delicate tip is protected by the cells of the root cap.

The plumule comes backwards out of the seed. Lateral (side) roots grow from the main root.

As its hooked stem lengthens, the plumule is pulled backwards through the soil. In this way, its delicate tip is protected from damage.

The shoot comes out of the soil and begins to straighten.

The leaves open out and begin to make food by photosynthesis. The seedling will now quickly gain in size and weight. By this time, the cotyledons are small and shrivelled, since their store of food has gone to the embryo.

Radicle   Testa splits.   Plumule   Lateral roots   Plumule

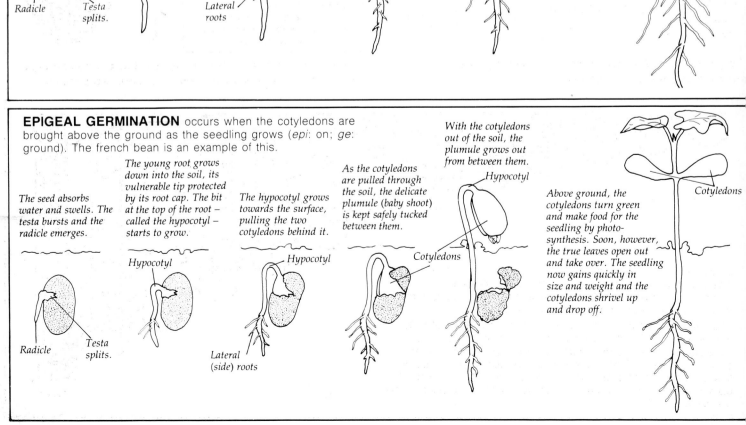

EPIGEAL GERMINATION occurs when the cotyledons are brought above the ground as the seedling grows (*epi*: on; *ge*: ground). The french bean is an example of this.

The seed absorbs water and swells. The testa bursts and the radicle emerges.

The young root grows down into the soil, its vulnerable tip protected by its root cap. The bit at the top of the root – called the hypocotyl – starts to grow.

The hypocotyl grows towards the surface, pulling the two cotyledons behind it.

As the cotyledons are pulled through the soil, the delicate plumule (baby shoot) is kept safely tucked between them.

With the cotyledons out of the soil, the plumule grows out from between them.

Above ground, the cotyledons turn green and make food for the seedling by photosynthesis. Soon, however, the true leaves open out and take over. The seedling now gains quickly in size and weight and the cotyledons shrivel up and drop off.

Radicle   Testa splits.   Hypocotyl   Hypocotyl   Lateral (side) roots   Cotyledons   Hypocotyl   Cotyledons

Plant growth

As an animal grows, new cells are produced by cell divisions all over its body. Plants are different. In plants, new cells are only formed in certain areas. These areas, where cell divisions are taking place, are called **meristems**. There is a meristem at the tip of every growing root and shoot. These provide the cells for the plant to get longer. This is called **primary growth**. There are other meristems, buried inside the stems and roots, which provide new cells to make the plant thicker (but no longer). This is called **secondary growth**.

The growth of a plant, however, is only partly caused by new cells being added to it. Most of the space inside a plant cell is taken up by the **vacuole**, which is mainly water. Newly-formed cells have no vacuoles. The biggest part of a plant cell's growth occurs when it develops vacuoles – a process called **vacuolation**. This goes on in the cells just behind the root or shoot tips. We can show this by marking root or shoot tips with ink, letting them grow, then seeing what happens to the ink marks. This is what we find:

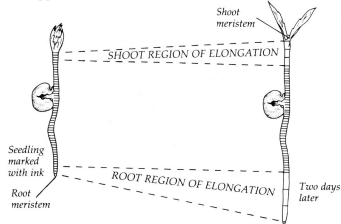

The parts of a root or shoot which are getting longer are called the **regions of elongation**.

Once a cell has fully grown, it starts to become different from other cells so that it can do its own special job for the plant. This development is called **differentiation**. The differentiating cells are found just behind the region of elongation. Various regions of cell development can be clearly seen in a long section of a root like that shown in the diagram below.

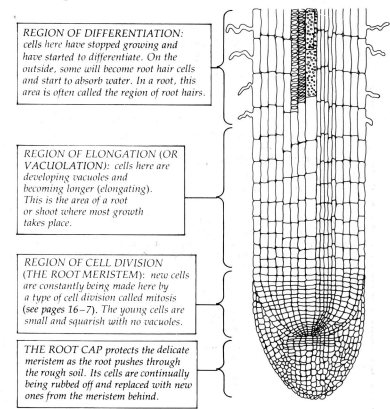

REGION OF DIFFERENTIATION: cells here have stopped growing and have started to differentiate. On the outside, some will become root hair cells and start to absorb water. In a root, this area is often called the region of root hairs.

REGION OF ELONGATION (OR VACUOLATION): cells here are developing vacuoles and becoming longer (elongating). This is the area of a root or shoot where most growth takes place.

REGION OF CELL DIVISION (THE ROOT MERISTEM): new cells are constantly being made here by a type of cell division called mitosis (see pages 16–7). The young cells are small and squarish with no vacuoles.

THE ROOT CAP protects the delicate meristem as the root pushes through the rough soil. Its cells are continually being rubbed off and replaced with new ones from the meristem behind.

Shoot development is similar to this, but there is no cap, and the presence of leaves makes it more complicated.

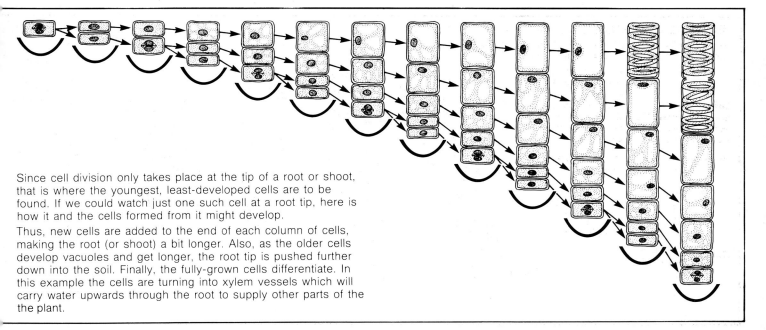

Since cell division only takes place at the tip of a root or shoot, that is where the youngest, least-developed cells are to be found. If we could watch just one such cell at a root tip, here is how it and the cells formed from it might develop.

Thus, new cells are added to the end of each column of cells, making the root (or shoot) a bit longer. Also, as the older cells develop vacuoles and get longer, the root tip is pushed further down into the soil. Finally, the fully-grown cells differentiate. In this example the cells are turning into xylem vessels which will carry water upwards through the root to supply other parts of the plant.

SECTION 17

The Endocrine System

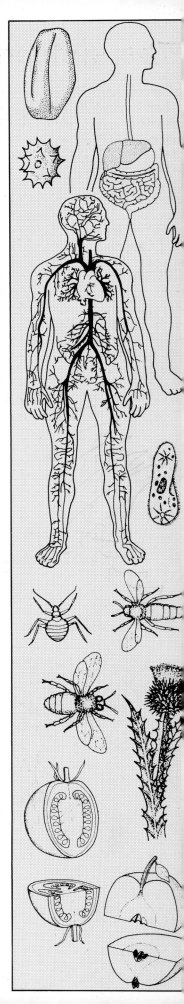

The endocrine system

The endocrine system consists of a number of **glands**. A gland is an organ whose cells make a useful substance known as a **secretion**, which they pass on (secrete) to other parts of the body. Some glands make their secretion and pass it into pipes called **ducts** which lead it to where it is needed. The salivary glands of the mouth are like this.

DUCTED GLAND

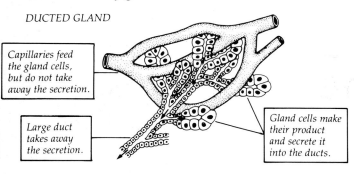

Capillaries feed the gland cells, but do not take away the secretion.

Large duct takes away the secretion.

Gland cells make their product and secrete it into the ducts.

.The glands of the endocrine system, however, are **ductless**. Their cells pass their secretion into the blood capillaries which run past them. The blood can then transport it rapidly to all parts of the body.

The ductless glands of the endocrine system make substances called **hormones**. A hormone is a chemical messenger. Carried by the blood to all parts of the body, a hormone will trigger certain organs into action when it reaches them. These are the **target organs** for that hormone. Some hormones have only one target organ, others have several.

DUCTLESS GLAND

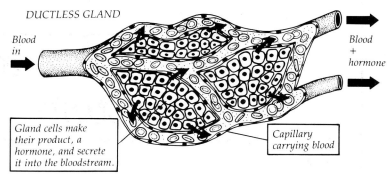

Blood in

Blood + hormone

Gland cells make their product, a hormone, and secrete it into the bloodstream.

Capillary carrying blood

The diagram below shows the position of some of the main glands of the endocrine system with the hormones they secrete.

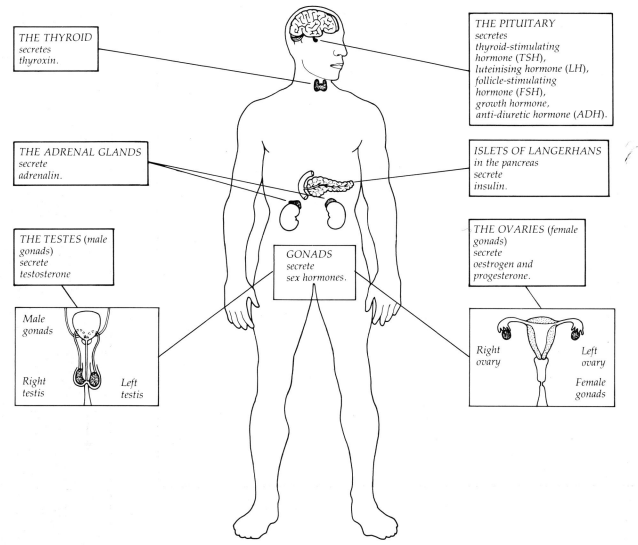

THE THYROID secretes thyroxin.

THE PITUITARY secretes thyroid-stimulating hormone (TSH), luteinising hormone (LH), follicle-stimulating hormone (FSH), growth hormone, anti-diuretic hormone (ADH).

THE ADRENAL GLANDS secrete adrenalin.

ISLETS OF LANGERHANS in the pancreas secrete insulin.

THE TESTES (male gonads) secrete testosterone

THE OVARIES (female gonads) secrete oestrogen and progesterone.

Male gonads

Right testis

Left testis

GONADS secrete sex hormones.

Right ovary

Left ovary

Female gonads

Hormones

Hormones are the chemical messengers produced by the ductless glands of the endocrine system. Released in tiny amounts into the bloodstream, they circulate all round the body until they reach their own target organ or organs. Only there do they have an effect. Thus, the ductless glands control the workings of other parts of the body.

Hormone molecules do not last long. The liver destroys them as they pass through it in the blood. So, if a gland is controlling a long-term process like growth, it must continually make fresh hormone. On the other hand, if the hormone's effect is needed for only a short time – to help control digestion, perhaps – the liver makes sure it does not overdo it. A few hormones are discussed below.

PITUITARY HORMONES

The pituitary is a small gland about the size of a pea. It is located underneath the brain. Despite its small size, it is known as the 'master gland' of the body. This is because a number of its hormones actually control other endocrine glands. So, if anything goes wrong with the pituitary, other parts of the body may be affected. Among the pituitary hormones which stimulate other glands are **thyroid-stimulating hormone (TSH)**, **follicle-stimulating hormone (FSH)** and **luteinising hormone (LH)**.

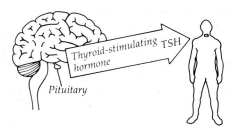

Target organ: thyroid gland

EFFECT
Stimulates the thyroid gland to make its own hormone, thyroxin.

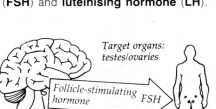

Target organs: testes/ovaries

EFFECT ON MALE
Testes begin to produce sperms.

EFFECT ON FEMALE
An egg ripens in one ovary. Both ovaries produce the female sex hormone, oestrogen.

Target organs: testes/ovaries

EFFECT ON MALE
Testes produce the male sex hormone, testosterone.

EFFECT ON FEMALE
Ovary releases the ripe egg and begins to produce another female sex hormone, progesterone.

Not all pituitary hormones stimulate other endocrine glands. Some have direct control over vital body processes. **Antidiuretic hormone (ADH)**, for example, adjusts the amount of water in the blood. If there is not enough, ADH causes more water to be reabsorbed into the blood from the kidney tubules. The kidneys will produce less urine and the blood will become more dilute. ADH is discussed on page 198. Another essential pituitary hormone is **growth hormone**.

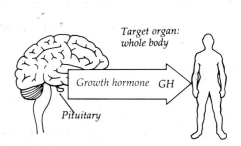

Target organ: whole body

EFFECT
In childhood, it is growth hormone which controls the growth of the body. For normal growth, the pituitary must make just the right amount. If it makes too little, very poor growth, or dwarfism, results. If it makes too much, excessive growth, called giantism, occurs.

The diagrams show three boys, aged 13. The boy in the middle shows normal growth. The one on the left suffers from dwarfism, while the one on the right suffers from giantism.

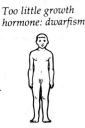

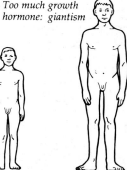

Too much growth hormone: giantism

Normal

Too little growth hormone: dwarfism

THYROXIN

Thyroxin is made by the **thyroid gland** in the neck. It controls the rate at which the tissues use energy (the metabolic rate) and so affects the performance of the whole body. It is especially important during growth and development. A child whose thyroid does not produce enough thyroxin will be stunted in growth and severely mentally retarded. This condition is called **cretinism**.

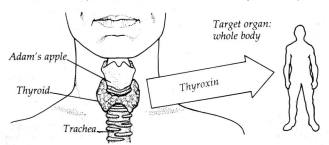

Adam's apple

Thyroid

Trachea

Target organ: whole body

Thyroxin

Sometimes the thyroid gland does not work properly in adults. If it cannot make enough thyroxin, the person becomes fat and slow to think and speak (**Myxoedema**). If it makes too much, the person becomes thin, nervous and over-active. Thyroxin production is stimulated by TSH from the pituitary.

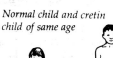

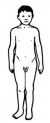

Normal child and cretin child of same age

OESTROGEN AND PROGESTERONE

Oestrogen and progesterone are female sex hormones made by the ovaries. They control reproduction by the female. In certain species, including humans, reproduction depends on a regular pattern of events called a **menstrual cycle**. In women a menstrual cycle usually lasts about 28 days. It begins (day 1) with the lining of the **uterus** breaking away and being shed, along with some blood, through the vagina. This is called **menstruation**, or having a period, and lasts about five days. A new lining then begins to grow. Meanwhile, an **ovum** (egg) begins to ripen inside one of the ovaries. About day 14 **ovulation** occurs – the ripe egg bursts from the ovary. If this egg is fertilised, then, by the time it reaches the uterus, the new lining will be in perfect condition to receive and nourish it. If, as usually happens, the egg is not fertilised, it dies and about day 28 menstruation begins again.

During a cycle, oestrogen and progesterone control the uterus. The ovaries, in turn, are controlled by follicle-stimulating hormone (FSH) and luteinising hormone (LH) made by the pituitary. It is the balance between each of these hormones in the woman's blood at any time that determines the stage which the cycle is at. The diagrams opposite indicate the changes which take place in ovary and uterus during a cycle and the levels of each hormone which are needed to cause them.

Apart from its role in menstrual cycles, oestrogen also causes the appearance of the female **secondary sexual characteristics** at puberty. These include the growth of breasts and pubic hair and the development of the more rounded shape of the female body.

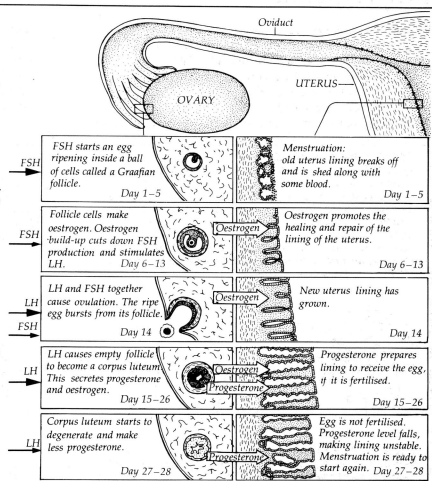

FSH — FSH starts an egg ripening inside a ball of cells called a Graafian follicle. *Day 1–5*

Menstruation: old uterus lining breaks off and is shed along with some blood. *Day 1–5*

FSH — Follicle cells make oestrogen. Oestrogen build-up cuts down FSH production and stimulates LH. *Day 6–13*

Oestrogen — Oestrogen promotes the healing and repair of the lining of the uterus. *Day 6–13*

LH — FSH — LH and FSH together cause ovulation. The ripe egg bursts from its follicle. *Day 14*

Oestrogen — New uterus lining has grown. *Day 14*

LH — LH causes empty follicle to become a corpus luteum. This secretes progesterone and oestrogen. *Day 15–26*

Oestrogen — Progesterone — Progesterone prepares lining to receive the egg, if it is fertilised. *Day 15–26*

LH — Corpus luteum starts to degenerate and make less progesterone. *Day 27–28*

Progesterone — Egg is not fertilised. Progesterone level falls, making lining unstable. Menstruation is ready to start again. *Day 27–28*

Oviduct · OVARY · UTERUS

TESTOSTERONE

Testosterone is made by the **testes**. It is the male sex hormone and causes the appearance of the male secondary sexual characteristics (see below). Production starts at puberty when luteinising hormone from the pituitary first reaches the testes.

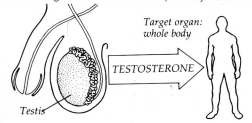

Testis · Target organ: whole body · TESTOSTERONE · EFFECT Voice breaks (becomes deeper) and hair grows on face, round sex organs and elsewhere. Sex organs grow. Body becomes more muscular.

INSULIN

Insulin is made in the **pancreas** by patches of cells called **islets of Langerhans**. Insulin's job is to lower the level of glucose in the blood when it gets too high. If the pancreas cannot make enough insulin, an illness called **diabetes** occurs.

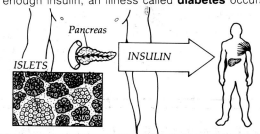

Pancreas · ISLETS · INSULIN · Target organs: liver and muscles · EFFECT The liver and muscles take glucose from the blood and store it as glycogen. This makes the blood glucose level fall.

ADRENALIN

Adrenalin is made by the adrenal glands which lie above the kidneys. It is often called the 'flight or fight' hormone, since its job is to prepare the body to take action in an emergency. When we get a fright, adrenalin is produced and quickly affects a number of organs. The liver converts glycogen to glucose to raise the blood sugar. The heart beats faster. Breathing speeds up. Blood is diverted from the gut to the muscles. These measures give the muscles the energy they need for extra effort. Other effects of adrenalin are shown opposite.

We do not actually have to be threatened with danger for these things to happen. Anything which makes us nervous or excited will cause adrenalin to be secreted.

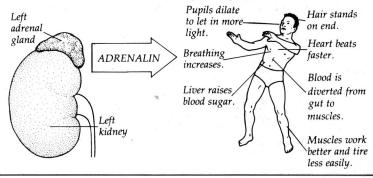

Left adrenal gland · ADRENALIN · Left kidney · Pupils dilate to let in more light. · Breathing increases. · Liver raises blood sugar. · Hair stands on end. · Heart beats faster. · Blood is diverted from gut to muscles. · Muscles work better and tire less easily.

Homeostasis

The conditions in which an organism lives are called its **environment**. To survive, an organism must be able to detect changes in its environment and respond efficiently to them. For multicellular animals like ourselves, this means that the various parts of the body must be carefully controlled so that they operate in harmony. This is called **coordination**. Coordination is achieved by the nervous system and the endocrine system. Orders sent by the nervous system are fast but short-lived, while those from the endocrine system are slower to arrive but their effect lasts longer. In fact, the two systems complement each other. In emergencies, for example, **adrenalin** makes the body 'super efficient' and ready for action. However, it is the nervous system which detects the threat in the first place and switches on the flow of adrenalin to cope with it.

As it happens, most of our cells never come into contact with the outside world – the external environment. Their environment is the quieter one of the **tissue fluid** which surrounds them. We call this the internal environment. Nevertheless, the cells can stand only very slight changes in this environment without being damaged. So, the body must constantly strive to keep it as steady as possible. Temperature, osmotic pressure (water content) and glucose

concentration are some of the conditions which the body will allow to vary very little. The devices which the body uses to control these things are known collectively as **homeostasis**.

Since the tissue fluid which makes up the internal environment comes from the blood, it is changes taking place in the blood which the body monitors and adjusts.

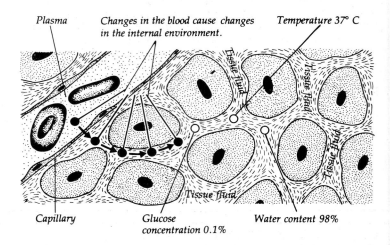

Plasma · *Changes in the blood cause changes in the internal environment.* · *Temperature 37° C* · *Tissue fluid* · *Capillary* · *Glucose concentration 0.1%* · *Water content 98%*

HOMEOSTASIS BY THE KIDNEYS

The kidneys are important organs of homeostasis. Among other things, they adjust the amount of water in the blood (see osmotic potential, pages 116–7). They do this by adjusting the amount of urine they produce. If we consume a lot of fluid, there will be too much water in the blood. The kidneys will then produce a lot of very dilute urine to get rid of the extra. If the body is short of water, the kidneys will produce only a very small amount of more concentrated urine. Usually, the situation is somewhere between these two extremes and the kidneys must make constant fine adjustments to the amount of water they allow out of the body.

The control centre for this job is in the brain. There, receptors check the condition of the blood which passes through them. If it is too concentrated (not enough water), they tell the **pituitary gland** to make **antidiuretic hormone** (**ADH**). This travels quickly in the bloodstream to the kidneys. There it causes more water to be reabsorbed from the kidney tubules into the blood (see page 119). Thus, less water is lost in the urine and the blood becomes more dilute. As more and more of this diluted blood returns to the brain, less ADH is made by the pituitary, until, finally, balance is restored.

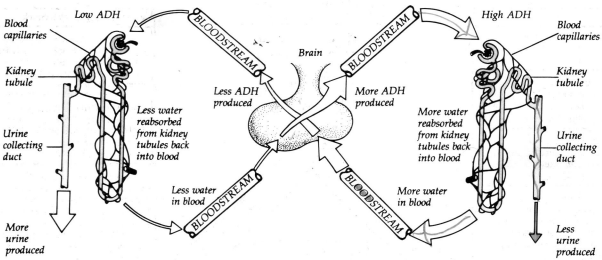

Low ADH · *Blood capillaries* · *Kidney tubule* · *Urine collecting duct* · *More urine produced* · *Less water reabsorbed from kidney tubules back into blood* · *Less water in blood* · *Less ADH produced* · *Brain* · *More ADH produced* · *More water reabsorbed from kidney tubules back into blood* · *More water in blood* · *High ADH* · *Blood capillaries* · *Kidney tubule* · *Urine collecting duct* · *Less urine produced* · *BLOODSTREAM*

This kind of control system is known as **feedback control**. Any change in the amount of water in the blood is fed back to the control centre and it acts to combat it. Too little water and ADH is produced. Too much water and ADH production falls. Thus, the water concentration of the blood is constantly changing. A feedback control system of this type makes sure, however, that it is always kept within acceptable limits.

CONTROL OF BLOOD SUGAR

The only sugar carried in any amount by the blood is **glucose**. The blood glucose level must be carefully controlled. If it gets too low, organs, especially the brain and heart, are deprived of their main energy source. If it gets too high, it causes the tissues to lose water by osmosis (see pages 116–7) and so dehydrates the blood. Changes in blood glucose are detected by the **islets of Langerhans** in the **pancreas**. They react by adjusting the amount of **insulin** they produce. This, in turn, causes the liver to either release or store glucose. The system is summed up in the diagram opposite. **Diabetes** is caused by the pancreas being unable to produce enough insulin. The blood glucose level rises and glucose begins to appear in the diabetic's urine. Diabetes can be controlled by careful diet and by injections of insulin. Other hormones, too, can affect blood glucose levels. In emergencies, **adrenalin** increases it (see page 197) to provide extra energy. In the longer term, **thyroxin** controls the rate at which the tissues use energy (the metabolic rate). Its activity thus affects the amount of glucose left circulating in the blood.

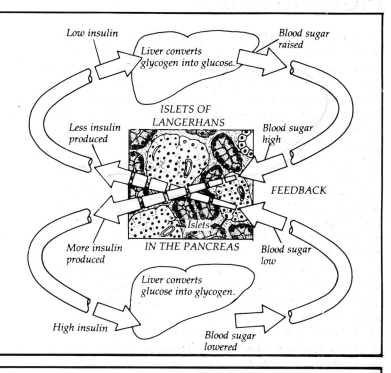

CONTROL OF BODY TEMPERATURE

Most animals are said to be cold-blooded. This does not mean that their blood is cold. It means that their body temperature tends to go up and down with the temperature of their surroundings. A more correct term for them is **poikilothermic** (*poikilo*: changeable; *therm*: heat). Poikilothermic animals can adjust their temperature in various ways. They can bask in the sun, for example, or cool off in the shade.

Birds and mammals are different. Their bodies have built-in systems which keep their body temperature steady even though the outside temperature rises and falls. They are commonly called warm-blooded animals, but a more accurate term is **homoiothermic** (*homoio*: same; *therm*: heat). Homoiothermic animals have a temperature control centre, or thermostat, in the brain. Information about the body temperature reaches this centre through the blood or nervous system. If necessary, it can then take steps to bring the temperature back to its proper level (around 37°C) in humans. This is another example of feedback control in homeostasis. It is summed up below.

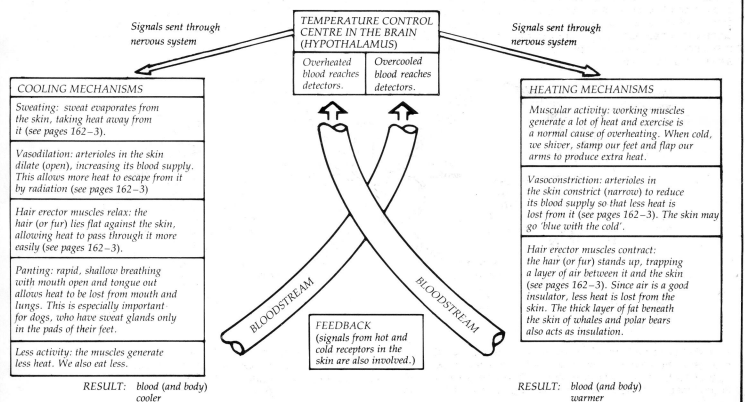

199

SECTION 18

Genetics and Evolution

Variation

No two living things are ever completely identical. There are always some differences between them. These differences are called **variations**. Variations are useful when we want to classify organisms into different groups. The more variations we find between two organisms, the farther apart we will group them. On the other hand, if two organisms are very similar, we may consider them to belong to the same species. Even organisms in the same species, though, are never exactly the same. There are always variations between them. There are two types of variation – **continuous variation** and **discontinuous variation**.

CONTINUOUS VARIATION

Continuous variation occurs when every member of a species shows a certain **characteristic** but not to the same extent. Take height, for example. Everybody is a certain height, but no two people are exactly the same. The characteristic varies continuously in the population from very small to very tall. The best way to show a continuous variation in a population is to draw a graph. The most common type of graph for this purpose is the **histogram** (bar graph). As large a sample of organisms as possible is measured. Then, since no two are exactly the same, a histogram is drawn in which each bar represents not one value, but a range of values.

The histograms opposite record two examples of continuous variation. The top histogram shows the heights of a random sample of 50 children, aged 12. The lower histogram shows the mass of a large number of broad bean seeds.

Although the variations are taking place in two very different types of organism, both histograms have the same bell-shaped outline. This is called a **normal distribution curve** and is typical of continuous variations. It tells us that, while small numbers of the population show the characteristic to a very large or very small degree, most are somewhere in between. The most common value is known as the **mode**.

Other examples of continuous variation include weight and handspan in humans, length of tail in other animals and the number of leaves, fruits or seeds produced by plants.

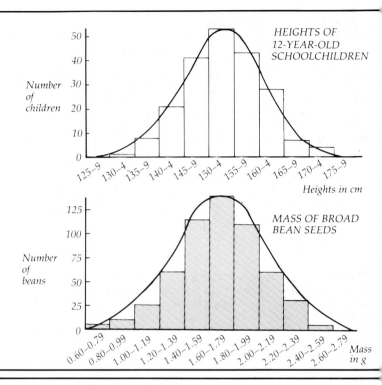

DISCONTINUOUS VARIATION

Discontinuous variation occurs when organisms must either have or not have a certain characteristic. There is no gradual change between two extremes. Human blood groups are one example. There are four distinct blood groups – O, A, B and AB. You either *have* one of these groups or you *do not have* it. There is no halfway. Discontinuous variations do not give normal distribution curves, though graphs are often drawn to show what proportion of a population has a specific characteristic. The graph opposite shows how the different blood groups are distributed in the UK. Other examples of discontinuous variation are shown below.

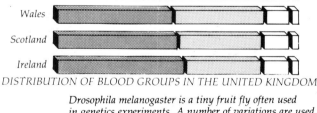

DISTRIBUTION OF BLOOD GROUPS IN THE UNITED KINGDOM

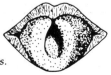

Tongue rolling: some people can curl the edges of their tongues without moving their lips.

Maize seeds

Full endosperm   Shrunken endosperm

Drosophila melanogaster is a tiny fruit fly often used in genetics experiments. A number of variations are used, for example:

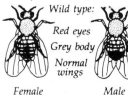

Wild type:
Red eyes
Grey body
Normal wings

Female   Male   Ebony body

Eye colour

Coloured

Colourless

Fingerprints come in several basic forms:

Loops   Whorls   Arches

Vestigial wings   Curly wings   White eyes

Every organism is different, even from members of its own species, so what causes the variations between them? In fact, they arise in two ways. The most important variations are passed on from parents to offspring. Dogs produce pups not kittens. Children resemble their parents, for example parents with blue eyes produce blue-eyed children. Variations like this which are inherited from parents are called **heritable variations**. Other variations are caused by the environment in which an organism lives. These cannot be inherited from parents and are called **non-heritable variations**.

All the many characteristics which make up an individual, including its appearance, are called its **phenotype**. Each phenotype is a blend of heritable and non-heritable characteristics.

HERITABLE VARIATIONS

Heritable variations are those which can be inherited from parents and passed on for generation after generation. All the discontinuous variations mentioned on the previous page are heritable. The information needed to build these characteristics is contained inside the nuclei of each organism's cells. When cells are dividing, we can see that the nucleus contains a number of 'threads'. These are called **chromosomes**. Each species has a set number of chromosomes in its nuclei. The human **chromosome number** is 46. The chromosomes of some other species are shown below.

Onion: 16 *Mosquito: 6* *Maize: 20*

The chromosomes carry the instructions which tell the organism how to develop. These instructions are called **genes**. Each chromosome carries a huge number of genes, each with its own little bit of information. You cannot have brown eyes, for example, unless your chromosomes carry the genes for brown eyes. The collection of genes which an organism has in its chromosomes is called its **genotype**.

If we look closely at an organism's chromosomes, we find that they can be sorted into pairs according to their size and shape. These similar chromosomes are known as **homologous chromosomes**. The little fruit fly, *Drosophila*, for example, has eight chromosomes which sort into four pairs.

Drosophila's 8 chromosomes *Arranged in 4 homologous pairs*

When **gametes** (sex cells) are made, they get only one of each homologous pair and so each gamete ends up with only half the usual number of chromosomes. This is called the **haploid number** of chromosomes (often written as n). Normal cells have the **diploid number** (2n). So, a normal (diploid) human cell has 46 chromosomes (2n=46), while a (haploid) sperm or egg has only 23 (n = 23). In *Drosophila* the diploid number is 8 (2n = 8), while the haploid number is 4 (n=4).

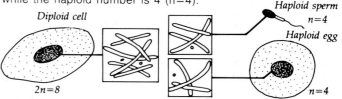

Diploid cell *Haploid sperm n=4* *Haploid egg n=4* *2n=8*

During fertilisation, the haploid nuclei of the male and female gametes fuse together. This gives a cell, the **zygote**, which now has the diploid number of chromosomes, and so half of the new cell's genes, have come from the male and half from the female. So, when the zygote goes on to become a new organism, some of its characteristics will resemble its male parent and some its female parent.

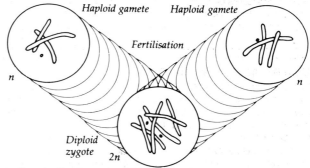

Haploid gamete *Haploid gamete* *Fertilisation* *n* *n* *Diploid zygote 2n*

Genetics is the branch of biology which looks at how variations are passed on from generation to generation. Since such heritable variations are caused by genes, genetics actually studies how genes are inherited.

NON-HERITABLE VARIATIONS

Non-heritable variations between organisms are those which are caused by the environment. These characteristics are said to be **acquired** not inherited. They cannot be passed on to the next generation. Scars, for example are non-heritable. If a locust loses a leg, its young will still hatch out with six legs, not five.

However, the environment can also affect the way in which heritable characteristics will develop. A tall variety of pea plant will end up small if it does not get enough water and the correct minerals. Its genes, which could have made it grow tall, do not get a chance to work. Similarly, if a child does not get enough vitamin D, it may develop rickets — a non-heritable condition. So, the phenotype of an organism is actually caused by its genotype and the effect the environment has upon it. Because of this, heritable characteristics which are easily affected by the environment are difficult to study in genetics and are usually avoided.

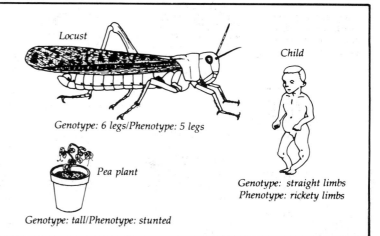

Locust

Genotype: 6 legs/Phenotype: 5 legs

Child

Genotype: straight limbs Phenotype: rickety limbs

Pea plant

Genotype: tall/Phenotype: stunted

Mendel

Genetics is the study of inheritance, that is the study of how characteristics are passed on from one generation to another. The basic laws of genetics were worked out in 1866 by an Austrian monk called Gregor Mendel. Mendel did this by carrying out breeding experiments on pea plants. When two individuals are bred together (crossed), their offspring are called **hybrids**. Knowing the **phenotype** (characteristics) of the parents, Mendel wanted to be able to predict the phenotypes of the hybrids. Other scientists had tried this before, but Mendel was the first to succeed. Modern genetics is based on his work.

Gregor Mendel (1822–84)

WHY WAS MENDEL SUCCESSFUL?

He studied a suitable organism.

Mendel used over 21 000 pea plants in his experiments. Peas grow quickly and each generation takes just one season to produce. Thus, he did not have to wait long to find out the results of his crosses. Also, although peas usually **self** **pollinate**, they are easy to **cross pollinate**. Mendel used both methods in his experiments. Finally, he had available a number of different varieties of pea plant which he could cross.

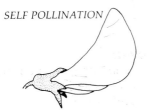

SELF POLLINATION

Pea flowers do not open to let insects inside and so they usually pollinate themselves.

CROSS POLLINATION: STEP 1

A flower bud is opened carefully. The stamens are removed before they are old enough to produce pollen. The bud is closed.

CROSS POLLINATION: STEP 2

Later, when the stigmas are ripe, pollen from another variety of pea is brushed on to them.

CROSS POLLINATION: STEP 3

The flower is enclosed in a bag to prevent insects bringing in other kinds of pea pollen.

He studied discontinuous variations only.

Peas, for example, have either yellow or green cotyledons with no confusing halfway shades. This made it easier for Mendel to record the results of a cross. The characteristics he studied are shown below.

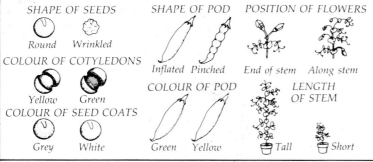

SHAPE OF SEEDS — Round, Wrinkled
COLOUR OF COTYLEDONS — Yellow, Green
COLOUR OF SEED COATS — Grey, White
SHAPE OF POD — Inflated, Pinched
COLOUR OF POD — Green, Yellow
POSITION OF FLOWERS — End of stem, Along stem
LENGTH OF STEM — Tall, Short

He studied one characteristic at a time.

Others studied a number of characteristics at the same time which made the results of crosses hard to interpret. Mendel would look at only one and ignore the rest. This gave him a clearer picture of what was happening, for example:

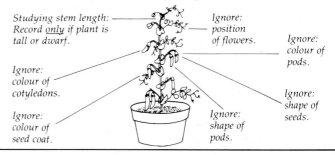

Studying stem length: Record *only* if plant is tall or dwarf.
Ignore: position of flowers.
Ignore: colour of pods.
Ignore: colour of cotyledons.
Ignore: shape of seeds.
Ignore: colour of seed coat.
Ignore: shape of pods.

He started with pure lines.

Before starting his experiments, Mendel had to be sure that the character he was studying would normally appear unchanged generation after generation. In peas, this is done by letting them self pollinate year after year and checking that the offspring always show the desired feature. Organisms which do this are called **pure lines** and are said to be **true breeding** for that characteristic. Pure lines are now always used in genetics experiments.

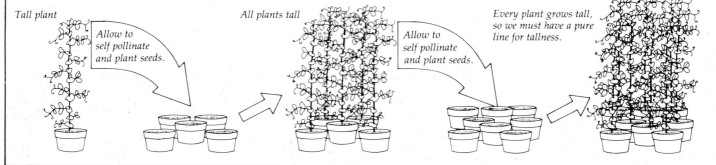

Tall plant — Allow to self pollinate and plant seeds. — All plants tall — Allow to self pollinate and plant seeds. — Every plant grows tall, so we must have a pure line for tallness.

Mendel's experiments

The F₁ generation

Mendel selected true breeding plants which differed in only one characteristic and crossed them. This is called a **monohybrid cross**. The starting plants make up the **parental generation** (P₁ for short) and the hybrids which result are called the **first filial generation** or F₁ generation.

Mendel crossed tall plants with dwarf plants and plants which gave round seeds with plants which gave wrinkled seeds. Here is what he found when he did this:

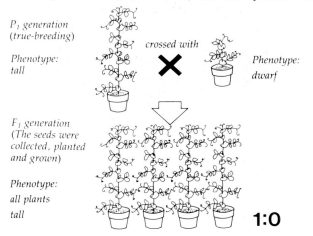

P₁ generation (true-breeding)

Phenotype: tall   crossed with   Phenotype: dwarf

F₁ generation (The seeds were collected, planted and grown)

Phenotype: all plants tall   1:0

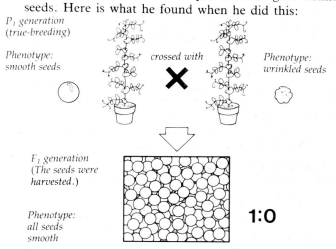

P₁ generation (true-breeding)

Phenotype: smooth seeds   crossed with   Phenotype: wrinkled seeds

F₁ generation (The seeds were harvested.)

Phenotype: all seeds smooth   1:0

The F₂ generation

In these two crosses and the others which Mendel did, all the F₁ plants had the same phenotype as just one of the parents. The other phenotype did not appear at all. To obtain the next generation, called the **second filial generation** or F₂ generation, was much easier. Mendel simply allowed the tall F₁ hybrid plants and plants grown from the F₁ round seeds to self pollinate.

Mendel never got exactly three to one in his F₂ generations.

However, in breeding experiments, if there is a large enough number of individuals produced in the F₂ generation, then this ratio will always be very close to three to one.

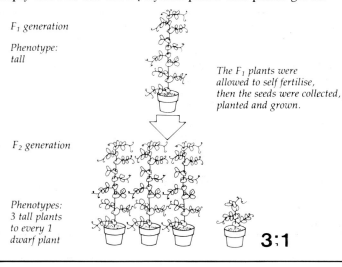

F₁ generation

Phenotype: tall

The F₁ plants were allowed to self fertilise, then the seeds were collected, planted and grown.

F₂ generation

Phenotypes: 3 tall plants to every 1 dwarf plant   3:1

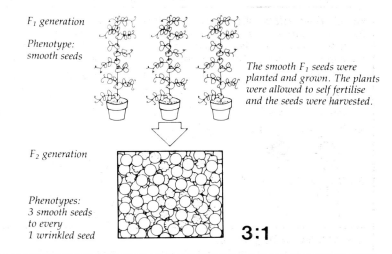

F₁ generation

Phenotype: smooth seeds

The smooth F₁ seeds were planted and grown. The plants were allowed to self fertilise and the seeds were harvested.

F₂ generation

Phenotypes: 3 smooth seeds to every 1 wrinkled seed   3:1

DOMINANT AND RECESSIVE GENES

Mendel said that the appearance of heritable characteristics was caused by microscopic factors in the cells. We now call these factors **genes** and we know that they are located inside the nuclei on the **chromosomes**. Since, in the F₁ generation, the gene for height seems to cancel out the dwarf gene, we call it the **dominant gene**. We call the dwarf gene the **recessive gene**. In genetics, genes are given symbols. Dominant genes are usually given a capital letter and recessive genes a small letter. Below are the genes which Mendel found to be dominant or recessive and the symbols for them.

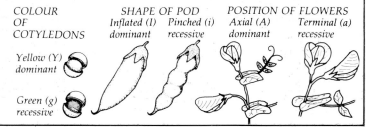

LENGTH OF STEM — Tall (T) dominant / Dwarf (t) recessive

SHAPE OF SEEDS — Round (R) dominant / Wrinkled (r) recessive

COLOUR OF SEED COATS — Coloured (C) dominant / White (c) recessive

COLOUR OF POD — Green (G) dominant / Yellow (g) recessive

COLOUR OF COTYLEDONS — Yellow (Y) dominant / Green (g) recessive

SHAPE OF POD — Inflated (I) dominant / Pinched (i) recessive

POSITION OF FLOWERS — Axial (A) dominant / Terminal (a) recessive

Mixing genes

Explaining Mendel's results

Heritable characteristics are caused by not one, but two **genes** carried inside the nucleus of every cell in an organism. Each pair of genes is located on a pair of **homologous chromosomes**, one to each chromosome. For an organism to be true-breeding, each gene must be identical. Such organisms are said to be **homozygous**. True-breeding tall or dwarf pea plants, for example, are homozygous. We write their **genotypes** as TT and tt respectively. F_1 hybrids, however, get one of each type of gene. They are said to be **heterozygous** and their genotype would be written as Tt. Different forms of a gene are called **alleles**. So, tall (T) and dwarf (t) are alleles of the gene for stem length in pea plants.

When gametes (sex cells) are formed, homologous chromosomes are separated and so each gamete gets only one from each pair of genes. We can now follow what happened when Mendel crossed tall and dwarf peas.

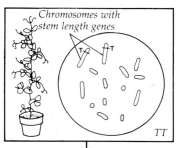

PARENT
Phenotype: tall
Genotype: TT
Notes: the plants are homozygous (true-breeding). The cells are diploid, containing 14 chromosomes (2n=14). One homologous pair carries the two genes for tallness.

Chromosomes with stem length genes

TT

Chromosomes with stem length genes

tt

PARENT
Phenotype: dwarf
Genotype: tt
Notes: the plants are homozygous. Their cells are diploid, containing 14 chromosomes (2n=14). One homologous pair carries the two dwarf genes.

GAMETES: pollen and ovules
Genotype: T
Notes: the gametes are haploid, containing 7 chromosomes (n=7). One chromosome carries a gene for tallness.

Fertilisation

GAMETES: pollen and ovules
Genotype: t
Notes: the gametes are haploid, containing 7 chromosomes (n=7). One chromosome carries a dwarf gene.

F_1 GENERATION
Phenotype: tall
Genotype: Tt
Notes: the plants are heterozygous. Their cells are diploid, containing 14 chromosomes (2n=14). One member of a homologous pair carries a tallness gene. The other has a dwarf gene. The tallness gene is dominant and the dwarf is recessive, so the plants are tall.

Tt

F_1 GAMETE FORMATION
Since the F_1 hybrid plants are heterozygous, they are now able to form more than one kind of gamete. 50% of pollen carries a tallness gene and 50% gets a dwarf gene. Similarly, 50% of its ovules carry a tallness gene and 50% get a dwarf gene.

GAMETES: pollen and ovules
Genotype: T (50%)

GAMETES: pollen and ovules
Genotype: t(50%)

F2 generation
Phenotypes: 3 tall/1 dwarf
Genotypes: TT(25%)/Tt(50%)/ tt (25%)

Notes: There are four ways (shown below) in which F_1 gametes can come together to form F_2 plants, with an equal (25%) chance of each happening. If enough F_2 plants develop, about 25% will be homozygous tall (TT), 25% homozygous dwarf (tt) and 50% heterozygous (Tt). Since tallness is dominant, these will also be tall. Thus, the F_2 generation yields 3 tall to 1 dwarf.

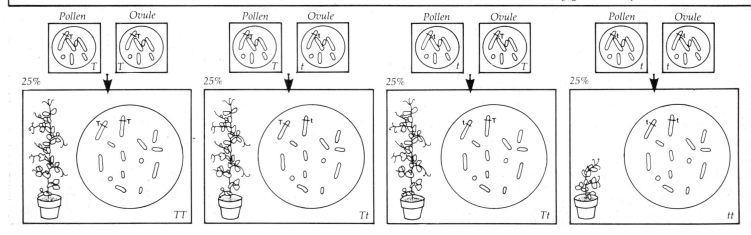

Pollen   Ovule   Pollen   Ovule   Pollen   Ovule   Pollen   Ovule

25%   25%   25%   25%

TT   Tt   Tt   tt

Since Mendel's time, similar breeding experiments have been carried out with many different organisms and the same sort of results have been obtained. Breeding experiments involving some animals commonly used in genetics are shown below. These organisms prove suitable for genetic experiments for the following reasons:

1 They are small and easily handled in large numbers.
2 They have a short **generation time**, i.e. they reproduce and mature quickly.
3 They are available in a number of strains which show **discontinuous variation**.

MICE

Mice can produce a new generation every three months. Among the varieties available for breeding experiments are mice with various colours of coat, for example:

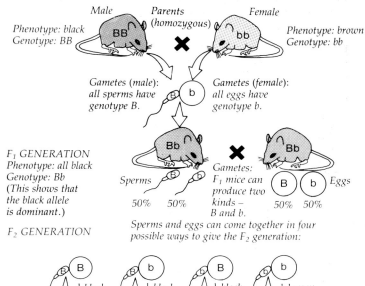

Male   *Parents (homozygous)*   *Female*

Phenotype: black
Genotype: BB

Phenotype: brown
Genotype: bb

Gametes (male): all sperms have genotype B.
Gametes (female): all eggs have genotype b.

F₁ GENERATION
Phenotype: all black
Genotype: Bb
(This shows that the black allele is dominant.)

Gametes: F₁ mice can produce two kinds – B and b.

Sperms   50%   50%   *Eggs*   50%   50%

F₂ GENERATION

Sperms and eggs can come together in four possible ways to give the F₂ generation:

$\frac{1}{4}$ black $\frac{1}{4}$ black $\frac{1}{4}$ black $\frac{1}{4}$ brown

BB   Bb   Bb   bb

DROSOPHILA MELANOGASTER

Drosophila melanogaster (see pages 202–3) can produce a new generation every two weeks. A number of different varieties are used in genetics experiments. Shown below is the result of crossing two strains with different wing types.

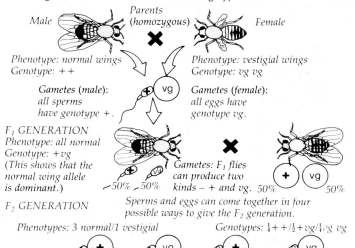

Male   *Parents (homozygous)*   *Female*

Phenotype: normal wings
Genotype: ++

Phenotype: vestigial wings
Genotype: vg vg

Gametes (male): all sperms have genotype +.
Gametes (female): all eggs have genotype vg.

F₁ GENERATION
Phenotype: all normal
Genotype: +vg
(This shows that the normal wing allele is dominant.)

Gametes: F₁ flies can produce two kinds – + and vg.

50%   50%   50%   50%

F₂ GENERATION

Sperms and eggs can come together in four possible ways to give the F₂ generation.

Phenotypes: 3 normal/1 vestigial   *Genotypes: $\frac{1}{4}++/\frac{1}{2}+vg/\frac{1}{4}vg\ vg$*

Normal   *Normal*   *Normal*   *Vestigial*

The back-cross

In an F₂ generation we always know the genotype of those organisms which show a recessive characteristic. They must be homozygous, otherwise the recessive allele could not **express** itself (show up). Brown mice, for example, can be of only one genotype – bb. Black F₂ mice, however, could be either homozygous (BB) or heterozygous (Bb). If we had such a male black mouse and we wanted to know its genotype, we would cross it with a female brown mouse. This is called a **back-cross** and it could give two possible results:

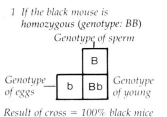

1 If the black mouse is homozygous (genotype: BB)

Genotype of sperm

	B
b	Bb

Genotype of eggs   *Genotype of young*

Result of cross = 100% black mice

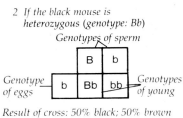

2 If the black mouse is heterozygous (genotype: Bb)

Genotypes of sperm

	B	b
b	Bb	bb

Genotype of eggs   *Genotypes of young*

Result of cross: 50% black; 50% brown

So, by the phenotypes of the young we can work out the genotype of the unknown parent.

The device used above to predict the results of the crosses is called a punnet square. The possible genotypes of the male gametes are put along one side and those of the female gametes along another. When the square is filled in, it shows the expected genotypes of the offspring and also the proportions of each type, if enough offspring are produced (see diagram opposite also).

INCOMPLETE DOMINANCE

Incomplete dominance occurs when alleles of a gene exist with neither one being dominant over the other. In such cases, heterozygous individuals have a phenotype midway between those of the two incompletely dominant alleles. In shorthorn cattle, for example, neither the white-hair allele (W) nor the red-hair allele (R) is dominant. Crossing gives the results shown below.

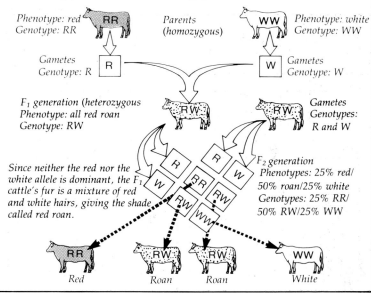

Phenotype: red
Genotype: RR

Parents (homozygous)

Phenotype: white
Genotype: WW

Gametes Genotype: R

Gametes Genotype: W

F₁ generation (heterozygous
Phenotype: all red roan
Genotype: RW

Gametes Genotypes: R and W

Since neither the red nor the white allele is dominant, the F₁ cattle's fur is a mixture of red and white hairs, giving the shade called red roan.

F₂ generation
Phenotypes: 25% red/ 50% roan/25% white
Genotypes: 25% RR/ 50% RW/25% WW

RR   *RW*   *RW*   *WW*
Red   *Roan*   *Roan*   *White*

Meiosis

The heritable characteristics of an organism depend on the types of **genes** which it has, in other words on its **genotype**. These genes are found in the nuclei of its cells on 'threads' called **chromosomes**. The cells of each species contain a particular number of chromosomes, known as the **diploid** number for that species (written as 2n). The chromosomes come in similar-looking pairs called **homologous** chromosomes. In human cells, for example, there are 46 chromosomes (2n=46), that is 23 homologous pairs.

When **gametes** (sex cells) are being made, each gamete gets only one out of each homologous pair and so ends up with only half as many chromosomes as a normal cell. This is called the **haploid** number of chromosomes (written as n). So, a gamete really has just one set of chromosomes (n), while a diploid cell has two (2n).

Gametes are formed in the sex organs of plants and animals by a kind of cell division known as **meiosis**. Since, during meiosis, the chromosome number is reduced by half, it is often called **reduction division**. Those cells which undergo meiosis and so produce gametes are called **gamete mother cells**.

The diagrams below show how the chromosomes behave as a diploid cell with 2n=6 undergoes meiosis.

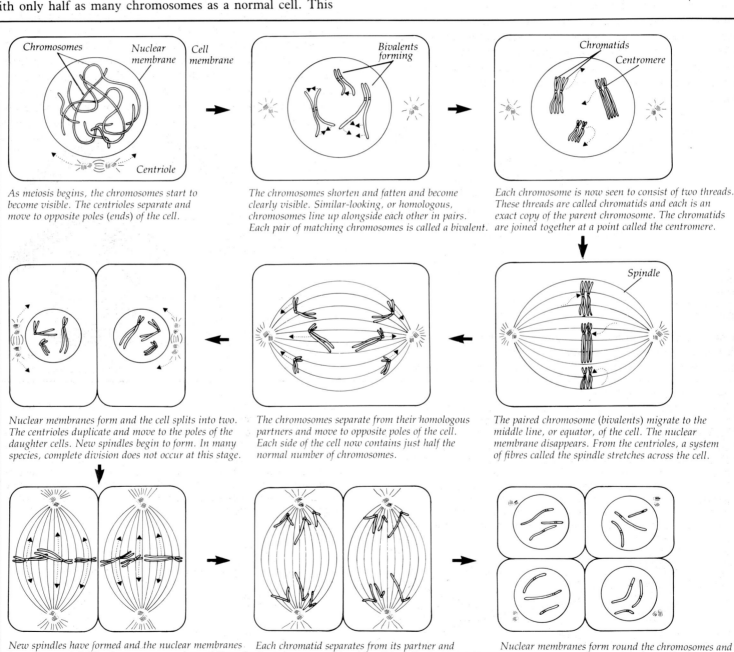

As meiosis begins, the chromosomes start to become visible. The centrioles separate and move to opposite poles (ends) of the cell.

The chromosomes shorten and fatten and become clearly visible. Similar-looking, or homologous, chromosomes line up alongside each other in pairs. Each pair of matching chromosomes is called a bivalent.

Each chromosome is now seen to consist of two threads. These threads are called chromatids and each is an exact copy of the parent chromosome. The chromatids are joined together at a point called the centromere.

Nuclear membranes form and the cell splits into two. The centrioles duplicate and move to the poles of the daughter cells. New spindles begin to form. In many species, complete division does not occur at this stage.

The chromosomes separate from their homologous partners and move to opposite poles of the cell. Each side of the cell now contains just half the normal number of chromosomes.

The paired chromosome (bivalents) migrate to the middle line, or equator, of the cell. The nuclear membrane disappears. From the centrioles, a system of fibres called the spindle stretches across the cell.

New spindles have formed and the nuclear membranes have disappeared. The chromosomes, each consisting of two chromatids joined at the centromere, migrate to the equators of the daughter cells.

Each chromatid separates from its partner and they move to opposite poles of the cell. The chromatids are now really daughter chromosomes and the ends of each cell have the haploid number (n=3).

Nuclear membranes form round the chromosomes and each cell splits. So, a diploid (2n=6) mother cell has now been converted into four haploid (n=3) gametes.

Sexual reproduction causes variation in a population, essential if the species is to survive and adapt to changing conditions. This is because the young are formed from the joining of two haploid (n) gametes – one from the male and one from the female. Thus, the diploid (2n) organism which develops has received half its chromosomes, and so half its genes, from one parent and half from the other. So, while it may resemble both parents in many ways, it can never be exactly identical to either. It is a new individual whose characteristics are determined by its very own combination of genes.

However, there is more to it than that. Every gamete, when it is made, must receive one chromosome from every homologous pair of chromosomes. It is a matter of pure chance which one out of each pair it gets. So, the more chromosomes an organism has, the greater is the number of different combinations which the gametes can have. In the cell shown below, for example, the six chromosomes could sort themselves in eight different ways to make eight different kinds of gamete.

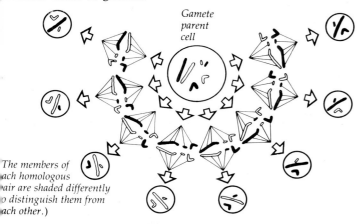

Gamete parent cell

The members of each homologous pair are shaded differently to distinguish them from each other.)

Now, while both members of each pair of homologous chromosomes carry genes which affect the same characteristics of their organism – stem length, coat colour,

etc – they are not the same. They will contain different alleles from each other. So, in meiosis, the **random assortment** of chromosomes into the gametes, as it is called, is actually a sort of 'shuffling' of the genes. This ensures that the members of a population get as many different combinations of characteristics from each other as possible. Consider human beings, for example. From our 46 chromosomes more than eight million different combinations of chromosomes can be 'shuffled' out to the gametes. No wonder even very close relations, such as brothers and sisters, can be so unlike each other.

Linked genes

Every chromosome carries a variety of different genes. Those genes which are on the same chromosome are said to be linked. Unlike other genes, linked genes will not tend to be separated when the chromosomes are 'shuffled' in meiosis. Since they are on the same chromosome, they tend to turn up together through the generations. In maize, for example, the alleles for coloured (C) or colourless (c) seeds and those for full (S) or shrunken (s) seeds are linked. Here is one example of how they behave:

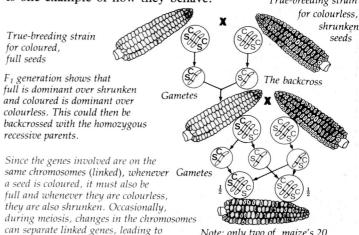

True-breeding strain for coloured, full seeds

True-breeding strain for colourless, shrunken seeds

F₁ generation shows that full is dominant over shrunken and coloured is dominant over colourless. This could then be backcrossed with the homozygous recessive parents.

Gametes

The backcross

Gametes

Since the genes involved are on the same chromosomes (linked), whenever a seed is coloured, it must also be full and whenever they are colourless, they are also shrunken. Occasionally, during meiosis, changes in the chromosomes can separate linked genes, leading to new combinations of characteristics.

Note: only two of maize's 20 chromosomes are shown here.

SEX CHROMOSOMES

Sex chromosomes determine the sex of an animal. There are two types of sex chromosome – **X-chromosomes** and **Y-chromosomes**. Each cell contains just two of them. Whether an animal is to be male or female depends on which two chromosomes its cells have. In mammals, for instance, females have two X-chromosomes. Their genotype is XX. Males, however, have one X-chromosome and one Y-chromosome, genotype XY. This means that a male mammal has one less pair of homologous chromosomes in its cells than a female. However, during meiosis, when gametes are being made, sex

chromosomes behave like the others and separate from their partners. Thus, each gamete gets only one sex chromosome. Since the female genotype is XX, all eggs must get an X-chromosome. The male genotype XY, on the other hand, means that males can make two kinds of sperm – half carrying an X-chromosome and half carrying a Y-chromosome. So, the sex of the future animal depends on which kind of sperm fertilises the egg. Since the chances are even, males and females emerge in roughly equal numbers.

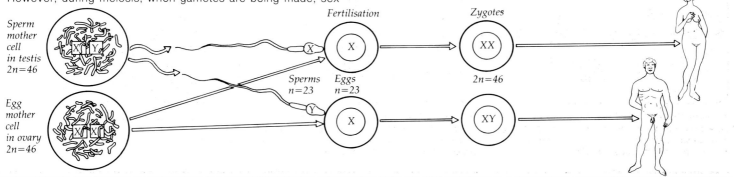

Fertilisation *Zygotes*

Sperm mother cell in testis 2n=46

Egg mother cell in ovary 2n=46

Sperms n=23 *Eggs n=23*

2n=46

Sex linkage

There are certain inherited defects which are much more common in men than in women. These conditions are said to be sex-linked. Among them are **red-green colour blindness** and **haemophilia**. They are caused by recessive genes carried on the X-chromosome. Since the Y-chromosomes are shorter than the X-chromosomes, they do not carry as many genes. Among their 'missing' genes are those which could influence the sex-linked characteristics.

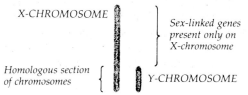

X-CHROMOSOME

Sex-linked genes present only on X-chromosome

Homologous section of chromosomes

Y-CHROMOSOME

So, for a male to suffer from a sex-linked condition, he need only inherit a single defective X-chromosome from his mother. Although its defective gene is recessive, his Y-chromosome can never carry the dominant gene needed to cover it up. Females, on the other hand, have, not one, but two X-chromosomes. Both would have to carry the defective gene before the defect would show up. Since one would have to come from the father and one from the mother, this is much less likely to happen. It is more common for a woman to be **heterozygous** for the trait, having one defective X-chromosome and one normal. In this case, she will not show the defective **phenotype**, but she can still transmit the defective gene to her children. She is said to be a **carrier**. A male cannot be a carrier. If he has the defective gene, he must show the defective phenotype.

Here are the children we would predict to be born to parents with various genotypes for a recessive sex-linked trait.

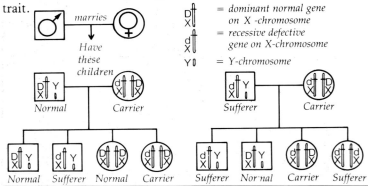

$\frac{D}{X}\|$ = dominant normal gene on X-chromosome

$\frac{d}{X}\|$ = recessive defective gene on X-chromosome

$Y\|$ = Y-chromosome

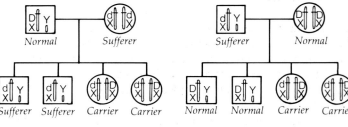

Normal / Sufferer   Sufferer / Normal

Sufferer / Sufferer / Carrier / Carrier   Normal / Normal / Carrier / Carrier

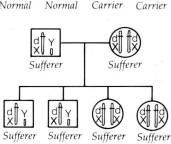

Sufferer / Sufferer

Sufferer / Sufferer / Sufferer / Sufferer

Note: some of these marriages, especially if the sex-linked condition is serious, are very unlikely to take place. Also, these are predictions only. For example, we might predict that half of a couple's sons will be affected, only to find that no sons are born to them, only daughters.

RED-GREEN COLOUR BLINDNESS

Red-green colour blindness is the inability to tell red from green. It is the most common sex-linked trait in humans, affecting about 8% of men, but only 0.5% of women. It is caused by a defective gene on the X-chromosome. Here are the families we would predict to result from the more common marriages involving this gene. Alongside them are the **Punnet squares** which are used to work them out.

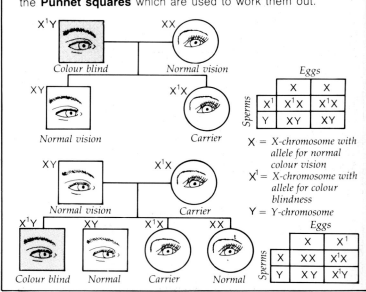

X = X-chromosome with allele for normal colour vision
X¹ = X-chromosome with allele for colour blindness
Y = Y-chromosome

HAEMOPHILIA

Haemophilia is a disease which prevents the blood clotting properly. This means that even a small injury can be very dangerous. The disease is caused by a recessive gene on the X-chromosome. It is very rare in women, although they can be carriers and transmit the disease to their sons. Queen Victoria, for example, was a carrier of haemophilia. The **pedigree chart** opposite shows how the gene was passed through the royal families of Europe. The carriers are only discovered by seeing which males actually develop the condition.

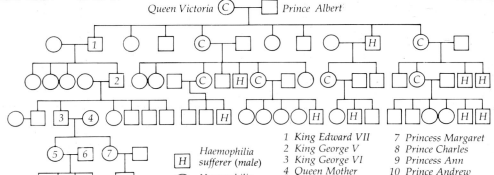

☐H☐ *Haemophilia sufferer (male)*

Ⓒ *Haemophilia carrier (female)*

1 King Edward VII
2 King George V
3 King George VI
4 Queen Mother
5 Queen Elizabeth II
6 Prince Philip
7 Princess Margaret
8 Prince Charles
9 Princess Ann
10 Prince Andrew
11 Prince Edward

Evolution

Life comes in an astonishing variety of forms. Almost two million different species of animals and plants have been discovered and new ones are being found every year. Even more different kinds are thought to have existed in the past, but have now died out completely. They are said to be **extinct**.

Many people believe that all these species were created in their present form by God a long time ago and that they have existed without changing ever since. Scientists, however, prefer another explanation. Scientists believe that all the different species alive today developed slowly and gradually, step by step, from the same simpler organism. This gradual change, or **evolution**, took thousands of

millions of years to happen. This idea of how life developed is called the **Theory of Evolution**. Many types appeared which were not well suited to their environment and these eventually became extinct.

From the Theory of Evolution, it follows that, if we were able to trace the ancestors of today's living organisms right back through time, we would find eventually that they all shared the same common ancestor. All the vertebrates alive today, for example, are thought to have evolved from simple fish-like animals. This evolution is believed to have taken over 400 million years. The simple evolutionary tree drawn below shows some of the stages through which the evolution of the vertebrates may have passed.

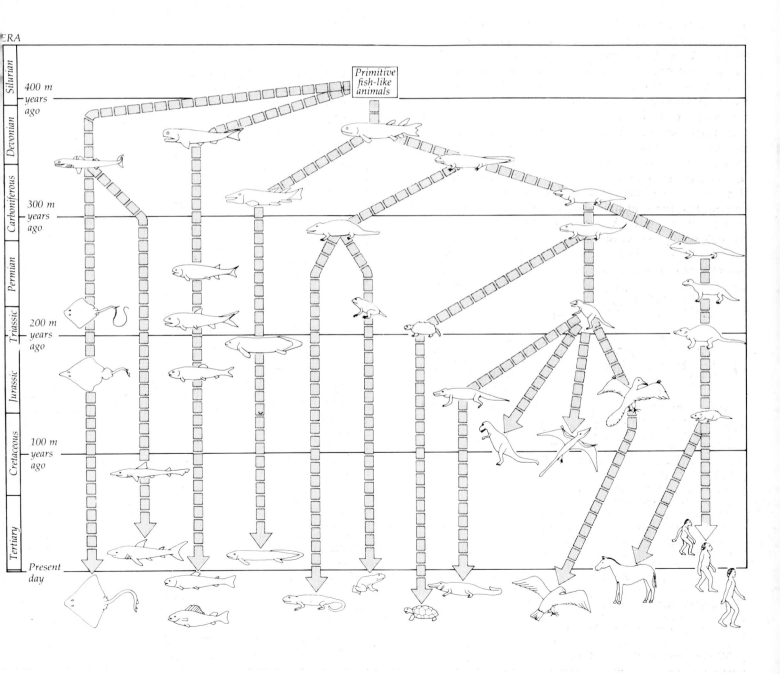

Evidence for evolution

The Theory of Evolution is an explanation of how the many kinds of plants and animals alive today came into being. Since the process is thought to have taken thousands of millions of years, there is no way to prove conclusively what actually happened. However, there is a lot of evidence to back up the theory. Suitable evidence has to show that, in the distant past, life on Earth was simpler and less varied than it is today. Also, it must indicate that, as time went on, more and more new types appeared, gradually becoming more complex and more advanced than the ones before. Furthermore, if today's very different creatures really do share common ancestors, then we would expect to find similarities between them – characteristics passed down to them from the same source. Among the evidence available is evidence from anatomy and from fossils.

EVIDENCE FROM ANATOMY

Homologous structures

When we compare the anatomy of different animals, we often find organs which are very similar in structure, although they may be used in different ways. These structures are said to be **homologous**. The limbs of many vertebrates, including humans, for example, are based on an arrangement of bones called the **pentadactyl limb** (*penta*: five; *dactyl*: finger). The pentadactyl limb structure is shown below and some of the uses to which it is adapted. The existence of this structure strongly suggests that these vertebrates share a common ancestor, whose descendants evolved in different ways. This is called **divergent evolution**.

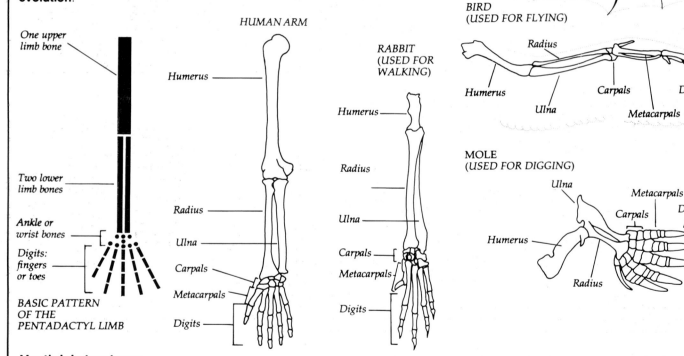

Vestigial structures

Many animals have organs in their bodies which seem to be of no use to them. These are called **vestigial organs**. In other species, however, the same organs exist, but they have a definite function. Dogs and humans, for example, have a similar set of muscles attached to the ears. The dog can use these muscles to turn its ears towards a sound, but we cannot. A rabbit's appendix is an important part of its digestive system.

Ours is often just a nuisance. We can see a further example in the whale's skeleton. It has no hind limbs, but it does have a vestigial pelvic girdle. This suggests that its ancestors, like other vertebrates, did have four limbs. The whales' watery environment, however, caused them to evolve differently. The hind limbs disappeared, leaving only a reduced pelvic girdle as evidence that limbs once existed.

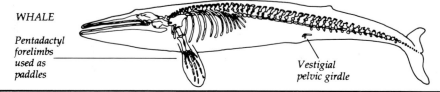

WHALE

Pentadactyl forelimbs used as paddles

Vestigial pelvic girdle

EVIDENCE FROM FOSSILS

When organisms die, their remains usually decompose and disappear completely. Sometimes, however, they are preserved for millions of years. These remains of ancient organisms are called **fossils**. Hard objects such as bones, teeth and shells or the woody tissues of plants are most likely to become fossilised. The existence of fossils provides us with a way of looking into the past to see what life was like many millions of years ago.

The best sources of fossils are **sedimentary rocks**. These rocks were formed from sediments such as sand, mud or silt which settled to the bottom of ancient seas. As the layers built up, tremendous pressures turned them into rock. Organisms buried in the sediments could only decompose very slowly. As they did so, their lost materials were replaced by minerals seeping into them. Gradually, the organisms turned to stone to be preserved as fossils in the newly-formed rock. As the diagrams below illustrate, the oldest sedimentary rocks and therefore the oldest fossils are to be found in the deepest layers of rock.

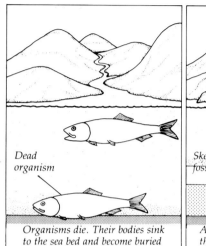

Dead organism

Dead organism

Organisms die. Their bodies sink to the sea bed and become buried by sediment.

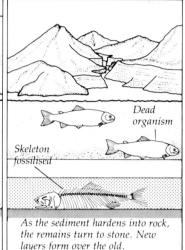

Dead organism

Skeleton fossilised

As the sediment hardens into rock, the remains turn to stone. New layers form over the old.

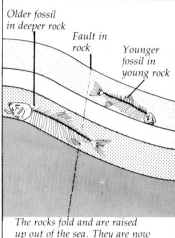

Older fossil in deeper rock

Fault in rock

Younger fossil in young rock

The rocks fold and are raised up out of the sea. They are now exposed to wind and rain.

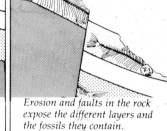

Erosion of rock exposes fossils.

Erosion and faults in the rock expose the different layers and the fossils they contain.

When large numbers of fossils are examined, we find what the Theory of Evolution predicts we should. Fossil organisms from the oldest rocks are few and simple in structure. As we go up the **fossil record**, however, organisms increase in number and variety and more advanced types begin to appear. The graph below summarises these findings.

Period	Algae, fungi and bacteria only	Cambrian — First invertebrates: graptolites, trilobites, shellfish, corals, echinoderms, crustaceans and other arthropods	Ordovician — First vertebrates – armoured fish	Silurian — First land plants, jawed fish, sea scorpions. Graptolites decline.	Devonian — Ferns, clubmosses, early seed plants, many types of fish, first amphibians appear.	Carboniferous — Giant clubmosses, ferns, horsetails, seed ferns, conifers and amphibians common. First reptiles and insects appear.	Permian — Reptiles common; amphibians decline. Giant clubmosses, horsetails, trilobites, many fish and corals extinct.	Triassic — First dinosaurs and mammals	Jurassic — Cycads, maidenhair trees and large ferns common; dinosaurs widespread. Flying reptiles and first birds appear. New corals and sea urchins appear.	Cretaceous — First flowering plants appear. Dinosaurs become extinct. Many kinds of birds and small mammals appear.	Tertiary — Flowering trees, grass, horses, apes, elephants and other large mammals appear. Later, ape-man appears.	Early Man appears.

600   500   400   300   200   100

Millions of years ago

So many good fossils of some organisms have been found that it has been possible to piece together their evolutionary history. The diagrams below, for instance, show how the horse is thought to have evolved. Similar schemes have been constructed for the giraffe and the camel. With many organisms, however, this is not possible. There are gaps in the fossil record. These are known as **missing links**. For many years, for example, no connection could be found between the birds and the reptiles from which they are thought to have evolved. Eventually, however, fossils of animals which seemed to represent a halfway stage between the two were discovered.

Selection

Organisms are faced with many different environments. A species will not survive unless it is suited to its own environment. The characteristics which allow an organism to fit into its environment are called **adaptations**. The pentadactyl limbs of the whale, for example (see page 138), are adapted as fins for swimming. Those of other vertebrates are adapted for other uses.

How have these different adaptations evolved? If organisms are descended from the same ancestors, how are they able to evolve until each species is adapted to its own ecological **niche** (see pages 102–3)? Also, environments change. Such changes have made many species extinct. They were well adapted to their old conditions, but could not fit into the new. Other species have been able to produce new adaptations allowing them to cope with the changes. How do these come about? This is what any Theory of Evolution must explain.

Various explanations have been put forward to explain how evolution comes about. The one which most biologists prefer is called the **Theory of Natural Selection**.

THEORY OF NATURAL SELECTION

The idea of **natural selection** was first suggested in 1858 by Charles Darwin and Alfred Wallace. The following year, Darwin expanded on the theory in a book called *The Origin of Species*. Since then, Darwin's ideas have been added to and modified by other biologists. They are now widely accepted as the best explanation of evolution. They are summed up in the diagrams below.

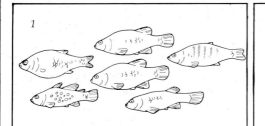

1. *Organisms are capable of producing large numbers of young in their lifetime. Some fish, for example, produce millions of eggs.*

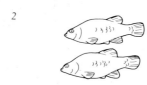

2. *Yet, in the wild, populations do not tend to increase. There may be 'good years' and 'bad years', but, overall, there will be little change.*

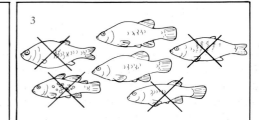

3. *Therefore, most organisms must die before they have a chance to reproduce. There is a struggle for existence.*

4. *Organisms of the same species vary. Every individual in a population will be different in some way from every other.*

5. *The characteristics which some organisms possess may give them a better chance of surviving than other members of the population.*

6. *The survivors will be able to breed and so pass on their useful characteristics to their offspring. These characteristics become more and more common in each generation.*

So, in a way, nature 'selects' some individuals and allows them to survive. This is what is meant by natural selection. The organisms which survive and breed are those which are best fitted, or adapted, to their environment. Darwin called this the **survival of the fittest**. There are many reasons why an individual could be the 'fittest' for survival. It might just happen to have the longest legs, as above, and so be able to escape predators. It could be the ancestral giraffe whose slightly longer neck allowed it to reach the best food. It could be the butterfly whose caterpillars were harder for birds to spot, or the plant whose seeds could survive through the harshest conditions and still be able to germinate.

Generation after generation, nature 'selects' the most useful characteristics in a population and allows them to be passed on.

As time goes on, large numbers of small changes add up and the population becomes more and more different from its ancestors. Other populations, descended from the same stock, may evolve in quite different ways if they are isolated in a different environment. Eventually, related organisms become so unlike that, given the chance, they can no longer breed successfully together. They have now evolved into separate species.

Once a species has become well adapted to its environment, its evolution slows down. It may remain little changed for millions of years. If its environment then changes, this may trigger off the evolution of new adaptations to cope with the changes. If it cannot achieve this, the species may become extinct. Its niche will then be occupied by some better adapted species.

ARTIFICIAL SELECTION

Nature is not the only agent of selection. Ever since people first started to keep animals and raise crops, they have been trying to improve them. This is done by selecting those individuals which have the most useful characteristics and allowing only them to breed. This is called **artificial selection**. Using artificial selection, breeders can cause domesticated animals and plants to evolve in the ways they want. The dogs shown below, for example, are all the same species. The huge variations between them have been brought about by artificial selection. The value of farm animals can also be increased by selective breeding. The graph below shows how this has improved the milk yield of dairy cattle. Many important new plant varieties, too, have been developed. Their high yields and resistance to disease could solve many food problems.

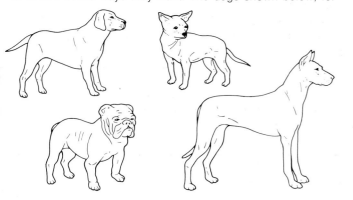

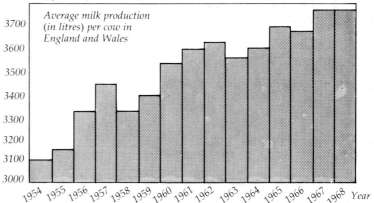

Average milk production (in litres) per cow in England and Wales

For evolution to be possible, heritable variations must be present in a population. These variations give natural selection something to work on. Heritable variations are caused by the different genes (see pages 206–7) which the individuals in a population possess. During sexual reproduction, new combinations of genes are put together, some coming from the male, some from the female. The most suitable combinations will survive and be passed on to following generations. However, new combinations of the existing genes in a population are not enough to account for the speed at which evolution can take place. There must also be a source of completely new genes. These are supplied by **mutations**.

When gametes are being made, they receive a copy of half of the parent's genes. Sometimes, mistakes are made in the copying process and new genes, or combinations of genes, are produced. These mistakes are called mutations. They are passed on to the offspring, giving them characteristics different from the rest of the population. Sometimes these characteristics are useful and the **mutants** will have an advantage. In this case, the mutant gene will become more common with each generation. Mutations, however, are usually both harmful and recessive, so, homozygous mutants are unlikely to survive. Heterozygous individuals may show no ill effects and the mutation will remain in existence. Then, if the environment changes, a once harmful or useless gene may suddenly be the best adapted and become common. Mutations are rare occurrences though radiation, for example X-rays, and certain chemicals can increase the rate of mutation.

NATURAL SELECTION IN THE PEPPERED MOTH

The Peppered Moth usually has silver grey wings with dark speckles. However, in 1848, at the height of the Industrial Revolution, a black mutant was discovered. This is known as the **melanic** form. Very soon, in heavily polluted districts, the melanic form became common and the pale type became rare. In country areas the melanic form remained almost unknown. Why had the moth population changed in this way? Well, Peppered Moths fly by night and rest on trees during the day. Experiments showed that in industrial areas the melanic form was almost invisible against the soot-blackened tree trunks. The pale form, however, was easily spotted and eaten by birds. In the country the opposite was true. The pale form was well camouflaged on the lichen-covered trees, while melanic types were quickly picked off. So, a change in the environment, namely increasing air pollution, followed by natural selection, has caused a change in the Peppered Moth population. The better-adapted moths were able to survive and breed and their useful characteristics spread rapidly through the population. Since the Clean Air Act was passed, many industrial areas have become cleaner and the process has gone into reverse.

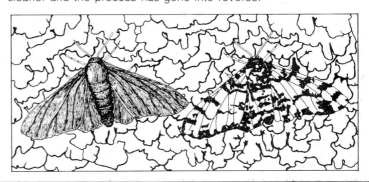

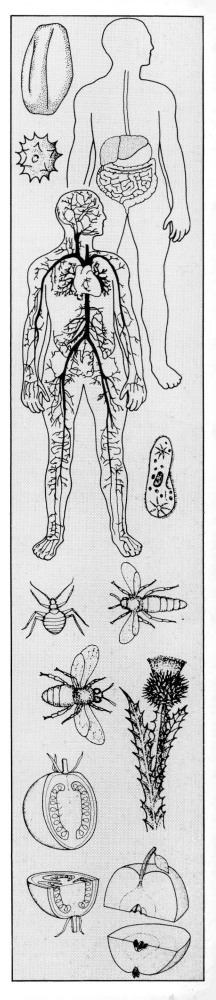

Soil

Soil forms just a thin covering over the surface of the land, yet this thin layer is vitally important to life. Good soils lead to abundant plant life. They give plants a firm base from which to stretch out their leaves to catch the sun's energy. From the soil, also, come the water and minerals which plants need for healthy growth. The plants, in turn, provide food and shelter for the animal community.

As well as a home for the roots of plants, the soil acts as a home for many living organisms (see page 220). The presence of these soil organisms affects the quality of the soil. Their constant activity improves the soil, making it a better place for plants to grow in. Without them, mature, fertile soils cannot develop.

The non-living 'skeleton' of the soil, upon which its living community is based, consists of rock particles, water, air and humus.

ROCK PARTICLES

Rock particles are tiny pieces of stone. These are slowly broken from the solid rock by the process of **weathering**.

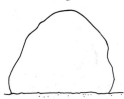

Parent rock before weathering

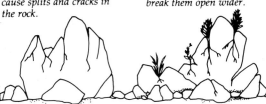

Frost and temperature changes cause splits and cracks in the rock.

Lichens first, then other plants, grow into cracks in the rock and break them open wider.

Weak carbonic acid in the rain dissolves away some of the rock minerals. The action of wind and water further wears down the rock.

Soil containing rock particles of different sizes

The soil particles which are produced by the weathering of rocks come in a variety of sizes. The largest are really small stones or **gravel**. The rest we sort into three grades depending on their size. These are called **clay**, **silt** and **sand**. All fertile soils are a mixture of the three. Such soils are called **loams**. Different mixtures give different kinds of soil, two examples of which are shown below. In the best soils various rock particles stick together to form **soil crumbs**.

Clay particles are very small, less than 0.002 mm in diameter. Adding **lime** causes clay particles to stick together. This improves a poor clay soil.

Silt particles are middling in size, ranging in diameter from 0.002 mm up to 0.02 mm.

Sand particles are the largest in the soil. They range in diameter from 0.02 up to 2.0 mm.

Clay loams tend to be heavy and difficult to dig. They do not drain well and may be cold, wet and contain little air. To improve their fertility, sand, lime or manure can be added to them.

Sandy loams are light and easier to work. They drain well and have plenty of air. However, they tend to be dry and to lose minerals easily. Manure or compost will improve a sandy loam.

Soil crumbs are clusters of rock particles of various sizes, stuck together by water and humus. A soil with good **crumb structure** drains well and is well aired. It lets roots grow easily through it and become firmly anchored in it.

HUMUS

Humus consists of the decaying remains of dead plants and animals and their wastes which have become mixed with the soil.

The remains and wastes of plants and animals fall upon the ground.

The decomposers, mainly fungi and bacteria, in the soil consume the debris, causing it to decay. Other soil organisms, such as earthworms, drag it underground.

The material gradually becomes humus, a combination of black, sticky liquid and fibres mixed in with the soil particles.

The sticky humus binds together rock particles of various sizes to make soil crumbs. Crumbs are good for a soil in a number of ways. The large spaces which form between the crumbs allow roots to spread easily through the soil, gripping it firmly as they go. Air, too, can easily get into the soil. Also, while humus keeps a soil moist, the spaces let excess water drain away quickly. Finally, soils with lots of crumbs are less likely to be blown away by the wind.

Good soils must also contain plenty of the **mineral salts**, such as **nitrates** and **phosphates**, which are essential for the growth of healthy plants. Humus affects this in two ways. Firstly, humus prevents minerals being **leached** (washed) out of the soil by rainwater. Secondly, humus consists of partly decomposed material. Eventually, it will be broken down completely by soil bacteria, leaving only its valuable minerals behind in the soil.

It is the black humus which makes the fertile upper layer, called **topsoil**, of soil dark in colour. The lighter-coloured **subsoil** contains no humus and few things can grow there.

WATER

Water is absorbed from the soil by the **root hairs** of plants. They do not just need the water itself, but also the minerals dissolved in it (see page 221). Without these they cannot grow.

The soil holds water in two ways. Firstly, the soil particles are covered in thin films of water. Secondly, water can fill the spaces between the particles. When most of these spaces have been filled with water, the soil is said to be **waterlogged**.

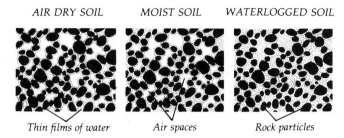

AIR DRY SOIL   MOIST SOIL   WATERLOGGED SOIL

Thin films of water   *Air spaces*   *Rock particles*

After a heavy rainfall, the soil will be full of water. The force of gravity pulls the water downwards out of the soil. Some of the water, however, is retained by the soil. The films round the soil particles are held too tightly to be removed. Also, some of the water in the soil spaces is held there by a force which can resist the pull of gravity. This force is called **capillarity**. We can watch capillarity in action if we put the end of a fine glass tube underwater. The water rises up the tube, against gravity. The thinner the tube, the higher the water will rise. The spaces between the soil particles behave just like tiny tubes. By capillarity, they hold on to water, which is then made available to plants. Capillarity can also move water through the soil from wet to dry areas, just as blotting paper soaks up ink. It can even draw water upwards.

The way a soil copes with water is important. A good soil must show good drainage, but also have good water retention.

CAPILLARITY

Drainage

Drainage takes place when more water falls on to a soil than it can hold. The excess water is drawn downwards, by gravity, out of the soil. Large spaces between the soil particles allow water to drain off quickly. Small spaces tend, because of their high capillarity, to slow down drainage.

Water retention

Water retention is the ability of a soil to hold water. If a soil holds too little water, plants will wither and die in it. If it holds too much, the soil organisms, including the roots of plants, will be deprived of oxygen. Small soil particles hold more water on their surface than large ones. Due to capillarity, soils with small spaces between their particles will hold more water than soils with large spaces. Also, humus absorbs water and so soils which are rich in humus will hold more water.

Thus, the drainage and water retention abilities of a soil depend on its particle sizes, its capillarity and its humus content. Here are how these factors operate in clay, sand and good garden loam.

CLAY drains poorly, but has high water retention. It can easily become waterlogged. Adding lime causes the particles to stick together to form crumbs. This improves the drainage.

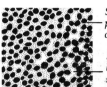

Small particles pick up a lot of water.

Small spaces between particles show high capillarity.

SAND drains quickly, but has low water retention. Minerals are easily washed out and the soil tends to be too dry. Adding manure improves a sandy soil.

Large particles hold little water.

Large spaces between particles show low capillarity.

LOAM drains well, but also has good water retention. These qualities are due to the humus content and the soil crumbs which good, fertile soils are rich in.

Water covers surface of soil crumbs and also gets inside them.

Large spaces let water drain through.

AIR

Air is an important part of any soil. Good soils may be up to 25% air. Organisms living in the soil, including the roots of plants, get the oxygen they need to stay alive from the soil air. As the diagrams opposite show, without enough oxygen, plant roots do not grow well and this affects the health of the whole plant. Equally important in the soil are the micro-organisms (see pages 228–9) which break down humus. These organisms release valuable minerals, such as nitrates, into the soil. Like plants, they are aerobic. This means that they cannot survive without oxygen. On the other hand, the denitrifying bacteria, which harm the soil by removing its nitrates from it, thrive in soils which contain little oxygen.

Soil air is held in the spaces between the soil particles. In sandy soils or in soils with good crumb structure, these spaces are large and can hold plenty of air. In clay or in hard-packed soils the spaces are small. Such soils hold little air and are said to be poorly **aerated**. Wet soils have little room for air and few things can grow in them.

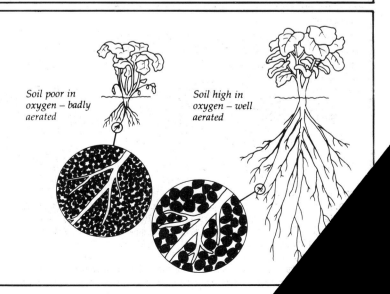

Soil poor in oxygen – badly aerated

Soil high in oxygen – well aerated

Life in the soil

Soil forms the **habitat** for a large **community** of different organisms. This community is affected by the soil in which it lives, but it also, in turn, affects the soil. The interactions between a habitat and its community make up an **ecosystem.** The plants which can grow in a soil and how well they can grow depends on the state of the soil ecosystem. The food web shown below is a very simple form of the type of web found in a soil ecosystem.

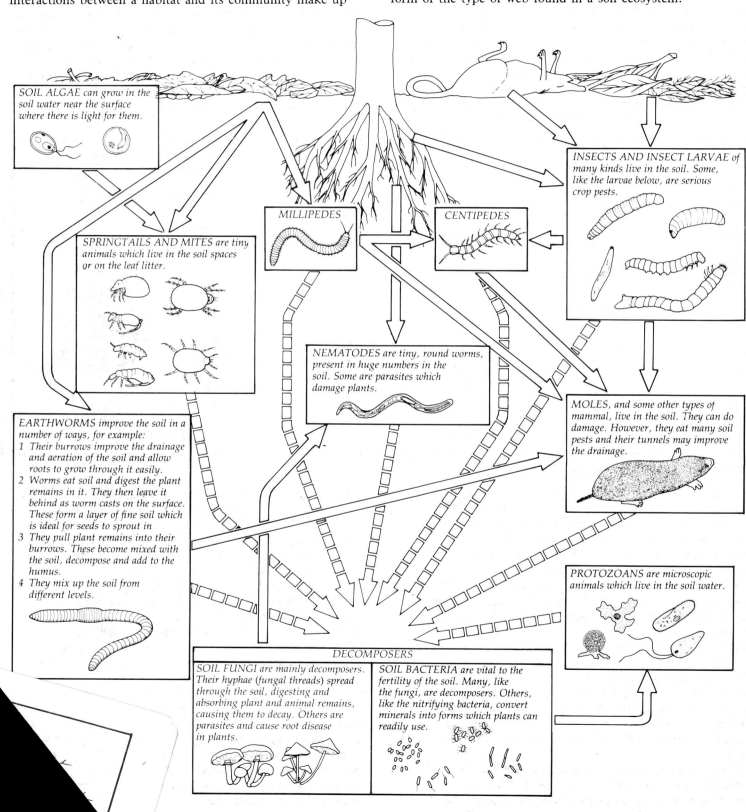

SOIL ALGAE can grow in the soil water near the surface where there is light for them.

SPRINGTAILS AND MITES are tiny animals which live in the soil spaces or on the leaf litter.

MILLIPEDES

CENTIPEDES

INSECTS AND INSECT LARVAE of many kinds live in the soil. Some, like the larvae below, are serious crop pests.

NEMATODES are tiny, round worms, present in huge numbers in the soil. Some are parasites which damage plants.

MOLES, and some other types of mammal, live in the soil. They can do damage. However, they eat many soil pests and their tunnels may improve the drainage.

EARTHWORMS improve the soil in a number of ways, for example:
1 Their burrows improve the drainage and aeration of the soil and allow roots to grow through it easily.
2 Worms eat soil and digest the plant remains in it. They then leave it behind as worm casts on the surface. These form a layer of fine soil which is ideal for seeds to sprout in
3 They pull plant remains into their burrows. These become mixed with the soil, decompose and add to the humus.
4 They mix up the soil from different levels.

PROTOZOANS are microscopic animals which live in the soil water.

DECOMPOSERS

SOIL FUNGI are mainly decomposers. Their hyphae (fungal threads) spread through the soil, digesting and absorbing plant and animal remains, causing them to decay. Others are parasites and cause root disease in plants.

SOIL BACTERIA are vital to the fertility of the soil. Many, like the fungi, are decomposers. Others, like the nitrifying bacteria, convert minerals into forms which plants can readily use.

Minerals in the soil

Plants, like all living things, consist mainly of water. If we drive off all the water, we will be left with a small amount of solid material. This makes up the **dry weight** of the plant. 95% of the dry weight of a plant is due to just three elements. These basic building blocks of the plant are atoms of carbon, hydrogen and oxygen. To obtain them, the plant absorbs carbon dioxide gas (CO_2) from the air and water (H_2O) from the soil. In photosynthesis (see pages 88–9), the plant combines these two raw materials to make sugar ($C_6H_{12}O_2$). From this it goes on to make the hundreds of different chemical substances it needs to live and grow.

To make many of these vital molecules, however, other ingredients are added. Proteins, for example, cannot be made without a supply of the element nitrogen. Chlorophyll molecules, which the plant needs to make its food, cannot be made without magnesium, and so on. These extra elements occur as mineral salts dissolved in the soil water, from which they are absorbed by the plant roots. In fact, if the roots of a plant are immersed in water which has all the essential minerals dissolved in it, the plant will grow quite happily. This is called **water culture**. If we miss out just one element from the culture solution, we can see what effect its absence has on the plant, for example:

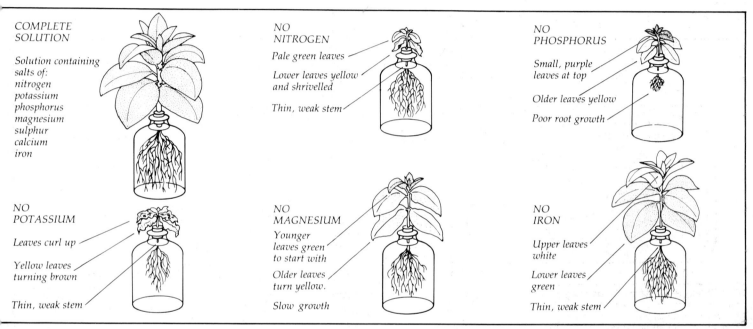

COMPLETE SOLUTION

Solution containing salts of:
nitrogen
potassium
phosphorus
magnesium
sulphur
calcium
iron

NO NITROGEN
Pale green leaves
Lower leaves yellow and shrivelled
Thin, weak stem

NO PHOSPHORUS
Small, purple leaves at top
Older leaves yellow
Poor root growth

NO POTASSIUM
Leaves curl up
Yellow leaves turning brown
Thin, weak stem

NO MAGNESIUM
Younger leaves green to start with
Older leaves turn yellow.
Slow growth

NO IRON
Upper leaves white
Lower leaves green
Thin, weak stem

Loss and replacement

The minerals in a soil come from the rock which formed it. Weak acids in the rain dissolve some mineral salts out of the parent rock and these end up in the soil water. As plants grow in the soil, they remove these dissolved minerals from it. If this is allowed to go on, the soil may become exhausted of its minerals until, eventually, plants can no longer thrive in it. Minerals may also be washed out of the soil by rainwater. This is called **leaching**. Leaching is a particular problem in fast-draining, sandy soils which are often less fertile because of it.

Given a chance, Nature itself will replace much of these lost minerals. Dead plants and animals and their wastes are all rich in minerals which came originally from the soil. These remains become mixed with the soil and get broken down by the **decomposers** until they form humus. Gradually, as they decay completely, their minerals are returned to the soil water to be available, once again, to plants.

When a field or garden is used to grow crops, this kind of natural replacement of minerals does not happen; the crop is harvested and the plants, with the minerals they contain, are removed from the ground for good. One way to replace the lost minerals is to get dead plant or animal material from elsewhere and dig it into the soil. In this way, the soil is kept rich in humus and future crops are kept well supplied with vital minerals. Farmyard manure, garden compost, leaf mould, bone meal, fish meal, even dried blood can all be used for this purpose.

The minerals which a soil lacks can also be replaced directly by the use of artificial fertilisers. Ammonium sulphate, for example, supplies both nitrogen (in the form of ammonium ions, NH_4^+) and sulphur (as sulphate ions, $SO_4^=$). Applied to the soil in the correct amounts, it dissolves in the soil water and rapidly becomes available to the plants.

To get the best out a piece of land, a different crop should be grown on it each year. This is called **crop rotation** (see pages 224–5). This ensures that plants which need a lot of one particular mineral do not exhaust it too quickly from that one field. The legume family, for example peas, beans or clover, is often used in crop rotations, since the bacteria that live in them actually add more nitrogen to the soil than the plants take out.

The nitrogen cycle

All living things need nitrogen. Many nitrogenous substances are absolutely essential to life. These include the proteins which are a part of every living cell. There is certainly no shortage of nitrogen in the world. 78% of the air is nitrogen gas, but, unfortunately, nitrogen gas is no use to most organisms. Plants, for example, must have their nitrogen mainly in the form of salts called **nitrates** ($-NO_3$) dissolved in the soil water. Animals must obtain theirs by eating plants or other animals so that they can digest and absorb their proteins. Certain bacteria, however, do have the ability to take nitrogen gas from the air and use it to make proteins and other nitrogenous compounds. This is called **nitrogen fixation**.

Once these bacteria have fixed the nitrogen, it becomes available for other organisms to use. In fact, the nitrogen may be used again by a variety of organisms, before it comes full circle and is returned as nitrogen gas to the atmosphere. This is called the **nitrogen cycle**. Every organism has its place in the nitrogen cycle. This includes two other important groups of bacteria called the **nitrifying bacteria** and the **denitrifying bacteria**. Their roles, and those of some of the other agents involved, are outlined in the nitrogen cycle drawn below.

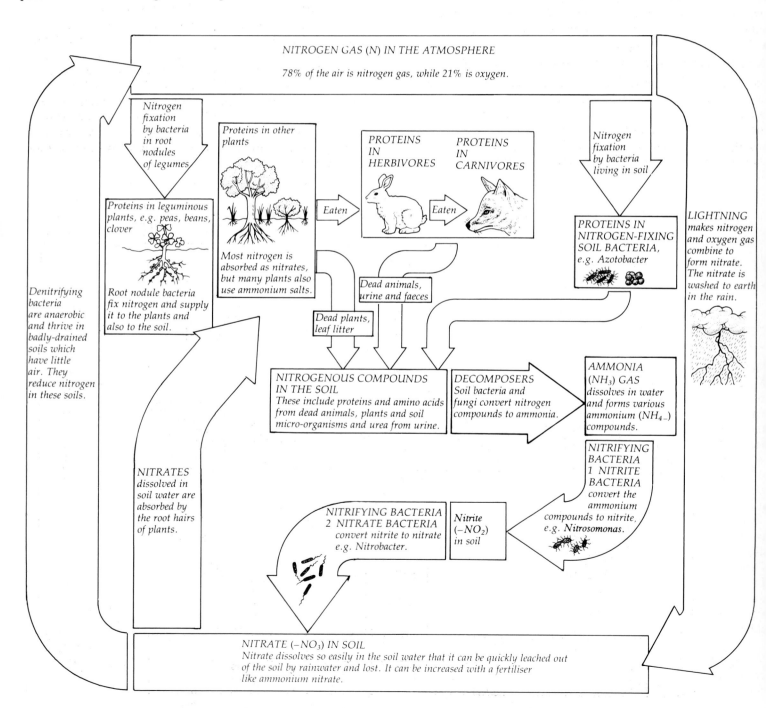

The carbon cycle

Living things are built of complex molecules based upon the element carbon. Such substances are called **organic compounds**. The carbon atoms for these compounds come from the small amount of carbon dioxide gas (0.03%) contained in the air. Certain organisms, chiefly the green plants, are able to absorb carbon dioxide and use it to make all the other carbon compounds which they need. This is called **carbon fixation** and it occurs in the process of **photosynthesis** (see pages 88–9) which we can sum up like this:

Water + Carbon dioxide → Food + Oxygen

Plants use these compounds for building materials as they grow and also as a source of energy. They get the energy out of them by the process of **respiration** (see pages 94–5) which we can write simply as:

Carbon compounds + Oxygen → Carbon dioxide + Water

Thus, respiration returns some of the carbon dioxide to the air. Photosynthesis and respiration are two quite separate processes in plant cells. For one thing, photosynthesis does not take place in the dark, but the plant must carry on respiration at all times. Like all organisms, plants need a non-stop supply of energy from respiration in order to stay alive.

Organisms which cannot carry out photosynthesis must get their carbon in the form of readymade organic compounds like proteins and carbohydrates. They do this by consuming other organisms, their dead remains or their wastes. Like the plants, they use part of this food for growth and part for energy and they release carbon dioxide in the process. Eventually, all organic matter is consumed by the **decomposers** – the fungi and bacteria which cause decay – and all the carbon atoms find their way back into the atmosphere as carbon dioxide, to be used again, sooner or later, by the plants. So the same carbon atoms are going round and round and being used again and again by all sorts of organisms. This is known as the **carbon cycle.**

Sometimes, carbon is taken out of the cycle for long periods of time. Plant or animal remains can be buried deep underground where they cannot decompose properly. They are transformed instead, over millions of years, into fossil fuels such as coal, oil and natural gas. This is called **fossilisation**. When we burn these fuels in our homes, cars or factories, the carbon which they contain is returned into the air, at last, as carbon dioxide. Thus, the combustion (burning) of fossil fuels must also be included in the carbon cycle illustrated below.

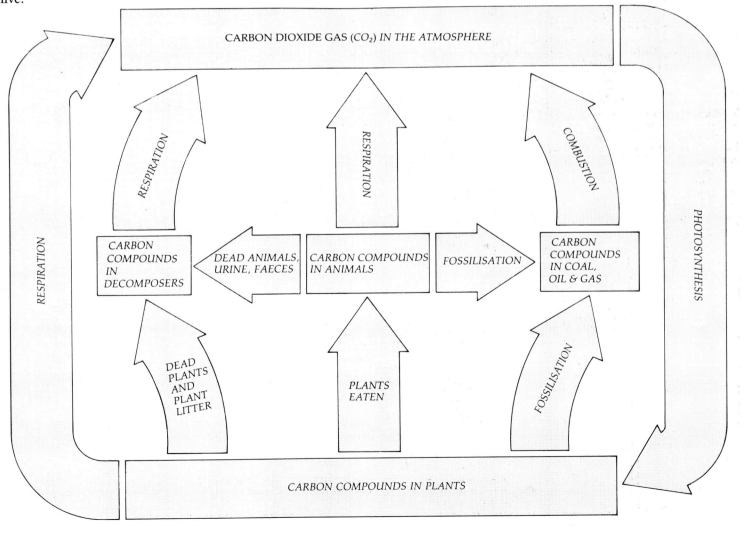

Using the land

A balanced natural ecosystem supports a wide variety of different plants and animals. The populations of the various inhabitants stay much the same from year to year, kept in check by natural forces such as the food available and the presence of predators. The soil is able to renew itself through the repeated cycling of its minerals (see the nitrogen cycle, page 222). However, when land is cleared to grow food, the balance of Nature is upset. The original species are evicted and in their place, one single crop is planted. This is called **monoculture**. Maintaining this new set-up is not without problems.

The problems of monoculture

Mineral exhaustion

All plants absorb minerals from the soil. Without these, their growth is poor. If the plants are removed by cropping, their minerals are not returned to the soil and the soil gradually becomes exhausted of its minerals and becomes less fertile. Also, each species takes more of some minerals than others, so these minerals become exhausted first.

Plant competition

If crops are planted too close together, the plants compete with each other for light, water and minerals. Their growth is slow and the harvest poor. The aim is to get as many plants as possible into a field, but to space them out so that they don't crowd each other. However, wild plants or weeds spread rapidly on to any cleared soil. They provide even stiffer competition as many of them grow much faster than cultivated plants and their demands for water and minerals may be much greater than the crop itself. Some weeds may produce several generations in one season. In this competition, the crop plant is usually the loser and the yield of a weed-infested crop can be very poor indeed. The presence of weeds also makes harvesting more difficult.

Weed infested – low yield   *Weed free – high yield*

Insects

Insects harm crops in a number of ways. They eat the leaves, stems or roots, they suck out their sap and they spread diseases. In a balanced ecosystem, their numbers are kept down by predators such as birds or other insects.

Disease

Plant diseases are caused by fungi, viruses and bacteria. In Nature, suitable host plants for disease organisms are well distanced and so the spread of disease is slow. In a monoculture, however, vast hordes of potential hosts are gathered together and infection can spread like wildfire. Crop diseases have caused disastrous famines (see page 229).

Tackling the problems

Crop rotation

Different plants require different minerals from the soil. They also take them from different levels since some have deeper root systems than others. So, if a different crop is planted in a soil each year, the soil does not become drained of its minerals. This is called **crop rotation**.

In any system of crop rotation, a **leguminous** plant (peas, beans, clover) is a must. These plants have **nodules** on their roots which contain **nitrogen-fixing** bacteria (see page 86). The bacteria convert nitrogen gas from the air into nitrate, an essential plant mineral. Growing these plants actually increases the amount of nitrate in a soil, and so makes it more fertile. Root crops such as turnips are also useful since they provide a good opportunity to clear out weeds before the next crop is sown. A typical four-course crop rotation is shown below.

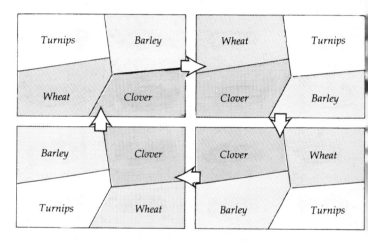

Organic fertilisers

Organic fertilisers include such things as farmyard manure and garden compost. Ploughed into the soil, usually in autumn, they decompose, releasing their minerals ready for the plants to use. They also improve the humus content and crumb structure of the soil (see pages 218–9). **Green manure** is the name given to crops such as peas or mustard which are sown, then ploughed back into the soil to improve it

Artificial fertilisers

Artificial fertilisers are chemicals such as ammonium sulphate and sodium nitrate. When added to the soil, they dissolve and their minerals are made available immediately to the plants. Their use does have certain disadvantages, though. Since the soil is having no organic matter added to it, its humus content falls and its crumb structure suffers. Also, artificial fertilisers are leached out of the soil by rain and washed into rivers where they cause **pollution**.

Pesticides

A pesticide is a chemical which kills organisms which cause damage to people, domestic animals, crops or property. Pesticides include herbicides, fungicides and insecticides.

Herbicides are chemicals which kill plants. Among the most widely used are the **selective weedkillers**. These kill broad-leaved plants which most weeds are, but not grass-type plants such as cereals. Their use can increase yields many times over.

Fungicides are chemicals which kill fungi, so preventing diseases such as apple scab and potato blight. They are also used to treat seeds before planting to protect them from diseases lingering in the soil.

Insecticides are chemicals which kill insects. The most well-known is DDT which has been widely used since 1945. Its use against crop pests has been very successful. It has also saved countless lives since it has been used against insects such as the typhus-carrying head louse and mosquitos which spread malaria.

Unfortunately, DDT and insecticides like it proved so effective that they came to be used carelessly on a vast scale. Huge areas of land were sprayed from the air. Aircraft spraying was even used to control midges. It soon became clear that this was having serious side effects.

Useful insects such as the natural predators of pest species were also killed. Freed from their natural enemies, new pests could appear to replace the old. No insecticide can kill every insect in a population. Some are **resistant**. They multiply rapidly and new chemicals have to be found to deal with the resistant strains.

Animals which had never been sprayed, such as fish and birds of prey, began to show signs of insecticide poisoning. They either died or failed to breed successfully. The animals worst affected were carnivores at the top of food chains. The reason is that many insecticides are **persistent chemicals**. This means that they do not break down easily, either in the environment or in the tissues of organisms. They are absorbed in low concentrations at the start of a food chain and passed along it, unchanged, from one animal to the next, becoming more concentrated at each stage, as the diagram shows. The top predator at the end of the chain receives a harmful or even lethal dose. Aquatic food chains are always worst affected, since insecticides are washed by the rain into rivers, etc.

CONCENTRATION ALONG A FOOD CHAIN

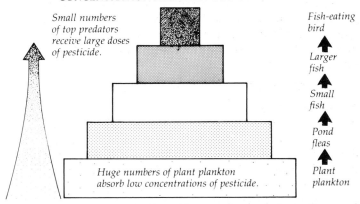

Small numbers of top predators receive large doses of pesticide.

Huge numbers of plant plankton absorb low concentrations of pesticide.

Fish-eating bird
Larger fish
Small fish
Pond fleas
Plant plankton

Other pesticides have similar effects and many, including DDT, have been banned. The newer pesticides are **biodegradable**. This means they break down into harmless substances.

Biological control of pests

Biological control involves using other organisms to control a pest. In the long run, it may be more effective than chemicals. The most common methods of biological control are to introduce a predator, parasite or disease which attacks the pest organism, but does no harm to others. Ladybirds, for example, can be used to eat the scale insect which damages citrus trees; myxomatosis has often been used to control rabbits.

SOIL EROSION
Bad farming methods can lead to topsoil being carried off by wind or water. This is called **soil erosion**. It can leave the land barren and useless. The main causes are listed here.

Wind erosion
When no organic fertilisers are used, the humus in the soil gradually declines. The soil becomes dry and light and is easily blown away in dry weather. When hedges and trees are removed to allow the use of larger machines, there is nothing to break the force of the wind and the situation gets worse. On poor, dry pastureland the soil is held in place by the plant cover. If this is **overgrazed**, wind erosion is likely.

Gulley erosion
Ploughing up or down a slope provides channels for rainwater to run along, washing soil away with it. This carves deep gullies which make the land useless for farming.

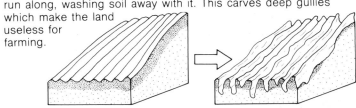

Gulley erosion is prevented by ploughing across, rather than up and down, the slope. This is called **contour ploughing**. The building of **terraced fields** also prevents gulley erosion.

Contour ploughing

Terracing

Deforestation
Trees growing on hillsides retain water and hold the soil in place. When they are chopped down, the soil is washed into the rivers. These become clogged and floods result. The quick run-off of spring rainwater and melted snow often leaves the region short of water when the floods are over. Replanting of trees and contour ploughing reduce these problems.

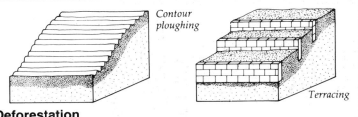

Trees felled

River silted

Sheet and gulley erosion

Sheet erosion
Sheet erosion happens when wet topsoil creeps slowly down a sloping field, leaving the upper parts thin and barren. Stone barriers built across the slope can slow it down. Contour ploughing can have the same effect.

SECTION 20

People and Micro-organisms

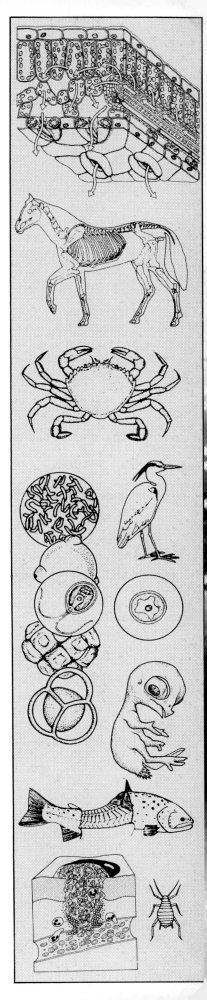

Micro-organisms

Micro-organisms (also called microbes) are tiny organisms which are invisible to the naked eye. It is only possible to see them in any detail with a microscope. Among the most important micro-organisms are the bacteria (see pages 20–1) and small fungi such as yeasts and moulds (see page 28). Viruses (see page 21) are often classed as micro-organisms, although they are not really living things at all.

Despite their tiny size, micro-organisms are vitally important to all other living things. Many of them do a lot of good (see page 21). Indeed, without their activities, life would be impossible. Others, unfortunately, are harmful. They ruin food and cause disease.

The decay and preservation of food

If food is left uneaten, it quickly goes bad. It looks unpleasant and it begins to smell. Louis Pasteur, a French scientist, discovered that the decay was caused by micro-organisms contaminating the food. As the organisms grow, they produce **enzymes** which liquefy the food so that they can absorb it. Pasteur found that if food (he used meat broth) was heated strongly, the micro-organisms were killed. This is called **sterilisation**. If the sterilised food was sealed off from the air immediately, it would not go bad.

Fresh broth — *Days later* — *Broth boiled and sealed* — *Days later* — *Still good*

Pasteur suggested that micro-organisms, floating in the air, land on food, grow in it and cause it to decay. Other scientists disagreed. They claimed that when air itself touched food, micro-organisms were created. They called it 'spontaneous generation'. Pasteur proved them wrong with a famous experiment. He boiled some meat broth in a special 'swan-necked' flask and cooled it very slowly. As the flask cooled, air was drawn in. Dust and micro-organisms, however, being heavier, got stuck in the bend and could not reach the broth. The broth, exposed to the air as it was, did not go bad, no matter how long it was left. A similar flask, with its neck broken off, did not work. The broth in it was bad within days.

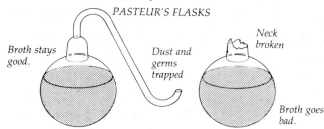

PASTEUR'S FLASKS

Broth stays good. — *Dust and germs trapped* — *Neck broken* — *Broth goes bad.*

We now know that bacteria and fungi produce tiny cells called **spores** which are carried around in the air. Spores are extremely tough and can survive, in perfect condition, for years. Some bacterial spores, in fact, can resist temperatures of up to 120°C. When a spore lands on a suitable source of warm, moist food, it quickly germinates, reproduces and spreads through it, digesting it and making it unfit to eat. Some contaminate the food with deadly poisons called **toxins**. If food is to be stored for any length of time, the growth of micro-organisms in it must be prevented. This is called food preservation.

Methods of preserving food

Several methods of food preservation have been in use for thousands of years. Others have been invented more recently. The most widely-used methods are listed below.

Drying
Micro-organisms cannot grow without water, so dried foods will keep for long periods. Common examples are cornflakes, dried milk and dried peas. Dried food is easy to store and transport, though drying often affects the flavour and texture of the food.

Pickling
Foods such as onions are stored in vinegar. The acetic acid in the vinegar kills the micro-organisms.

Osmotic methods
Foods like honey, jam, salted fish and raisins which have a high concentration of sugar or salt will not go bad. The high osmotic potential (see pages 116–7) of their surroundings prevents the micro-organisms from taking in water and so they cannot grow.

Canning
Food is cooked, sealed in a can and heated under pressure to a very high temperature. All micro-organisms and their spores are killed. As long as the can is not pierced, the food will stay good. Tinned food has been known to last for a hundred years.

Pasteurisation
Bacteria, including some which cause serious diseases like TB, grow rapidly in milk. To prevent this, the milk is heated to 72°C for just 15 seconds. This kills most bacteria without spoiling the flavour of the milk.

Ultra high temperature
Milk is suddenly heated with scalding steam to 132°C for just 1 second, then packed in sterile cartons. If unopened, UHT milk will keep for six months.

Refrigeration and freezing
Low temperatures, unlike high, do not kill micro-organisms, but they do slow down or halt their growth. The length of time for which food can be kept safely depends on how low the temperature is (see scale, page 230). If food is frozen too slowly, large ice crystals form inside its cells. These damage the cell walls of fruit and vegetables which become mushy when thawed out. Clarence Birdseye found that quick freezing solved this problem.

Freeze drying
Food is frozen solid, put in a vacuum, then slowly warmed. The ice evaporates off, leaving the food dried. When water is added, the food's texture and quality are unharmed.

Micro-organisms and disease

Organisms which cause diseases are called **pathogens** and many micro-organisms are pathogenic. Pathogenic organisms are **parasites**. They invade the living body of their host, feeding on and destroying its tissues. The host sickens and often dies. That such tiny organisms should be responsible for so much of the suffering and misery in the world seems almost unbelievable. It is not surprising that only in the last century did scientists such as Pasteur and, especially, a German named Robert Koch begin to prove the connection. Disease takes its toll not only of humans, but also of organisms which support them. Domestic animals catch many of the same diseases we do and also others, such as foot and mouth in cattle and distemper in dogs, which we do not. Equally important to us are plant diseases.

Plant diseases

Damage to crops by micro-organisms has caused both poverty and famine. Bacteria and viruses are responsible for many serious crop diseases, but fungi are the worst offenders. From 1845–61, for example, a million people in Ireland died from starvation because a fungal disease called potato blight wiped out their crops. Another million were forced to emigrate.

Wheat rust, corn smut, Dutch elm disease and 'damping off' of seedlings are all the result of fungal infection. Chemicals called fungicides can be sprayed on crops to protect them.

Human diseases

The diseases caused by pathogenic micro-organisms are **infectious**. This means that they can be transmitted from one organism to another. Disease organisms are commonly called germs. The diseases they cause can be contracted by humans in the following ways:

From the air—Droplets coughed or breathed out by an infected person, or dust particles in the air, may contain disease organisms or their spores. When breathed in, these may cause the disease.

By contact—Certain diseases may be transmitted by contact with an infected person. These diseases are said to be **contagious**. They include smallpox and impetigo. Sometimes, indirect contact through a sufferer's clothes, bedding or possessions may be enough.

Food and drink—Food and drink may be contaminated by airborne germs or by infected humans or animals, especially from their faeces. Personal hygiene, food hygiene and clean water supplies are essential because of this risk.

Through wounds—Some pathogens, such as tetanus bacteria, enter the body through breaks in the skin. Rabies is contracted from the bite of an infected dog. Fleas transmit plague from rats to humans when they pierce the skin to feed on blood.

After infection, it takes some time for the first symptoms to appear. This is called the **incubation period**. During this time, a person, without knowing it, may be a **carrier**, spreading the disease to other people. For this reason, persons suspected of having a serious disease are kept in **quarantine** even though they seem to be perfectly healthy.

When a disease is always present in a region, it is said to be **endemic**. A sudden outbreak affecting a lot of people is called an **epidemic**. Details of a few diseases are given in the table below.

DISEASE	CAUSED BY	METHOD OF TRANSMISSION	SYMPTOMS	TREATMENT/PREVENTION
TUBERCULOSIS (TB)	Bacteria	From the air or infected milk	Coughing, fever, breathlessness – once a serious killer disease	Rest, isolation, antibiotics, BCG vaccination, X-ray screening
CHOLERA	Bacteria	Drinking water contaminated by faeces	Severe vomiting and diarrhoea leading to death from loss of water	Replacing fluid direct into a vein, vaccination
IMPETIGO	Bacteria	By contact especially among children, highly contagious	Blisters, which form yellow crusts, on face, hands and knees,	Cured by antibiotics
FOOD POISONING	Bacteria	Contaminated or improperly cooked food	Vomiting, diarrhoea – some forms of food poisoning are very dangerous	Strict hygiene when handling food, proper cooking and storage
SYPHILIS	Bacteria	Sexual intercourse – it is a type of venereal disease (VD).	Sores on sex organs. If untreated, paralysis, blindness, madness may develop years later.	Penicillin
TYPHOID	Bacteria	Drinking infected water	Fever, headache, cough, rash	Fluids, antibiotics, vaccine, clean water supplies
WHOOPING COUGH	Bacteria	By contact or from the breath of an infected person	A 'whooping' cough, fever, convulsions (a severe disease of childhood)	Vaccination
POLIOMYELITIS	Virus	From breath or contaminated food, highly infectious	Mild fever, then severe pain in the limbs and permanent paralysis/death	Vaccination
CHICKENPOX	Virus	From breath or contact, highly infectious disease of childhood	Fever, small red blisters all over the body which dry and flake off	None, but one attack gives immunity for life.
MEASLES	Virus	Droplets in the air, highly infectious	Fever, runny nose, sore eyes, rash all over body, sometimes serious	Vaccination, though one attack gives immunity for life.
INFLUENZA ('FLU')	Virus	From breath	Chills, fever, headache, cough, aches and pains	Bed rest, fluids
SMALLPOX	Virus	By contact, highly contagious. Can be caught from patient's clothes and bedding.	Fever, severe headache and backache, rash on face and limbs, leaving scars (often fatal)	Vaccination is thought to have got rid of this disease for good.
YELLOW FEVER	Virus	Injected into the blood by a type of mosquito — serious disease in the tropics	Fever, aches, yellow skin, death from kidney or heart failure	Vaccination
RINGWORM	Fungus	By contact or from wet floors, highly contagious	Red, scaly, itchy patches, usually ring-shaped, on head, armpits or feet (where it is known as athlete's foot)	Antibiotics, if it becomes serious

Fighting germs

Germs, many of them very dangerous, are all around us. Usually, though, they must be given a chance to attack in force before they can cause real harm. On these pages we will look at the defences, some natural, some man-made, which we can array against them.

Attack from the air

All the air passages from the nose to deep down in the lungs are kept covered in greasy **mucus**. Airborne germs get stuck to this and the soiled mucus is then swept away by the beating of countless tiny **cilia** (see page 110). Nasal mucus also contains an **enzyme** which kills germs. If necessary, germs are expelled violently by coughs and sneezes. We should always use a handkerchief, of course, to prevent them from being passed on to others.

Attack through the skin

The outer layer of the skin is made of tightly-packed, but dead, cells. It forms a tough barrier which keeps most germs away from the living cells beneath (see pages 162–3). Many micro-organisms, mostly harmless, live on the skin. Washing can never remove them all, but it does reduce their numbers and so lessens the risk of infection. If the skin is broken, we can help its defence system (see below) by washing the wound and applying an **antiseptic**. An antiseptic is a chemical, safe to us, which can kill most germs. This gives the body a better chance to deal with the remainder.

The value of antiseptics was first shown in 1865 by Joseph Lister, a surgeon. In those days, many surgical patients died, not from their operation, but from bacterial infection of their wound. Lister began spraying an antiseptic called carbolic acid on his patients' skin, his surgical instruments and all round the operating theatre. The death rate fell dramatically.

Another type of skin is the **conjunctiva** which covers the eyeball. Tears, which contain a natural antiseptic, are used to keep it flushed clean.

Attack in food

The body can usually deal with all the germs in food. Some are killed by hydrochloric acid in the stomach and some by digestive enzymes in the intestine. However, food is an ideal growth medium for micro-organisms and, given the opportunity, they can multiply rapidly in it. Temperature control is vital. This diagram shows how temperature affect the growth of bacteria in food.

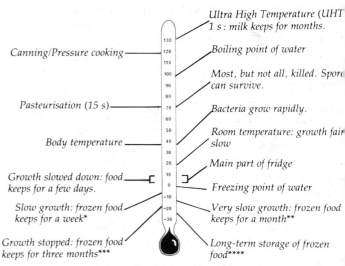

Ultra High Temperature (UHT 1 s : milk keeps for months.

Canning/Pressure cooking — 130 120 110

Boiling point of water — 100

Most, but not all, killed. Spore can survive. — 90 80

Pasteurisation (15 s) — 70 60

Bacteria grow rapidly.

Body temperature — 50 40 30

Room temperature: growth fair slow

Main part of fridge — 20

Growth slowed down: food keeps for a few days. — 10 0

Freezing point of water

Slow growth: frozen food keeps for a week* — -10 -20

Very slow growth: frozen food keeps for a month**

Growth stopped: frozen food keeps for three months*** — -30

Long-term storage of frozen food****

PLUGGING THE GAPS

When the skin is cut, the body's defence and repair squads go into action. The cut bleeds at first and this helps to clean it out. Blood platelets then begin to pile up to plug the leak. The complex chain reaction of blood clotting begins. This involves various things – some such as **platelets, calcium ions** and **vitamin K** in the blood, others in the damaged tissues. The end result is that fibrinogen, a soluble plasma protein, is turned into solid threads of fibrin. The fibrin forms a net across the cut and red blood cells and platelets are caught up in it to form the clot. The clot then shrinks, squeezing out any fluid and the cut is sealed.

Meanwhile, white blood cells have gathered in strength to eat invading bacteria – a process called **phagocytosis** (see pages 132–3). The phagocytes can actually slide out of the blood vessels to 'chase' germs. They also mop up any debris. New tissue can then grow to repair the skin.

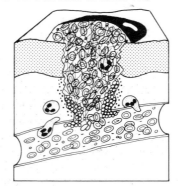

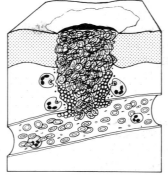

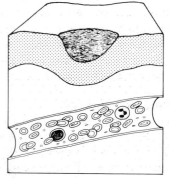

Platelets cluster round the cut to restrict blood loss.

⊚ = red blood cells   ⌐ = fibrinogen
◉ = white blood cells   ⫽ = fibrin
° = platelets

Fibrinogen changes to fibrin. The net of fibrin threads traps blood cells to form the clot. Phagocytes wriggle out of the blood vessels to 'hunt' germs.

Clot shrinks to squeeze out fluid and dry up. Phagocytes devour germs and damaged tissue.

New tissue grows to repair damage. Remains of clot forms into a scab.

So, while proper cooking kills germs, mere warming (30–40°C) encourages them. Both things can happen, for example, in a frozen turkey which has not been completely thawed out. After cooking, the outer meat is safe. Inside, though, where it was still frozen, it may only have been warmed up. It could now be teeming with food poisoning bacteria.

Precautions should also be taken to keep dangerous germs away from food in the first place. Clean kitchens, utensils and dishes, washed hands, especially after using the toilet, are all essential. Flies and other animals should be kept away from food.

The battle for the blood

Antigens and antibodies

When the outer defences fail, **lymphocytes**, cells found mainly in the blood and lymph nodes (see pages 132–3), take over. They react to chemicals called **antigens** carried by the invaders and they produce proteins called **antibodies** to counter them. Antibodies work in several ways.

Some antibodies stick the germs together in clumps. They can no longer get into the tissues and are eaten by **phagocytes**.

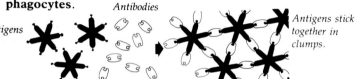

Antibodies. Antigens. Antigens stick together in clumps.

2 Some antibodies stick to the germs and cause them to burst.

Antigen. Antibodies.

Antigens dissolved.

3 Some antibodies stick to the germs and their presence makes it much easier for the phagocytes to attack them.

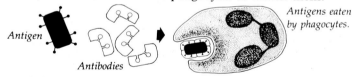

Antigen. Antibodies. Antigens eaten by phagocytes.

4 Some bacteria give out poisons called **toxins**. Some antibodies stick to the toxin making it harmless. These antibodies are called **antitoxins**. Viruses, too, can be neutralised in this way. They are then eaten by phagocytes.

Antibodies are very **specific**. Each type gives protection against just one disease. Measles antibodies, for example, are useless against chickenpox virus.

Active immunity

When an unfamiliar germ gets into the blood, it takes some days before the right antibody can be produced to combat it. The germ gets a chance to spread and we fall ill. This is the danger period if the disease is serious. The next time around, however, the system 'recognises' the antigen and speedily produces large numbers of the right antibodies. The germ is exterminated before it can take a hold. We are now said to be **immune** to that disease. This type of immunity is called **active immunity**.

Immunisation

One attack of a disease such as polio or smallpox can cause death or permanent damage. For protection, **vaccines** are used. Vaccines contain germs or their toxins which have been made harmless in some way. They still, however, cause antibodies to be formed against them. Then, later on, if we are exposed to the active germs, we are already immune to them. This is called **immunisation**. The actual process of giving a vaccine, usually by injection, is called **vaccination**. The first vaccinations were performed more than 200 years ago by a doctor named Edward Jenner.

Passive immunity

Sometimes an unprotected person is exposed to infection and there is no time then for vaccination to be effective. With some diseases, it is possible to inject antibodies themselves into the blood. This prevents damage being done. Since the body itself does not have to make the antibodies, this is known as **passive immunity**. Tetanus antitoxin, for example, can be obtained from horses' blood for this purpose. The effect, though, is only temporary.

Antibiotics

Antibiotics are chemicals made by micro-organisms which can kill, or stop the growth of, bacteria and fungi. The first antibiotic was discovered by Alexander Fleming in 1929. A blue mould called *Penicillium* accidentally got on to an agar plate on which he was growing bacteria. He noticed that no bacteria could grow near the mould. A germ-killing substance was later isolated from the mould and called **penicillin**. Countless lives have been saved by penicillin and, although many antibiotics have since been discovered, penicillin is still among the best. Man-made drugs which act as antibiotics are now also available. Unfortunately, antibiotics have no effect on viruses.

Disinfectants

Disinfectants, like antiseptics, are chemicals which kill germs. However, they are too poisonous to be used on or in the body. Instead, they are used to clean places such as toilets and sinks, and in hospitals where the risk of infection is high.

Asepsis

For some things, it is not enough to reduce the number of germs around. They must be eliminated completely. This is called **asepsis**. In an operating theatre, for example, the air is drawn in through a filter to remove germs. The operating team's clothes and instruments are sterilised by heating them to 120°C in a kind of pressure cooker called an **autoclave** and the theatre itself is cleaned with disinfectant. Aseptic techniques are also essential when doing experiments with micro-organisms. Otherwise, the experimenters could be infected or their cultures could be contaminated.

Pollution
and
Conservation

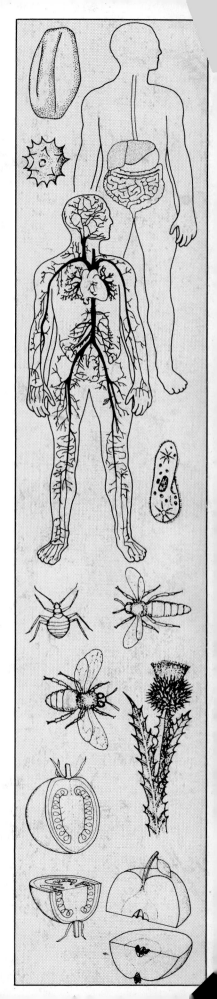

Pollution

Pollution is the release of harmful substances into the environment. These are called **pollutants**. Some pollutants are said to be **biodegradable**. This means that they are cleaned from the environment naturally, mainly by the decomposers—saprophytic bacteria and fungi. Others, however, usually man-made chemicals, are **persistent**. They can remain in the environment, unchanged, for many years. If such chemicals enter food chains, they may become concentrated to dangerous levels. No part of the environment is safe from the threat of pollution.

Air pollution

The chief causes of air pollution are the burning of coal and oil in homes, factories and power stations and the exhaust fumes of cars, buses and lorries. The main air pollutants are listed below.

Smoke

Smoke is made mainly from carbon particles (soot). It discolours the buildings in towns and cities and is a cause of lung diseases such as bronchitis (see page 110). It also affects plants. It covers their leaves, shutting out the light, and clogs up their stomata (pores). Plant growth is poor in smoky areas.

Carbon dioxide (CO_2)

Strictly speaking, carbon dioxide is not a pollutant, since plants cannot grow without it. However, the amount of carbon dioxide in the atmosphere has risen by around 10% in the last hundred years and is still rising. Some scientists fear that this could trap the sun's heat and cause the Earth to become warmer. They call it the 'greenhouse effect'. This could melt the polar ice caps and there would be disastrous floods all over the world. On the other hand, smoke and dust might reduce the sunlight and make the world cooler. No one knows.

Sulphur dioxide (SO_2)

Sulphur dioxide is a poisonous gas. While it does no harm to most people, it can affect sufferers from asthma and bronchitis, and make their condition worse. Its most serious effects are on plants. It destroys their leaves and reduces their growth. Even when discharged high into the air, its harmful effects continue. It dissolves in water to form acid which returns to the Earth as **acid rain**. This ruins the stonework of buildings. It can also acidify soils, making them unsuitable for plants. When washed into lakes and rivers, it kills off the fish.

Carbon monoxide (CO)

Carbon monoxide is a poisonous gas. It combines with **haemoglobin** (see pages 132–3), the red, oxygen-carrying protein in the blood. This reduces the body's oxygen supply and can lead to suffocation. Fortunately, carbon monoxide concentrations in the air are never high enough for that. However in a busy city street, shoppers may be exposed to fairly high levels. Smoking cigarettes, though, would give them a bigger dose.

Lead

Lead is added to petrol to improve engine performance. It is then expelled in the exhaust fumes. Although the amount is small, it can build up inside the body over a period of time and can cause damage, particularly brain damage, especially to children. Some countries have passed laws banning or restricting the use of lead in petrol.

Smog

For five days in December 1952, a mixture of smoke and fog, known as smog, hung over London. During that time, 4000 people are thought to have died from its effects.
Smog is caused by a weather condition called a **temperature inversion**. Normally, warm air carrying pollutants rises upwards and disperses them. During a temperature inversion, however, a blanket of non-moving warm air traps a layer of cold air beneath it, often for days. Smoke and fumes become concentrated and smog results. In hot, sunny cities like Los Angeles in California, car exhaust fumes, trapped by temperature inversions, are turned by sunlight into chemicals which sting the eyes and irritate the nose. This is called a **photochemical smog**.

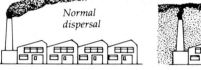

Normal dispersal

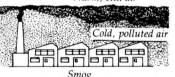

Warm, still air

Cold, polluted air

Smog

Tackling air pollution

After the 1952 London smog, the first Clean Air Act was passed in Britain. This established **smokeless zones** all over the country. These are areas in which only smokeless fuels may be used. Smog is now virtually a thing of the past in Britain. Industry, too, has helped. Emissions from factory chimneys are cleaned to remove smoke and sulphur dioxide. Higher chimneys disperse the smoke more effectively, though it may later be deposited, perhaps as acid rain, in other countries. Many birds and other animals, which had abandoned the cities, have now returned. Afterburners and filters can be fitted to cars to reduce the pollution from their exhausts. The use of these has made the Los Angeles air five times cleaner than it was.

Monitoring air pollution

Smoke pollution can be measured by drawing air through a filter to catch the solid particles and then weighing them. This shows London's air to be twenty times cleaner than it was in 1952. Simple measurements can be made by wiping the soot from leaves in different places and comparing them by eye. Some organisms are useful indicators. Lichens are very sensitive to sulphur dioxide, though some species can tolerate it more than others. A study of the type and amount of lichen growth in an area gives a good idea of the level of air pollution.

Water pollution

Clean water is so essential for the health and well-being of human beings and all other organisms that its pollution is particularly serious. Some of the chief pollutants of water are listed on the next page.

Sewage

Raw sewage consists of human faeces and all the other wastes which we flush down our toilets and sinks. It provides a perfect food for bacteria and other microbes which can quickly convert it to harmless substances. In sewage plants, they are allowed to do just that in gravel beds supplied with plenty of air. This is how sewage is 'treated'. The treated sewage can then be pumped safely into a river. Often, though, sewage plants cannot cope and they are forced to discharge raw sewage. With this abundant supply of food, bacteria in the river multiply rapidly and absorb all the oxygen from the water. Soon, few other organisms can live there. One which can is a little red worm called *Tubifex*. It can survive because it contains haemoglobin (hence its colour) and can absorb efficiently what little oxygen is left. The presence of these worms is a sign that water is poor in oxygen.

Given the chance, the river can recover and, further downstream from the plant, a greater variety of organisms will be found. Unfortunately, in heavily populated areas, there may be a number of sewage plants. The river can be turned into one vast sewer. A useful indicator that water has been polluted with human faeces is the presence in it of a bacterium called *E coli*. This organism is always present in faeces and, although it is harmless, many of the bacteria which live with it are not. Water containing *E coli* is unfit to drink.

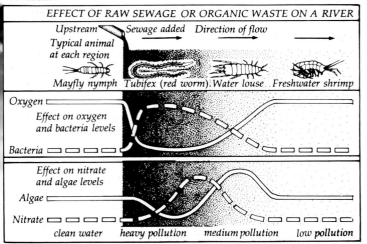

EFFECT OF RAW SEWAGE OR ORGANIC WASTE ON A RIVER

Upstream — Sewage added — Direction of flow

Typical animal at each region

Mayfly nymph   Tubifex (red worm) Water louse   Freshwater shrimp

Oxygen

Effect on oxygen and bacteria levels

Bacteria

Effect on nitrate and algae levels

Algae

Nitrate

clean water   heavy pollution   medium pollution   low pollution

Detergents

Detergents from homes and factories can create mountains of foam across rivers. This absorbs oxygen, keeping it away from the organisms below. Detergents in sewage cause problems at the treatment plants by killing the microbes upon which the treatment process depends.

Excess fertilisers

Fertilisers, such as nitrates and phosphates, are washed from farm land into the rivers. They stimulate the growth of algae which form a mat over the surface of the water. This is known as **algal bloom**. It deprives the plants below of light and so harms the animals which depend on them. It is also expensive to remove if the water is to be used for drinking. Treated sewage, which is rich in nitrates, and detergents, which are rich in phosphates, also cause this problem.

Toxic industrial waste

Industries discharge chemicals such as acids, alkalis, cadmium, mercury and lead. In high concentrations, these can kill everything in a river, making it biologically dead. Even in small amounts, some chemicals may be dangerous if they are passed along food chains.

Organic industrial waste

Effluent from paper mills, sawmills, dairies and food factories is organic and, like sewage, can be broken down by bacteria. Its effect on a river is similar to that of sewage.

Oil

Oil forms a thin film over the surface of lakes and rivers which prevents the water from absorbing oxygen. It is biodegradable, however, and its effects are temporary. The greatest threat of oil pollution actually comes from the sea. Millions of tonnes of oil either spill, or are dumped into the sea each year. Sea birds are the first to suffer. Covered in oil, they are unable to fly or swim and their feathers no longer keep them warm. They either starve, die from cold, or are poisoned trying to clean themselves. When oil slicks come ashore, beaches are fouled and shore animals and plants are killed.

Land pollution

Large areas of good land have been made derelict by the dumping of waste. This includes the domestic refuse collected by the council and the huge slag heaps piled up by industry. More harmful in the long run, though, are chemicals applied to the land. The pesticides used in agriculture and certain highly poisonous industrial wastes may be gradually washed by the rain deep down into the ground. If they find their way into public water supplies, they could render them unfit to drink for many years.

Noise pollution

Noise isn't really a pollutant. However, since its presence in the environment can be both unpleasant and harmful, the term 'noise pollution' is often used. Noise is measured in units called **decibels** (dB). A sound we can only just make out registers zero decibels (0 dB). This is called the **threshold of hearing**. Sounds above 120 dB become painful and this is the **threshold of pain**. Continued exposure to this kind of noise damages the inner ear and leads to permanent deafness. People who work near noisy machinery are especially at risk and must wear ear plugs for protection.

Radioactive waste

Radioactive elements give off invisible rays which can cause cancer or lead to the birth of deformed children. The radiation gradually decreases to a safe level, but, with some substances, this can take thousands of years. Hospitals and industry use radioactive sources, but the biggest producers of radioactive wastes are nuclear power stations. At present, most of this has to be stored since there is no satisfactory way of disposing of it. Nuclear explosions in the atmosphere are another source of radiation. These produce dust called **radioactive fall-out**. This can become concentrated in food chains, including those involving humans, and reach dangerous levels.

Resources and conservation

The things we need to support our way of life are called **resources**. Some resources are renewable—as they are used up, Nature replaces them. Others are non-renewable—supplies of these must eventually run out. Some non-renewable resources, however, can be used more than once. For example, if a piece of iron is allowed to rust, it is lost for ever. If it is salvaged and processed, it can be used again and again. This is called **recycling**.

Human beings make more demands upon the resources of their environment than any other species. As the graph below shows, these demands can only increase since the human race is undergoing a population explosion (see page 66). If essential resources are not to run out, they must be conserved, so that they will always be there for us to use and so that the Earth will always be able to maintain the organisms which live upon it.

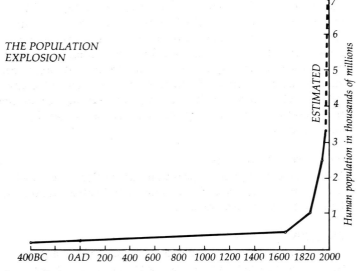

THE POPULATION EXPLOSION

Land

Our survival depends on having enough land to grow food. Yet, each year, all over the world, valuable land is used up to provide houses, factories, roads and airports. Fertile valleys are flooded to supply water and power, while careless farming causes soil erosion and creates new deserts. As populations increase, more and more land is gobbled up. The habitats of wild plants and animals are destroyed and many species are in danger of becoming extinct. There are a number of steps we can take to relieve this problem, if not solve it:

Bringing new land into food production
Most suitable land is already being used. Improved farming methods can be used to improve crop yields, although these can create problems (see pages 224–5). Irrigation schemes, where they are possible, may make some new land available.

Using wild animals for food
Some land, in Africa for example, is unsuitable both for farming and for cattle, yet it provides an ideal habitat for wild animals such as antelope and buffalo. These could be hunted to produce extra food. The numbers being killed, however, have to be controlled. Overhunting of the American bison reduced its population from 60 million to almost none in less than a century. Only legal action saved the animal from extinction. A similar thing happened to the whale.

Reclamation
The need to use agricultural land for building can be reduced, if derelict land can be used instead. One way to do this is to fill old quarry and mine workings with refuse and building rubble from the towns. 13% of New York City is built on land which has been reclaimed in this way. Old slag heaps and bings can be levelled and planted to make parks and playing fields.

Conservation
Laws have been passed to prevent building on farm land round our towns and cities. These are called **green belts**. They stop the cities from sprawling across the countryside until they meet each other. Areas such as national parks, bird sanctuaries and nature reserves have been set aside to preserve natural habitats and the organisms which live there.

Water

Human health and survival depend on plentiful supplies of fresh, clean water. As populations increase, so does the demand for water. In many parts of the world, where rainfall is low, poor water supplies make life very difficult. Even countries which have plenty of rain may have difficulty in meeting the demand for water. Some reasons for this are:

Increasing domestic use
Apart from water used for drinking, cooking and washing, large amounts may be used flushing toilets, in washing machines, dishwashers, cleaning cars, sprinkling lawns, etc. Much of this is wasted.

Increasing industrial use
Industries use huge amounts of water. For example, it takes 200 tonnes of water to produce one tonne of steel. It even takes 6 litres of water to make just one packet of crisps.

Inadequate collection
Piped water supplies need reservoirs to collect and hold the water. For a big city, this could involve flooding large areas of nearby land. This may not be possible or desirable.

Pollution
Many lakes and rivers which could be valuable sources of water cannot be used because of pollution.

Water, at least, is a renewable resource. The water we throw away is cleaned and recycled for us by Nature. This is known as the **water cycle** (see page 124). Even so, with waste and pollution on the one hand and rising demand on the other, water could become increasingly scarce.

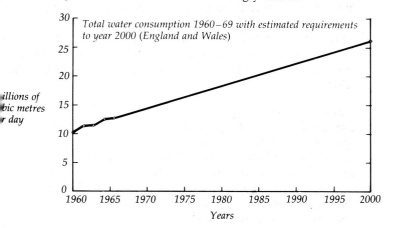

Total water consumption 1960–69 with estimated requirements to year 2000 (England and Wales)

Fish

Fish supplies more than 3% of the world's protein. As population increases, even more will be needed. It should be possible to supply this. Modern fishing fleets use sonar to find fish, efficient gear to catch them and special ships to process them far out at sea. There are, however, two main threats to the world's fish stocks:

Overfishing

Fish is a renewable resource and adult fish produce huge numbers of young. Certain species, though, are more hunted than others. With modern technology, it is quite possible to catch a particular species of fish faster than it can reproduce. This is overfishing. Eventually, there are not enough left to catch. This almost happened to the herring, once one of our most common table fish. Only laws, backed by scientific research, limiting the amount of fish caught, can prevent this. The mesh size of nets must also be controlled to allow young, immature fish to escape and breed.

Pollution

Waste dumped at sea or washed into the sea from rivers can ruin fishing grounds. Even small amounts can enter food chains and make valuable fish unfit to eat.

Forests

About 20% of the land area of the world is covered by forests. These forests are important in a number of ways. They prevent soil erosion and floods and they provide habitats for other organisms. They also act as the Earth's lung, absorbing vast amounts of carbon dioxide and replacing it with equally vast amounts of oxygen.

Apart from this, there is an increasing demand for timber and timber products such as paper. Forests, of course, are a renewable resource. The trouble is that once a tree has been cut down it takes a long time to replace it. If mature trees are felled faster than young ones can grow, whole forests could disappear for ever. Forest resources should be conserved in the following ways.

1 Natural forest should not be used for timber. This is especially important for the huge tropical rain forests of South America and Asia. The ecosystems of these areas are so delicate that, once the trees are removed, they quickly become wasteland.

2 Timber should only be taken from special plantations and cleared areas should be able to reseed themselves naturally, fast enough to replace losses. In Britain, the Forestry Commission has the job of managing timber resources.

3 Paper can be used again. Although recycled paper is not good quality, it can be used to make cardboard and paper bags, so reducing the pressure on the forests.

Energy

People use energy for cooking, heating, lighting, transport, etc. Industry also uses huge amounts of energy. As population and industry expand, so too does the need for energy. At present, our chief sources of energy are fossil fuels such as coal, oil and gas. These fuels, however, are non-renewable and will not last for ever. Oil and gas could be completely used up by early next century, although coal should last a lot longer. Coal, though, is a source of many valuable chemicals and, in the long run, burning it may not be a good idea. The energy problem can be tackled in various ways.

Preventing waste

More efficient engines, improved home insulation, etc., all save energy. Waste heat from factories and power stations can be used to heat nearby homes.

Nuclear power

Nuclear power stations could provide part of the energy now supplied from fossil fuels. However, they create problems of possible accidents and radioactive waste. They are also based on a non-renewable resource—uranium ore.

Renewable energy sources

The search is now on for supplies of energy which are renewable. These include wind energy, tidal energy, solar energy, wave energy, and geothermal energy, that is energy from the heat of the Earth itself.

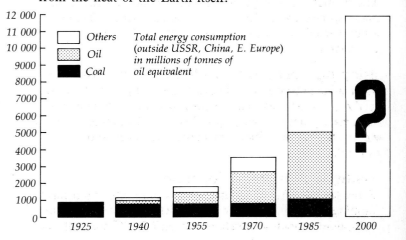

Total energy consumption (outside USSR, China, E. Europe) in millions of tonnes of oil equivalent

Others
Oil
Coal

Index

241